Virus-Induced Enzymes

NUMBER XXIV OF THE COLUMBIA BIOLOGICAL SERIES

VIRUS-INDUCED
ENZYMES

Seymour S. Cohen

COLUMBIA UNIVERSITY PRESS / NEW YORK AND LONDON

1968

Seymour S. Cohen is Hartzell Professor and Chairman of the Department of Therapeutic Research and Charles Hayden American Cancer Society Professor of Biochemistry in the School of Medicine of the University of Pennsylvania.

As a progressive scientific discipline, it [biochemistry] belongs

to the present century. . . . By its essential or ultimate aim

I myself mean an adequate and acceptable description of molecular

dynamics in living cells and tissues.

FREDERICK GOWLAND HOPKINS, 1933 (314)

INTRODUCTORY REMARKS

It was a great pleasure to be invited to present the Jesup Lectures at the Department of Biology of Columbia University, particularly because I received the degree of Ph.D. from the Department of Biochemistry of that University. The occasion permitted me to meet many old friends and teachers with whom I have happily shared the distinction of one-time membership in a Department truly significant in the history of our discipline. To have been trained in the Department of Biochemistry and later to be asked to lecture in the Department of Wilson, Morgan, and numerous other great scholars, and to follow in the series distinguished by Mayr, Pontecorvo, Simpson, and many others of comparable eminence, brought a responsibility and challenge probably too formidable to meet successfully. No matter; in meeting this challenge I was compelled to reexamine my research efforts in biochemical virology over many years and to think about what it all may have meant in terms of the progress of biology and biochemistry. Having undertaken this type of contemplation while on sabbatical leave at the Institut du Radium in Paris, I could always ascribe the deficiencies of the Lectures to the numerous enjoyable distractions of life in Paris rather than to the inadequacies of the work or to my interpretations thereof.

I interpreted the task of a Jesup Lecturer as that of fulfilling two roles. First, I shall discuss the contributions of my laboratory at the University of Pennsylvania within the context of the major problems in an active area of biological research. Secondly, I shall indicate the manner in which the significant contributions of that period of progress provided a jumping-off point for the new problems which now confront biology and biochemistry. In line with this interpretation I particularly welcomed the invitation because it afforded an opportunity to present in one place a picture of our efforts in biochemical virology since the early 1950s. The lectures can have the additional role of expanding the historical record of the contributions of biochemistry to our present knowledge of virus multiplication. It is my intention, however, to develop only one of the major lines of our work in biochemical virology, that of the discovery, nature, and relations of virus-induced enzymes, the specific area with which I have been concerned for the past fifteen years.

Although studies in this specialized area have been treated in several reviews, there has not previously been a comprehensive discussion of the subject. This may be an appropriate time to take stock before the literature becomes entirely unmanageable.

Only two other volumes devoted almost entirely to the biology of bacteriophage have appeared in recent years. The most recent one (90), comprised of essays in honor of the important contributions of Max Delbrück, affirms in numerous places rot only his antipathy to biochemical approaches to the problems of phage multiplication, but also the reluctance of many of his students and collaborators to adopt a biochemical or chemical methodology in their early work. The discussions in that volume therefore both consciously and unconsciously are limited quite severely, although these limitations are not reflected in the misleading title chosen by its editors, *Phage and the Origins of Molecular Biology*. The essays are undoubtedly of interest within the context of that portion of phage biology determined by the group of workers within the sphere of Delbrück's influence. However, my feeling is that a truly complete historical record of the development of phage and molecular biology must include the biochemical contributions. In a recent review Kendrew (364) deplored the virtual omission among the contributions in that book of any reference to the study of molecular structure. Studies of molecular structure are obviously a strong line of work, in addition to studies of the biological and biochemical contributions on which molecular biology is based. Kendrew also questioned the assumption of the editors and most of the contributors that the central theme of molecular biology is concerned almost exclusively with biological information.

Although a different kind of effort, the book written earlier by G. Stent (693), *The Molecular Biology of the Bacterial Viruses,* nevertheless anticipated in title, content, and organization the bias and predilections cited above. In my view this volume also distorts by omission and commission the history of this subject with respect to the biochemical contributions. The distortion is particularly marked in the subject of virus-induced enzymes and, since this is to be the point of focus of my lectures, it seemed to me that I have no choice but to attempt some corrections of the record.[1]

In an introduction to a book of this kind it is common practice to indicate compelling reasons for the author's concern with the subject under discussion for a major portion of his adult life. My reasons can scarcely be described as deliberate choices. As a result of many events characteristic of my time and origins my entrance into both biochemistry and virology can only be described as a series of fortunate accidents. I stumbled into the former after graduation from college in the late thirties. After receiving the Ph.D. degree, I was the fortunate recipient of an early Fellowship of the National Foundation for Infantile Paralysis; it enabled me to work

[1] ". . . while mistakes of a factual nature in scientific results or theories are rapidly corrected, those concerning the historical development are perpetuated through sheer laziness and may remain unchallenged for more than a century. Such mistakes are very seldom corrected by the scientific historian, who has only a bird's-eye view of the development of the subject and often does not realize their importance. The task of correction thus falls to the scientist who happens to be interested in the history of the growth of his own subject and is reluctant to rely on those statements which are often the result of a long chain of copying and perpetuation of the original mis-statement. However unpleasant it is to challenge mistakes made by distinguished investigators, the great importance of the subject makes it necessary to do so for the benefit of those who wish to assess the state of the subject as it was before the more recent developments." Keilin (358).

on viruses with Dr. Wendell Stanley. The fellowship was but one of many positions for which I had applied, in most instances unsuccessfully. I have worked on one or another aspect of the biochemistry of viruses since the spring of 1941, first because of the requirements of the position, second because the problems were interesting and developed from one important puzzle to another, and finally because I discovered that I could make discoveries. In my doctoral studies under Professor Erwin Chargaff I detected phospholipids and nucleic acid in the microsomal fraction of lung tissue. The pursuit of phosphorylated constituents became focused on nucleic acids in viruses in my very first position, and I have continued to study the biochemistry of the nucleic acids for all of my professional career. At first I studied the nucleic acids in cells and in viruses because the substances were present in my preparations and because my training suggested that they ought to be better characterized. Only after a long period of the growth of biochemical virology did it become clear that the nucleic acids have important physiological and genetic roles that need to be unraveled.

To have worked in the biochemistry of the nucleic acids and viruses for many years without a clear biological perspective, other than the romantic but stimulating notions of "Microbe Hunters," may seem shocking to many younger men. It is fashionable now to begin communications with "We asked the following question. . . ." In those early years I also asked questions which were far less precise in current terms, because the subject of my unsophisticated curiosity encompassed enormous areas of ignorance and seemed to warrant an initial survey of the lay of the land. Many parts of the chart of the New World have now been filled in, at least in outline, and I dare say that the detailed exploration of key areas is clearly more justifiable now than it was ten to twenty-five years ago. I do not consider that even our present chart of virus multiplication is adequately sketched either in broad outline or in detail. Believing that there are many ways to make discoveries, I seem to take my pleasures in observing the existence of broad lacunae whose outlines and subsequent details I can explore and chart. It was in an effort to fill a probably significant gap that G. R.

Wyatt and I looked at the base composition of phage DNA and, after discovering 5-hydroxymethylcytosine, pursued this exotic substance to the broad area of virus-induced enzymes.

When I studied plant viruses as a postdoctoral fellow or the typhus vaccine during World War II, my orientation and method of work were essentially those of a chemist. Observing that the biochemical study of virus-infected cells was nonexistent, and contemplating such an exploration, I was compelled to think about the potentialities and difficulties of various biological systems. In 1945, in the laboratory of Dr. Dale Coman, I started to examine animal cells in tissue culture and concluded very soon, in the limitations of my position and the urgency of my youth, that such systems were not yet ripe for the biochemistry that I could then apply. Moving then to the T-even phage systems, under the guidance initially of Dr. Thomas Anderson and then that provided by the rigorous course taught by Dr. Max Delbrück at Cold Spring Harbor in 1946, I found it easy to appreciate the advantages conferred by an appropriate biological system. That the biochemistry of virus multiplication should be developed on a sound biological base was not to be denied, and the apparent primacy of this orientation was well exemplified for me in the words of Hopkins (314): "In exploring and cultivating the fields of nature, the chemists were best provided with the machinery for this cultivation, but the biologists knew best the lay of the land."

All members of the small group of biochemists, including Earl Evans, Frank Putnam, and Lloyd Kozloff, who had also begun the chemical dissection of phage multiplication, were convinced of the need to use the two disciplines in attaining our goals. For many years, however, it was not possible to establish either the validity or the pressing importance of the biochemical methodology among most of the committed biologists. Indeed, it was not until the relatively late period of study described in this volume that many of the same biologists chose to adopt chemical approaches to the problems whose outlines they had drawn; by that time these approaches had become patently inescapable if the biological phenomena were to be dissected to their molecular bases.

xii Introductory Remarks

The rejection of "biochemistry" and the adoption of the term "molecular biology" by the genetically oriented microbiologists in the last decade is one of the most striking and interesting phenomena of modern biology. This event is of no less interest to historians of biochemistry than to those of cellular biology. After 1952 the phage biologists relinquished the idea that cellular biology had a mystical core impenetrable to biochemical concepts. Nevertheless, in formulating more and more precisely the problems of inheritance which interested them, they felt that they could afford to bypass innumerable apparently irrelevant facts and techniques of biochemistry. Of course, it should be noted that the bulk of the licensed biochemists were themselves ignoring the biological advances in this area, advances which would within a decade compel their interest and participation. That Hopkins had defined the role of biochemistry in such a way as to encompass aid to the geneticists had been ignored by both biochemists and molecular biologists. I have thought that "Molecular Biology" was born as a result of the need of biologists engaged in microbial and viral physiology to affirm their identity and their presumably special role by adopting a new name. Biochemists and molecular biologists, now meeting more frequently on common experimental ground, often operate amidst administrative chaos of their own making, quite apart from the confusion which has resulted in the preparation of students for work in contemporary biology.

I do not mean to imply that I believe that only administrative questions now separate biochemists and molecular biologists. Now that the concession of the importance of biochemistry by molecular biologists is evident very often in the nature of their laboratory efforts and the chemical sophistication of their biological predictions, the two groups still do very different kinds of experiments in large part.

I have also developed reservations concerning the view that, at present, biologists know best the lay of the particular land with which I am concerned, although I am sure they did in the initial stages of the revolution in virology. After all, the land has become far more cultivated, and in some lots in fashionable districts the terrain is being turned over, square foot by square foot. It is now clear that phage biology, despite its beauty and elegance in providing test systems for certain problems of phage multiplication, has avoided numerous critical physiological aspects of the overall problem. It has failed to question distortions of the nature of bacterial cytology and physiology, and it currently provides an inadequate guide to the training of students who might become capable of solving numerous critical phage problems. I need only to say the words "bacterial membrane" to substantiate these points.

If I were asked, "Who today and in the immediate future will know best the lay of this land?" I should now choose a suitably trained biochemist, firmly schooled in the biology of cells and of phage and other viruses, at a level equivalent to a broad and rigorous equipment in thermodynamics, physical organic chemistry, enzymology, and intermediary metabolism. Of course, in so doing I merely affirm that most problems of virus biology, unlike some other biological problems, must be resolved within dimensions characteristic of chemical interactions.

Having made these general remarks on what I conceive to be the past, present, and future of the position of biochemistry among the disciplines engaged in virology, I am freer to consider the structure of these lectures. I shall not attempt to describe all our present knowledge of the physiology of virus multiplication. I shall present the results of some fifteen years of experimental work, among more than twenty in phage biochemistry, which bear particularly on the general phenomenon of the virus-induced production of enzymes. Our own studies fall fairly naturally into six sections, which served as a rough guide to the lectures. The stages of our work are presented in the accompanying table which includes the names of my numerous able collaborators, each of whom made outstanding and creative contributions to our story.

The table shows that, having discovered the presence of a new virus-unique pyrimidine, 5-hydroxymethylcytosine, in the T-even phages and its absence in the host nucleic acids, we were led to pursue successively the problem of its metabolic origin in infected cells and the nature of the enzyme which catalysed its synthesis.

1. Existence and structure of   1952   G. R. Wyatt
   5-hydroxmethylcytosine
   (HMC)

2. Metabolic origin of HMC   1953–55   M. Green, H. D.
   thymineless death, unbal-   Barner, J. L. Stern
   anced growth

3. Enzymatic synthesis of   1956–59   J. G. Flaks
   dHMP, dTMP (discovery
   of early enzymes)

4. Characterization of dCMP   1959–61   L. I. Pizer
   hydroxymethylase

5. *De novo* synthesis of dCMP   1962–64   C. Matthews, F.
   hydroxymethylase   Brown

6. Control of synthesis of virus-   1963–66   M. Sekiguchi, C.
   induced proteins   Freda, A. Raina

Having discovered this enzyme and its apparent absence in uninfected cells, we undertook to investigate one of the most investigated problems of the recent period of cellular physiology, the
genetic control and phenotypic expression of a protein, in this
instance, a virus-induced enzyme. After the demonstration of the
origin *de novo* of one such enzyme, we were led to examine the
control of synthesis of different classes of proteins, determined in
a virus genome. Although this record of discovery might not itself
warrant six lectures, the exploration of virus-induced enzymes began
in problems apparently central to the development of modern biology. Since our discovery in 1957 of the enzyme which synthesizes
the virus-specific pyrimidine, the field of virus-induced enzymes has
grown enormously, comprising perhaps a half to a quarter of current work in biochemical virology. Indeed, in 1967, within a decade
after that discovery, it appears that twelve or eighteen lectures,
rather than six, might begin to cope with existing data. The need
to present our specialization in six lectures compels me to exclude
the whole of the relevant data of plant and animal virology and of
other highly important areas of bacteriology. Pleading lack of time
and space, I shall confine my attention to the field of certain DNA

phages and, despite this restriction, nevertheless feel overwhelmed by the scope and detail of the relevant literature.

To explain the slow pace of our initial lectures and our concern with the early history of phage biochemistry, much of which may be quite familiar to my audience, I express the belief that the inception of the subject of virus-induced enzymes represents a slowly achieved turning point in the thinking about the physiology of virus multiplication. Before the discovery of the new pyrimidine and the enzyme responsible for its synthesis it was commonly thought that an infecting virus merely used the preexisting machinery of the host cell. Our discoveries showed clearly that at least one group of viruses expanded the metabolic machinery in an infected cell. Even though other viruses failed to contain comparable new and esoteric compounds, our early studies of the induction of thymine synthesis in phage infection demonstrated that the biosynthesis of the commonly found enzymes might also occur as an evolutionary adaptation important in the survival of many viruses. The expansion of the metabolic machinery of virus-infected cells is now known to be a general phenomenon, although highly specific and often quite puzzling in its biological import.

That enzymes were synthesized which were not present in the viruses themselves but which were nevertheless important for virus multiplication helped to explain early perplexing data on the course of protein synthesis in phage infection. The distinction we were able to make between the nonviral enzymes which appear early and the viral proteins which appear late provided a partial framework for the dissection of stages of the multiplication of DNA phages, as recorded in the accompanying chart. This distinction also became

Stages of a Cycle of Multiplication of T-Even Phages

Adsorption	1. Synthesis of early proteins
Penetration	2. Synthesis of viral DNA
Multiplication	3. Synthesis of late proteins
Lysis	4. Self-assembly

a basis for a comparison of the patterns of polymer biosynthesis in other virus systems. The numerous references in current virological literature to "early" and "late" proteins in animal or plant virology, as well as in many phage studies, stem from this event in the dissection of the cycle of T-even phage multiplication. In addition, this dissection of the cycle stimulated studies of the possible mechanisms of control of sequential syntheses of early and late proteins, that is, the problem of the sequential and piecemeal phenotypic expression of a virus chromosome present in its entirety within the host from the moment of infection. This problem is obviously one of the most, important in developmental biology, and the phage system may provide, in miniature, a system amenable in our time to dissection at the molecular level. Thus the subject of our discussion can provide an entry to the understanding of contemporary effort in both virology and cellular physiology, and it simultaneously ties such effort to the broad sweep of work in both genetics and embryology.

The historical fact that the flood of work on the DNA phages has been among the major currents which have shaped modern biology has not been lost on the phage workers themselves. Many of us are taking one occasion or another to step back, to try to recapture some of the flavor of work and of discussion in the not too distant past, and to obtain some deeper insights, if possible, into what really happened. It may be that the amateurism of such efforts, contributed by distinguished workers now in their anecdotage, will contribute more readily to an eventual psychoanalytic history than to a broader discussion of the personal and group characters which formed this current. However, using these memorabilia, a true historian of this period may eventually appear who will ask how the phage workers managed to hide and to grow in the crevices of American science, and then emerged to multiply first in the ruins of the Long Island Biological Laboratory at Cold Spring Harbor, and finally throughout the world.

It is natural that some of the current "historical" efforts will distort the intellectual history of phage biology, as I have noted earlier.

Keilin [1] has suggested some of the reasons why the correction of historical error cannot be left to an examination of the literature by the interested student. I may suggest some other reasons which relate to the state of the virus literature itself. One of the more interesting points, virtually inherent in all literature, as discussed recently by Medawar, Feynman, [2] and others, suggests that an investigator rarely indicates in the introduction to his paper or elsewhere why he did the experiments leading to his publishable results. I hope that as a result of my participation in much of the early biochemical history, I may help to clarify some of these obscurities.

In addition, I suggest that the literature in phage biology and biochemistry is in a particularly weak and incomplete state. The close intercommunication of members of a phage community which has produced results very rapidly has led to the view among some members that the detailed publication of results is not necessary. In other instances, particularly among biochemical contributors, considerations of priority seem to have led to the publication of fragmentary announcements. Indeed, some major laboratories working in this field have never published a single extensive and carefully refereed paper. For these reasons also we can well imagine that not only will certain data be difficult to find but also, even if they are located, some useful controls on their presentation will be missing. Because I have tried to collect and evaluate this literature over many years, it is possible that I can contribute by trying to present my own view of historical "reality seen through a temperament."

In closing this introduction I express my gratitude to many individuals in addition to my collaborators whose scientific contribu-

---

[2] "We have a habit in writing articles published in scientific journals to make the work as finished as possible, to cover up all the tracks, to not worry about the blind alleys or to describe how you had the wrong idea first, and so on. So there isn't any place to publish in a dignified manner, what you actually did in order to get to do the work, although there has been, in these days, some interest in this kind of thing . . . So, what I would like to tell you about today is the sequence of events, really the sequence of ideas, which occurred . . . ." Feynman, 1966 (205).

tions I have acknowledged earlier. Numerous investigators have kindly given me their papers in advance of publication, making it possible for the lectures and this volume to be reasonably up to date. My old friend, Dr. Raymond Latarjet of the Institut de Radium in Paris, provided every physical necessity to the pursuit of this activity during our very pleasant stay in Paris from January through July, 1967. I am particularly happy to thank Mrs. Betsy Van Camp at the home office in Philadelphia who was a tower of support and strength during the periods of preparation and writing of the lectures while we were away in Paris. Also I am grateful to my good friends, Dr. Jerard Hurwitz and Dr. Ernest Borek, for numerous suggestions which have undoubtedly helped to strengthen the book. Finally, I must call attention to the splendid efforts of Elaine P. Cohen and our children, Michael and Sara, who over the many years not only survived the day-to-day course of the experimental work and more recently the preparation of lectures, but were also pleased with discoveries, real or apparent, doleful and comforting in disasters, real or imaginary, and suitably impressed with the call to prepare the Jesup Lectures.

CONTENTS

Virus-Induced Enzymes

NUMBER XXIV OF THE COLUMBIA BIOLOGICAL SERIES

The study of viral infections is continually yielding results that could not have been predicted from results that went before. At best, this means that progress is being made. At worst, it means that our field of endeavor is in a healthy condition, amenable to progress. HERSHEY, 1952 (303)

Chapter 1

BIOCHEMICAL VIROLOGY
BEFORE
5-HYDROXYMETHYLCYTOSINE

I choose to divide the history of virology into three major periods; a chemical orientation has been important only in the last two. In the first period are the important events from the discoveries of the three major groups of viruses as etiologic agents of diseases in plants, animals, and bacterial cultures to the analysis and restriction of pathogenesis as a result of immune and epidemiologic phenomena; these discoveries mainly precede the chemical phases of work in virology. That this initial division is not totally adequate is clear from the fact that antiviral vaccines were devised long before the discoveries of tobacco mosaic virus in the 1890s by Iwanowski (326) and Beijerinck (45). Furthermore, many viruses, such as those of mouse leukemia, are being isolated at present by classical methods. Nevertheless, the "first" period began with studies in which the problem of the biological nature of the infectious agent was posed almost immediately. Beijerinck, who discovered so many of the organisms which provoke the microbial physiologist, was apparently the first to conclude that a virus, the etiologic agent of the tobacco mosaic disease, was not merely a

small microbe or cell (45). Loeffler and Frosch (455) soon thereafter described the tiny virus of the foot and mouth disease. After
some years Twort (764) and d'Hérelle (300) independently discovered the bacterial viruses. Twort also defined the conditions
necessary for *in vitro* growth of the pathogenic Johne's bacillus. In
so doing he was the first to define a specific and characteristic nutritional requirement for a bacterium (765), thereby establishing
a cornerstone for bacterial nutrition and comparative biochemistry.
The book by Stent (693) presents an interesting and informative
description of the earliest years of work and thought on the nature
of bacterial viruses, leading from d'Hérelle, Gratia, Bordet, and
Wollman to Burnet and eventually, in the more recent periods, to
Delbrück and Lwoff. Since the intellectual history of this particular period of biological investigation is not my immediate concern, I shall not comment further on these important events.

The Beginning of Chemical Virology   Despite numerous earlier
efforts to characterize the size and shape of infectious virus agents,
the publication of Stanley (691) in 1935 on the isolation of ordered
aggregates of tobacco mosaic virus (TMV)(the "crystallization" of
TMV) is the most useful starting point in dating the beginning of
the second period, the beginning of chemical virology. For the
first time, chemically definable particles had been separated from
the cell; they had the two major characteristics of genes, the abil-
ities to reproduce themselves and to elicit additional specific physiological responses, such as the synthesis of a specific viral protein,
in a suitable cellular environment. In subsequent years, virology
attempted to define the physical and chemical nature of many
types of virus particles. Not only did this seem important to problems of virus disease, but it was also hoped that some of these
viruses might provide insights to the minimal requirements for
genetic determination and duplication. In pursuit of these ends
Stanley had shown the applicability of the methods of protein isolation and characterization to the isolation of a virus, and he organized laboratories which thoroughly explored the chemistry of
isolated virus particles.

Bawden and Pirie (39, 40) were the first to show, in 1936, the presence of ribose nucleic acid (RNA) in this virus. This finding and the discovery of the infectivity of RNA some twenty years later (216, 250) constitute one of the major chemical facts which distinguishes the RNA viruses from any known cells. Thus a viral genetic system can exist and be based entirely on RNA, instead of on DNA, which is exclusively present in the genetic systems of cells. This extraordinary phenomenon poses the still unsolved problem of the evolution of such RNA-based biological and biochemical systems. The existence of deoxyribose nucleic acid (DNA) in a bacterial virus had also been described in 1936 by Schlesinger (639). In addition to being the first to find DNA in a phage, Schlesinger had developed techniques applicable to the physicochemical characterization of phage particles and had made many observations on these viruses. His numerous previously forgotten or ignored contributions have been emphasized quite properly by Stent (693).

The physicochemical characterization of the plant viruses by the newly developed methods of Svedberg and Tiselius, among others, was carried out in English and German laboratories, as well as Stanley's laboratory at the Rockefeller Institute at Princeton. I participated in the work of the latter laboratory in 1941 and 1942; in that period we isolated and characterized RNA from TMV (141). Virus RNA was found to be far larger than a tetranucleotide, which P. A. Levene had postulated to be the size of RNA generally. The group assembled by Stanley at that time, M. Lauffer, G. L. Miller, and C. A. Knight, was doing most careful work in defining the physical chemistry and composition of plant viruses. Indeed, the thorough studies of Lauffer, who used the methods of protein chemistry, led to estimates of the dimensions for particles of tobacco mosaic virus (419) which are only a shade different from the dimensions revealed by the electron microscopy of workers such as Anderson (692). It can be said that electron microscopy of the viruses actually validated in large part the hydrodynamic theories commonly used by protein and polymer chemists at that time to interpret their data on sedimentation, diffusion, viscosity, and so on.

In this period, studies of the isolation and characterization of viruses and virus components had also encompassed numerous animal viruses. Such studies culminated during World War II in the application of this new-found knowledge to the development of virus vaccines. For example, Stanley's laboratory shifted its direction to the isolation and characterization of influenza virus as a step in the development of an influenza vaccine. In the same kind of effort I returned to Columbia University and then moved to the University of Pennsylvania to participate in the characterization and purification of the antigens of *Rickettsiae prowazeki*, then thought to be more like a virus, from the rather crude typhus vaccine.

At some point in my early postdoctoral period, I recall asking why virtually no biochemical work was being done on the multiplication of tobacco mosaic virus. It was and still is virtually impossible to do on plants or plant tissue cultures infected by plant viruses the numerous types of simple experiments which I eventually did in the phage systems. However, I was not then equipped to understand the nature of the biological difficulties in plant or animal systems being studied at that time.

From "Free Genes" to Infected Cells   In the third and most recent period of virology, in which we are still immersed, major efforts have progressed beyond the viruses alone, as representatives of "free genes," and have focused on the exploration of events in infected cells. In indicating this new major direction, I do not imply that studies on the isolation and characterization of virus particles did not continue. Indeed, in recent years the analysis of virus multiplication and assembly has itself compelled a more detailed dissection of the structure of the virus particles.

The new interest may properly be said to have begun with Delbrück (195), and his emphasis on the analysis on phage multiplication in defined populations containing infected and uninfected bacteria. The contributions of d'Hérelle and Burnet, although often quite relevant, did not lead to a continuing broad front of biological experimentation, and may therefore be viewed as interesting but indecisive in this respect. The facts contributed by Delbrück himself were not enough to produce that broad front of work, but the totality of his influence expressed in his time and place did have that effect. Among his contributions is certainly the organization of a community of investigators who agreed to apply their various disciplines to a relatively small group of bacterial viruses, which infect a common nonpathogenic bacterium; they also agreed to discuss their findings and thoughts together rather frequently.

This community of phage workers concentrated its efforts on a group of T phages which multiply in *Escherichia coli*. The three morphological types within the tadpole-shaped T group have been summarized by Bradley (70). In addition to differences in size within the group, the elaborate tail apparatus of the T-even phages, T2, T4, and T6, possesses two coaxial hollow tubes, of which the outer one is a contractile sheath, T1 and T5 have long tails without contractile sheaths, and T3 and T7 have very short tails. The serologically related T-even phages, T2, T4, and T6, soon absorbed the largest portion of experimental interest. By the time I began in this field, numerous biological reagents and data had become available, for example, specifically adsorbing hosts, antisera, adsorption rate constants, and the duration of the period of multiplication in infected cells. The T-even phages were also known to contain large amounts of DNA and protein (736). All of the rapidly growing store of biological information affirmed the feasibility of biochemical work with T-even phages, whose size and composition are compared in Table 1 with some other bacterial viruses.

The elegant electron microscopic description of the tadpole-shaped T2, containing DNA within its head, and of the tail-first attachment of the virus to the bacterial whale, has recently been elaborated in great detail by Simon and Anderson (667). The process of virus attachment, injection, and transfer of DNA from virus to bacterium has been summarized by these workers and is illustrated in Fig. 1. My work, as well as that of most biochemists

Table 1. Properties of Some Bacterial Viruses (474)

DOUBLE-STRANDED DNA

	Molecular Weight (10⁻⁶)			Dimensions (Å)	
Virus	Virus	DNA	% GC †	Head	Tail
T2, T6	210	120	35	950 × 650	1000 × 200
T4	210	130	35	950 × 650	1000 × 200
T5	~180	84	39	650 × 650	1700 × 100
T7, T3	37.5	22	48	500 × 500	150 × 100
λ	~66	33	50	570 × 570	1400 × 70
α	68	25–39	52	300 × 300	1215 × 90

SINGLE-STRANDED DNA OR RNA

	Molecular Weight (10⁻⁶)		Base Ratios				Dimensions (diameter of sphere)
Virus	Virus	DNA or RNA	A †	T(U) †	G	C	
φX174	6.2	1.6	24.6	32.7	24.1	18.4	200–250
f2	~6	1	22.2	25.2	25.9	26.5	200–250
MS2	3.6	1	23	25	27	25	200–250
R17	4.2	1.3	23	25	26	25	200–250

† G-guanine; C-cytosine; A-adenine; T-thymine; U-uracil.

interested in this field, with the exception mainly of Kozloff, has been concerned with the phenomena of intermediary metabolism and polymer synthesis subsequent to the injection of viral DNA into the bacterium. At present, very few biochemical details concerning the initial and terminal stages of a cycle of virus reproduction are available.

The early experiments begun in Delbrück's school have seemed to me to embody a methodology somewhat different from that which I adopted as the basis of chemical work. He treated a bacterium as a sealed container into which a virus had been in-

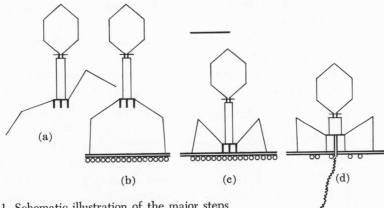

Figure 1. Schematic illustration of the major steps
in the attachment of T2 and T4 phages to the
E. coli cell wall (667).

serted and from which virus progeny had emerged; the quantitative yield and the qualitative nature of the progeny were to permit inferences concerning the nature of the intracellular process.
Delbrück seemed to feel that the major and simplest approach
was that afforded by control of the input or parental virus. Indeed, I once wagered that I could prove to him that the period
of multiplication of a virus inside its bacterial host (the latent
period) was not independent of nutritional conditions, as he had
suggested in his class in 1946. In retrospect, his early view appears
to contain many of the limitations of the phage biology of the period. If the bacterium is indeed a virtually sealed phage dupli-
cator, essentially inert to the medium in which it is placed, there
is really very little to be done to alter the experimental conditions,
other than to change the input virus and to examine the progeny
carefully. That this fundamental experiment is powerful in its own
right cannot be gainsaid; it is in fact the key experiment of phage
genetics, and its ingenious variations represent a large part of the
armamentarium of molecular biology. The contrary notion, that the
host cells were not invariant elements but were responsive to
environmental conditions and could be followed by numerous
other parameters, including the fate of metabolites present in the

media, was merely a part of my inheritance as a biochemist which I undertook to apply.

Whereas much phage physiology made use of populations of bacteria infected at low ratios of virus to bacteria, that is, multiplicities, ≤ 0.1, in order to avoid obscuring the quantitation and nature of the phage yields as a result of intrabacterial recombination of infecting viruses, a very few experiments had been designed by biologists to explore the effect of infection on the bacterium itself. High multiplicities, about 20 to 50, produced a striking lysis without virus multiplication in certain systems (159); multiplicities of 5 to 10, in which the proportion of uninfected cells is far less than 1% of the total, produced unusual light-scattering changes during T-even phage infection (173). The latter system—cells infected at a multiplicity of about 5 virus particles per bacterium, in which virus multiplication developed without premature lysis and the proportion of uninfected cells (about 0.5%) could not contribute significantly to the physiology of the culture—seemed best suited for following the fate of metabolites and cellular substance during infection. This design made available a relatively homogeneous population of infected cells, actively synthesizing virus substance and virus particles during a period otherwise unavailable to phage biologists, at least during this early phase of the work. The path was thereby opened to a minute-by-minute dissection in the intermediary metabolism of infected cells and eventually to the enzymology of virus infection.

This experimental design also permitted us to take advantage of a peculiarity of the T-even phage systems. The wild type T-even phages, which are designated r^+, produce small turbid plaques on lawns of sensitive bacteria, as distinct from the r mutants, which produce larger clear plaques. As Doerman showed (173), superinfection of r^+-infected bacteria by r^+ phages inhibits bacterial lysis and permits a continued biosynthesis and multiplication of virus. Thus the multiple infection of cells, permitting superinfection by readsorption after liberation of virus from a small percentage of infected cells that lysed early, establishes an extended period for biochemical work in r^+ systems, 2 to 3 hours at 37°. This lysis-inhibited system is in contrast to the 20- to 30-minute period of multiplication occurring in cells infected at low multiplicity (<0.1) with r^+ strains or in cells multiply infected (≥ 1) with r strains. The latter types of systems have been preferred by the biologists more concerned with the nature and quantity of initial and final products.

It was not until about 1952 that some phage "biologists" began to embark on chemical experiments, for example, intracellular changes in specific polymers, isotope incorporation, assembly of polymers, and studies with populations of infected cells under conditions of multiple infection. This methodology then became a common feature of their armamentarium, as well as that of phage biochemists. My use of 1952 as a critical year in the history of phage biology rests on more than our own surprising discovery of 5-hydroxymethylcytosine in that year. As we shall see below, this year did represent an unusual stage in that history, because it was a year of reassessment in several important laboratories. The discovery of a new pyrimidine at that time also affected the decisions that were to determine new directions of work. This reassessment also took place in my own laboratory, and I wish to record briefly the results of our own phage work until that time, as well as that of others, to help to understand the context in which a virus-specific pyrimidine emerged on the unsuspecting phage community.

OUR WORK ON PHAGE INFECTION BEFORE THE NEW PYRIMIDINE

Inhibition of Host Synthesis   My decision to work with phage stemmed from an earlier decision to develop a biochemistry of infected cells, modified by the realization that animal virus-infected tissue cultures were not yet suitable to this end. My work in phage began in a collaboration in 1945 and 1946 with T. F. Anderson, who has done so much on electron microscopy and phage structure and adsorption. Having no experience in cellular metabolism,

I thought it would be helpful to learn to use Warburg respirometers and then to determine the effect of T-even phage on the respiration of growing cultures of *E coli*. Respiration, energy metabolism, and Warburg respirometers were very fashionable at that period in the history of biochemistry. The effect of this particular fashion can be detected in other early metabolic studies with plant and animal virus infections.

That my work has been confined almost entirely to T-even phages is clearly a matter of historic accident; that T2, for example, is so extremely virulent was known only in the sense that infected cells lysed, liberating phage. At that stage in our knowledge, T-even infection might have permitted the multiplication of numerous cell constituents as well as of virus. Our studies in respiration (122) produced the novel result that the rate of respiration that prevailed immediately before infection was maintained without change during infection with active virus or with ultraviolet-irradiated virus, which cannot multiply. We interpreted this to mean, first, that energy metabolism is maintained in virus multiplication, as common sense would dictate to be useful and desirable for this process, and, second, that infected cells had lost some truly important metabolic activities, for example, the ability to multiply themselves and to synthesize cellular enzymes involved in respiration. Monod and Wollman (515) soon showed that the synthesis of certain other enzymes, particularly the inducible β-galactosidase, could not develop in *E. coli* infected by the virus ϕII. In my early discussions of these results I thought that this phenomenon might be a common feature of virus multiplication. In actual fact, multiple infection of a growing culture by numerous phages, ϕX174 for example, is now known to be accompanied frequently by an increasing rate of respiration, or of other biochemical parameters of growth, which are halted abruptly only by lysis. The T-even phages are different from most phages because they do turn off the synthesis of host polymers almost instantly, although they do not affect respiration during virus multiplication.

Table 2 lists the many host enzymes whose synthesis is stopped by T-even phage infection. Such information is hidden as essentially uninteresting incidental observations in many papers. I do

Table 2. Arrest of Synthesis of Bacterial Enzymes after T-even Phage Infection — Partial List

System Studied	Reference	System Studied	Reference
Respiratory systems, over-all glucose utilization	(122)	Orotate + PPRP → uridylate	(390)
β-Galactosidase	(515)	Inorganic pyrophosphatase	(390)
RNase	(563)	Adenine + PPRP → adenylate	(390)
Protease	(563)		
Formic dehydrogenase	(563)	CMP, UMP, AMP kinases	(558)
Apyrase	(563)	DNA-dependent RNA polymerase	(558)
Aspartate carbamyl transferase	(430)		
		CCA enzyme	(558)
Dihydroorotic dehydrogenase	(430)	DPNH oxidase	(597)
		Polynucleotide phosphorylase	(644)
Alkaline phosphatase	(430)		
Amino acid-activating systems	(390)	Thymidine phosphorylase	(350)
		Deoxyribose 5-phosphate aldolase	(350)
PPRP synthetase	(390)		
Serine hydroxymethylase	(571)		

not doubt that I have failed to detect in the literature some others which should be added to this list. An apparent increase was detected initially in the activity of DPNH oxidase, an enzyme considered to be a component of the bacterial membrane. This result was finally interpreted to arise from a change of state of this membrane component during infection (597).

The arrest of synthesis of bacterial enzymes and other structures such as ribosomes reflects the abrupt cessation of synthesis of bacterial messenger RNA. It is my suspicion, on which I shall elaborate later, that the solution of the mechanism of this phenomenon, which has been an outstanding mystery for twenty years,[3] may well provide one of the most fundamental insights into the

[3] "On peut, comme l'ont fait Cohen and Anderson, concevoir que le virus détourne l'une des réactions essentielles du métabolisme cellulaire. Hypothèse particulièrement intérressante, puisqu'on pourrait espérer déterminer le stade métabolique ou la chaîne des réactions intéressés. Nous n'en sommes pas là." Monod and Wollman, 1947 (515).

nature of bacterial structure and function. Such a perspective is conceivable despite the uncommon quality of the phenomenon; extreme pathology, which is uncommon, exaggerates critical properties of the norm, at least potentially outlining these normal properties with ever greater clarity. The extreme virulence of the T-even phages manifested in numerous important areas of metabolism has fulfilled precisely this function in the dissection of the metabolism of infected cells. I shudder to think how difficult life would have been in 1946 if we had started our work with T3, for example.

Synthesis of Viral Polymers   My analyses of polymeric components in infected cells began with the nucleic acids, because I had had some experience with these substances and more or less specific colorimetric methods were available for pentose and deoxypentose nucleic acids. Furthermore, this was an area in which the composition of the virus was quite different from that of the host bacterium. Unlike the bacteria, or indeed unlike essentially all cells which contain both DNA and RNA, the T-even viruses contain DNA alone, in about 50% of their dry weight. That the T-even phages were devoid of RNA was proved in our own work (122, 109), although earlier analyses from other laboratories had suggested that T2 contained variable amounts of RNA depending on the medium of origin (736).

Our results in the study of nucleic acid metabolism were of course intimately tied to the inhibitory activity of the T-even phages in cellular growth. Our primitive colorimetric analyses made it possible to see that the RNA content of the cells, unlike the accumulation of large amounts of RNA in normal growth (109, 110) or in other types of DNA-phage infection, did not increase appreciably. On the other hand, after a brief and reproducible delay of 7 minutes in our system of infected cells, the rate of synthesis of DNA was markedly increased (5- to 10-fold)(109), the DNA apparently capturing the phosphorus previously destined for RNA. That this new DNA was probably entirely virus DNA was strongly suggested by the isolation of most of the newly synthesized DNA in virus particles.

In the summer of 1948 I performed a joint experiment with A. H. Doermann, who had recently learned how to effect the premature lysis of infected cells in order to count fully active phage held within the bacterium. He had found that active intracellular phage was present only in the second half of the latent period. We estimated both DNA synthesis and internal phage, that is, new intracellular progeny phage, in the same population of infected cells and showed that accumulation of this apparently virus DNA preceded the appearance and maturation of virus (112). This result suggested that phage synthesis involved a stepwise synthesis and assembly of virus components to form virus from materials such as DNA, itself inactive as free phage. Phage multiplication was therefore totally unlike cell multiplication. In the latter process, intact cells capable of multiplication never disappeared. As is well known, the molecular basis of the disappearance of infecting phage became clear in 1952 with the Hershey-Chase experiment (306), which revealed the selective injection of phage DNA into the bacterium.

In tracing the synthesis of polymers in infection, we also estimated protein synthesis, possibly being among the last in our time to apply the micro-Kjeldahl method to such studies. These results in 1947 clearly demonstrated that protein synthesis, like respiration, was also maintained at a constant rate from the very beginning of infection. Curiously, other analysts were unable to confirm this result for many years (563), and only in 1954 did Hershey and colleagues do so, using the incorporation of ^{35}S to label newly formed proteins (308). This series of results, first obtained in 1946 and 1947, thus set the stage for the demonstration of early virus-induced enzymes in 1957; energy production and protein synthesis are maintained after infection, but the synthesis of virus DNA begins only after an initial lag. In 1947 we also showed by means of the inhibitory amino acid analogue 5-methyltryptophan (123) that without the very earliest protein synthesis in infected cells a subsequent synthesis of virus DNA did not occur (109, 110). That the rate of such DNA synthesis, when it did begin, was essentially a function of the amount of synthesis of early proteins was established in 1955 in the work of Burton (86).

Having performed analyses with this system by "classical" methods, I then moved to the use of isotopes, which, although not very widely used as yet and new in my hands, nevertheless had been extensively employed in the Department of Biochemistry at Columbia while I was a student. My experiments with ^{32}P revealed that T2 and T4 virus DNA was derived largely from exogenous phosphate (109, 111). In retrospect, this particular result seems quite banal, since the T-even phages do compel a relatively enormous synthesis of DNA. I suspect that it was the "daring" use of this "new" tool, taking on a bit of the glamour of the recently exploded bomb and representing the beneficences thought to be derivable from nuclear energy, that colored the reception of these experiments.

I also studied the incorporation of ^{32}P-orthophosphate into fractions of infected cells and detected such incorporation not only into DNA but also in small amount (109, 111) into crude RNA and lipid fractions. In 1947 we lacked paper chromatography and ion-exchange chromatography and were therefore unable to prove that the ^{32}P contained in an RNA fraction really represented a part of ribonucleotide derived from RNA. I suggested that the ^{32}P in the RNA fraction was present as a contaminant and thereby missed the existence of messenger RNA. In 1953 Hershey also reported on the presence of ^{32}P in such a fraction (304) and showed that it had some apparent metabolic activity as well as sensitivity to enzymatic degradation. Speaking as a chemist, I am unwilling to accept his early evidence as a satisfactory proof of incorporation of ^{32}P into RNA in infected cells and consider that the first rigorous demonstration of this point is that of Volkin and Astrachan (776, 778) who used ion-exchange chromatography to reveal the presence of ^{32}P in derived ribonucleotides.

Alternative Paths of Glucose Utilization   The striking difference between the polynucleotides accumulated during growth and during virus infection led me to consider for the first time the problem of the possible interrelation of carbohydrate metabolism and phosphorus utilization. An ambitious program of work in this connection fully occupied our laboratory from 1947 to 1952. Indeed, we are still engaged with aspects of the observations and ideas derived from this effort. In formulating a working hypothesis (109), we imagined that the pathways of formation of ribo- and deoxyribose phosphate derivatives were different, although linked by some common intermediate. I guessed that infection could shift the path of phosphate as follows:

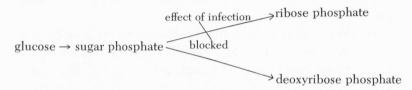

We know some twenty years later that this speculation is not justified and that ribonucleotides are converted directly into deoxyribonucleotides. The exact form of the hypothesis did not matter in 1947, however; virtually nothing was known of the origin of either ribose or deoxyribose at that time, nor were these reactions being investigated. It seemed reasonable to believe that our naive hypotheses would improve as we worked.[4]

It had been known that two paths of utilization of glucose 6-phosphate did exist, but only that of anaerobic glycolysis had been neatly dissected in numerous classical studies. Late in the 1930s Warburg and Dickens had begun to explore an oxidative pathway which led through 6-phosphogluconate to unidentified pentose phosphates. This work had not been developed since 1939; it was a casualty of World War II. In re-exploring the phosphogluconate pathway and its products, we developed numerous new chemical and biological methods of analysis (115) and detected numerous

---

[4] However, it was evident to me that in order to begin at all I knew too little about bacteria and their enzymes. After an exciting sabbatical year in the laboratories of André Lwoff and Jaques Monod in preparation for this effort, I began to work on this problem in 1948 in collaboration with Dwight McNair Scott.

new enzymes of carbohydrate metabolism. We did in fact detect the enzymatic formation of D-ribose-5-phosphate (139) from 6-phosphogluconate, although a major product in our enzyme system was an unknown pentose phosphate. Horecker and his collaborators demonstrated that D-ribulose-5-phosphate was the primary product of phosphogluconate oxidation and the immediate precursor of ribose-5-phosphate. Lim and I (443) recently demonstrated an additional enzyme in *E. coli* which also converts D-ribulose-5-phosphate into D-arabinose-5-phosphate, the latter being a precursor of an important cell wall constituent in gram-negative bacteria (121).

The demonstration of the existence of enzymes for both paths of glucose utilization in our host *E. coli* led us to ask whether both paths actually operated in this organism, whether ribose was actually derived from the phosphogluconate path in intact cells, and whether infection did in fact reduce the contribution of the phosphogluconate pathway to glucose utilization. For this purpose I used 1-^{14}C-glucose with the first available samples of this radioactive sugar prepared by H. Isbell of the National Bureau of Standards. From the $^{14}CO_2$ liberated by the bacteria it was easy to show that both pathways were actually used in growing *E. coli* (113). Although many sophisticated variations of this experiment and of the calculations have been performed with this as well as more elaborately labeled substrates, our initial range of values defining a partial use of the phosphogluconate path in normal growth still holds. Furthermore, infection with a T-even phage did reduce the extent of utilization of this pathway and increased the relative contribution of the anaerobic pathway. It is true, I think, that numerous insights into alternative paths of carbohydrate metabolism began and developed in the context of the study of phage multiplication.

In later years, students in our laboratory, M. Lanning and M. Loeb, demonstrated that ribose originated as a product mainly of the phosphogluconate pathway and that deoxyribose originated from ribose in both growing and infected bacteria (413, 414, 452, 453). Furthermore, we showed that extracts of infected cells reduce

ribonucleotides to deoxyribonucleotides more actively than do uninfected cells, although the significance of this result is not yet entirely
clear (128, 127). It has been possible to show that the enzymes of
the phosphogluconate path are present in infected cells (640) and
can operate in such cells (138), but the mechanism by which the
infection reduces the use of this path is still obscure.

Briefly, then, over a period of five years and longer we had
demonstrated and clarified numerous complexities in the utilization
of carbohydrate as a precursor for ribose and deoxyribose phosphate.
We had, in addition, eliminated our naive hypotheses about the
steps in the metabolism of glucose which might be controlling
nucleic acid metabolism in phage infection. By the end of 1951 and
the beginning of 1952 we had decided to look elsewhere for controlling mechanisms in virus multiplication.

On DNA and Phage Biology in 1952   It is my contention that by
the end of 1951 the work on the T-even phages, despite the exciting
discoveries of Lwoff and his collaborators on lysogeny, had reached
a temporary plateau. The growth of T-even virology in fact resembles a diauxie rather than an unbroken exponential curve of
progress and understanding. An examination of the papers given at
Royaumont in the summer of 1952 shows that this is so (616).

Stent has stated (90), "In 1952 the fifty or so stalwarts, gathered
at the Abbaye de Royaumont near Paris for the first International
Phage Symposium, knew by then that the phage DNA is the sole
carrier of the hereditary continuity of the virus and that the details
uncovered hitherto were to be understood in terms of the structure
and function of DNA."

In contrast to Stent's assessment of the consensus at that time, the
actual content of the papers does not indicate such a clear perspective. Actually few (four) of the twenty papers on the T phages
were directed to the nature and role of phage DNA; nine others
were concerned with the definition of the biology of lysogeny,
colicines, and so on. That phage DNA was essential to virus multiplication seemed likely at that time. However, Hershey was still
exhibiting a characteristic caution about whether phage DNA was

in fact the phage determinant, remarking that, "Parental DNA components are, and parental membrane components are not, materially conserved during reproduction. Whether this result has any fundamental significance is not yet clear." Hershey did comment on "intracellular viral DNA, which rightly or wrongly, we are now inclined to associate with vegetative phage," but neither he nor any of the participants at Royaumont referred to the work of Avery (20). In a sense the situation was a replay of the previous history of the reception of Avery's experiment, as the crucial experiment of Hershey and Chase (306) apparently did not receive the immediate recognition of its now universally acclaimed significance, at least in the proceedings at Royaumont.

Wyatt and I submitted our report (820) of the discovery of a new pyrimidine in T-even phage DNA to be read at that Symposium; a footnote added in proof records the identification of the new base as 5-hydroxymethylcytosine, which occurred late in the summer of 1952. Our paper merely states that, "In correlating the possible specificity of DNA with chemical structure, it is of interest to compare the nucleic acids of genetically related and unrelated viruses."

It may seem a small and trivial point to debate whether phage workers saw the functional significance of DNA in 1952 or 1953. I do not believe it to be a small point in terms of the intellectual history of this branch of science. The critical experiments were in fact available in 1952, but most of the engaged workers were reluctant to reach the appropriate theoretical and programmatic conclusions. The problem is not to be glossed over; why indeed did this occur in phage biology, even as in the study of transformation? I really cannot say. In 1947 I had tested isolated T-even phage DNA for "transforming" activity (109) but was unable to detect such activity in these tests of genetic recombination. I seem to have decided that the theoretical implications of transformation did not need to concern my plans for future work. It is appropriate to recall that the infectivity of viral RNA was not detected (or apparently sought) until 1956, some twelve years after Avery's work and four years after the Hershey-Chase experiment. The infectivity of a virus DNA was demonstrated in 1957. Before 1953 only John Northrop (538) had asserted in print the now obvious statement, "The nucleic acid may be the essential autocatalytic part of the molecule, as in the case of the transforming principle of the pneumococcus (Avery et al., 1944), and the protein portion may be necessary only to allow entrance to the host cell."

PHAGE PHYSIOLOGY IN 1952

The Box Was Not Sealed   I have commented briefly on the conceptual content of the two major types of phage experiments: one-step growth curves at low multiplicity, and chemical studies at high multiplicity of infection. In order to dissect nutritional requirements for phage multiplication, we had in fact used both types of experiments. For example, in work with 5-methyltryptophan we had shown that this inhibitor affected the latent period and the virus yield when the inhibitor was added to cultures infected at low multiplicity at various times during the latent period (130), and affected DNA synthesis when added to cultures infected at high multiplicity (109, 110). In other studies, cells grown in rich nutritional conditions were shown to have different latent periods and burst sizes (131) or different rates of DNA synthesis when infected in less rich media (132). Prototrophic cells, being sensitive to the variation of numerous components of the medium, were evidently more pliable than had been suspected by phage biologists. Nutritional requirements for protein and nucleic acid synthesis could be demonstrated easily (131, 132) with infected cells, as they were with auxotrophic infectible strains (593).

Free Virus and Vegetative Phage   The experiments of Doermann (174) on premature lysis revealed the difference between extracellular virus and an intracellular phage component capable of genetic continuity. Hershey and Chase (306) showed that this difference occurs initially with the injection into the bacterium of the viral chromosome, comprised largely of DNA, and the separation of the viral DNA from virus protein present in the microsyringe left on the outer wall of the now infected bacterium. The stimulation of numerous steps of multiplication by the insertion of the viral DNA, including the stimulation of synthesis of virus DNA before the completion of intact particles, has been noted above.

The Development of Isotopic Methods   The use of radioactive phosphorus to label exogenous precursors of virus DNA (111) was developed further by Evans (199) and his colleagues (400) to show that some viral DNA was derived from DNA-P present in the host. This process was shown to involve the degradation of host DNA to small components; in confirming this result we found that intraceullular virus produced early had the highest content of pyrimidines derived from host DNA (794). This finding indicated a fairly rapid reutilization of components of the degraded host DNA.

The data for other phages were far less adequate, but Putnam and his co-workers (590) had also observed the use of bacterial DNA to form T7 DNA, a result extended by Labaw (406) to T1, T3, and T5. These results have been interpreted to indicate a non-specific transfer of the degradation products of host DNA; that is, large specific polynucleotide fragments of bacterial DNA did not serve as precursors of viral progeny. Other viral components, nitrogen, amino acids, were also clearly derived *de novo* from exogenous components (199). The totality of the data on the T-even phages has excluded the concept of the utilization of a major host polymer, as such, as a precursor in the synthesis of viral polymers.

In such tests both host and medium components had been labeled. This technique was eventually extended to the labeling of parental virus DNA to determine the fate of the viral chromosome during the replication of the progeny. Graham and his collaborators had shown that phage DNA is extensively degraded under conditions of multiple infection, but not in single infection (429, 261). Even under the latter conditions a series of technical difficulties, such as those preventing a total isolation of progeny, obscured the significance of the experimental result, which was that about half of the parental phosphorus appeared in the progeny (399). This amount was nevertheless far greater than that involved in the transfer of parental protein to progeny.

The possibility that phage DNA was actually bipartite, that is, part transferred and part degraded, was eventually excluded. It was not until 1961, however, that it was proved that the viral chromosome consisted of a single DNA molecule (157, 84, 373). The transfer of parental phage DNA to progeny was demonstrated to be dispersive, with small pieces appearing among different progeny molecules (696, 392). The replication of T-even phage DNA is now believed to be semiconservative (399), as is *E. coli* DNA, and the dispersion of parental DNA among progeny arises from numerous recombinational events (392) whose chemical mechanisms are beginning to be clarified, as we shall see in Chapter 4.

The Year of the Pulse   In 1952 at Royaumont, reference was also made (303) to the introduction of the isotope pulse by Maalöe and his postdoctoral collaborators. This powerful technique, in which isotopes or other substances, such as analogues, are given to the cells for brief periods and eliminated subsequently by flooding the system with normal metabolites, has been very important in the dissection of the latent period. Some of our early experiments with 5-methyltrytophan and its reversal by tryptophan (130) are essentially pulse experiments, but we did not generalize the technique and extend it to isotope experiments.

Reference was also made at Royaumont (303) to experiments with ^{35}S which indicated that virus protein is synthesized relatively late during the latent period. In 1954 Hershey and his collaborators (308) showed by means of this type of experiment that ^{35}S-sulfate incorporated into protein early in infection did not enter phage to a significant extent, whereas ^{35}S-sulfate incorporated 10 minutes after infection did appear in phage progeny. Only after this experiment had been performed was it clear that proteins synthesized early after infection were not phage structural proteins, even though they were essential for the synthesis of phage DNA.

Peeking into the Box   At that time, when increasing thought and effort were also being directed to a minute-by-minute analysis of events occurring in the latent period and to the premature disruption of the irrefragable bacterial barriers, efforts were initiated to visualize the internal contents of the infected cells. By means of the electron microscope Luria, Delbrück, and Anderson (464) had detected T-even phage apparently at the moment of emergence from infected cells during lysis. When cells were disrupted prematurely by rapid decompression, some tailless particles were detectable in the extracts before the appearance of intact infectious phage (433). Noninfectious phage head coats are also liberated by lysis from proflavine-treated infected cells (162), and, although it appears clear that they relate to an early stage of maturation of phage, it is still by no means certain whether they ever contained DNA.

Luria and Human (465) had applied the Feulgen technique to infected cells in 1950 and had detected the apparent disruption of the bacterial nucleoid after infection, as well as the accumulation of DNA within infected cells. Not until many years later was the visualization of components in ultrathin slices of infected bacteria developed. The difficult work of Kellenberger and his collaborators on such a project did not begin to bear fruit until 1957. At that time they detected a pool of fibrillar phage DNA between 7 and 10 minutes after infection. This component condensed slightly later in infection into dense particles, apparently devoid of an external membrane (363, 360). As noted earlier, the relation of the formation of the coat proteins to the packaging of the condensed DNA is still obscure; this important problem is discussed in Chapter 5.

5-Hydroxymethylcytosine and Its Impact   In the years 1951 and 1952 many workers had seemingly exhausted the old experiments and had begun to reach out for new approaches to the understanding of phage multiplication. As our work on carbohydrate metabolism was slowly reduced, it seemed desirable to learn more about the base composition of phage DNA. Several apparently contradictory observations on this material were puzzling, and rigorous analyses were called for. G. R. Wyatt, who had recently published such base analyses on the DNA of insect viruses and had been the first to detect 5-methylcytosine in DNA, agreed to a collaborative effort on the analysis of various preparations of phage and phage DNA. A collaboration in which we defined the base composition of the DNA of *Rickettsia prowazeki* had been quite productive (818). As is well known, we went on to detect a new pyrimidine in the T-even phage DNA; it replaced cytosine in this material (819).

This result was unsuspected when we began, and quite startling to me when it emerged. I had undertaken to organize a course in comparative biochemistry at the time and had already become suspicious of the validity of a key biochemical dogma of the time, namely, the "unity of biochemistry." This hypothesis focused on many apparently ubiquitous biochemical compounds and processes known in the 1940s, and neglected numerous other esoteric "irrelevancies." It proposed not only a monophyletic biochemical evolution but a general methodology of biochemical research as well, developing the notion that results obtained with one type of biological material could be readily extrapolated to all biological material. Even today discussion of the hypothesis may be conducted in a far more knowledgeable and sophisticated way without a decision about its validity being immediately and clearly evident. In the early 1950s the hypothesis tended to stultify biochemical research in some areas, producing, for example, a curious resistance to the formal possibility that major pathways of carbohydrate metabolism in addition to the Emden-Meyerhof path of anaerobic glycolysis might exist simultaneously in cells. Nevertheless, I still expected to find normal nucleic acid bases in virus DNA, accepting at one layer of consciousness the dogma which I questioned at another. Our work on carbohydrates, pyrimidines, and, more recently, polyamines has led me to conclude that appeal to existing knowledge is often dangerous in planning programs of study. In many cases it is still necessary to look to Nature for primary biochemical data.

We had informed Hershey of our discovery before the Royaumont meeting, and he announced his confirmation (303) of the discovery of a new pyrimidine at that symposium. This finding meant to him that "the quantitative chemical distinction between bacterial and viral DNA now seems to be feasible." He began almost immediately to exploit this difference in numerous biochemical experiments. One important result obtained by the comparison of the disappearance of the cytosine and the appearance of the phage pyrimidine was the discovery of the relatively slow rate at which bacterial DNA is actually degraded (307). Such a result obviously bears on the mechanism of inhibition of bacterial synthesis in T-even phage infection by suggesting that the degradation of the host genome does not account for the very rapid arrest of synthesis of all host nucleic acids and proteins.

Using these distinctive nucleic acid markers, Hershey also estimated the initiation of synthesis of phage DNA, the size of the pool of precursor phage DNA, and so on. I do not believe that most of these results (304) were qualitatively new on the whole, despite the methodological elegance of the experiments. Because so much phage DNA is being synthesized, parameters of accumulation of T-even phage DNA may be measured adequately for most purposes by colorimetric procedures. For example, Vidaver and Kozloff (770) used the appearance of the new pyrimidine to estimate the inception of synthesis of phage DNA in normal infection and obtained the same value I had obtained earlier by colorimetry (109). In this study these workers also confirmed our observation that cells infected with ultraviolent-irradiated phage capable of multiplicity reactivation did not effect a partial synthesis of phage DNA (124) proportional to the presence of undamaged genetic units. This result was contrary to the mechanism of a readily dispersable and reaggregable genome that had been proposed to account for multiplicity reactivation (461).

The substance of these remarks is that in mid-1952, although T-even virology was still relatively unfocused on a central role for DNA, except for the efforts of a very few workers, the major trend to biochemical study had nevertheless begun. In following that trend, the discovery of 5-hydroxymethylcytosine emerged unexpectedly and gave impetus to new types of work, including our own. Knowledge of the existence of the pyrimidine seems to have helped seduce important workers into metabolic study. Insight concerning the probable role of phage DNA became broadly apparent to phage workers only after the discovery of the structure of DNA by Watson and Crick (792, 793); this was communicated to virologists generally in the Cold Spring Harbor Symposium in the summer of 1953.[5,6] In the year intervening between the advent of our knowledge of the structure of the new pyrimidine (the summer of 1952) and that Symposium, we were able to determine numerous new properties of phage DNA and its components, and to obtain metabolic evidence for virus-induced acquisition of metabolic function, which was also presented at that meeting (114).

[5] "By 1953, phage workers had for the first time what Delbrück used to call a party line. For the first time, too, biologists were in possession of a chemical structure that said something about function. . . ." A. D. Hershey, 1966 (90).
[6] This interpretation of the early history not only is contrary to the remarks of Stent, as indicated earlier, but also indicates that the preface to the second edition of *General Virology* by Luria and Darnell (463) badly confuses the timing, sequence, and meaning of events in 1952 and 1953.

For nothing is born in the body / In order that we may be able to
use it, / But, rather, having been born, / It begets a use.

Chapter 2

FROM VIRAL PYRIMIDINES
TO VIRUS-INDUCED
ACQUISITION OF FUNCTION

As noted in Chapter 1, the discovery of the new viral pyrimidine,
5-hydroxymethylcytosine, occurred in analytical studies of the base
composition of viral DNA. Initially the studies were undertaken
mainly to characterize these materials more completely and to see
if differences could be detected between one-step mutational pairs
of r^+ and r strains. Obviously, we had no idea at that time of the
possible number of viral genes in the T-even phages or of the nature
of the chemical change in DNA which might accompany a mutational change in one viral gene.

In addition, Wyatt and I wished to clarify some aspects of our
own earlier studies in relation to a then recent report of the non-
existence of cytosine in T-even phage. In 1951 Smith and Wyatt
(680) had observed a cytosine-like base in strong acid hydrolysates
of phage DNA. Weed and I had studied the metabolic precursors
of phage pyrimidines (794). After a hydrolysis of phage DNA in
dilute acid, we had detected a substance which behaved like 3',5'-
deoxycytidine diphosphate. Both groups had referred to the base as
cytosine. Nevertheless, Marshak reported in the same year that
cytosine was not present in acid hydrolysates of T-even phage DNA
(486).

Marshak's important paper was weak in two critical respects: he accounted for only three-quarters of the bases presumed to be present in the phosphorus-containing nucleotides in DNA, and his chromatographic solvent permitted a fraction of the new pyrimidine, which still remained after hydrolysis, to migrate with obscuring guanine. Although it might be imagined that virus DNA possessed an abnormal phosphorus content, we had shown five years earlier that virus DNA was apparently normal with respect to the equivalence of purines and pyrimidines, since the molar ratio of diphenylamine-detectable deoxyribose to phosphorus was 0.5 (122). Marshak had hydrolysed DNA with concentrated perchloric acid (487), which I had used in 1945 to free all deoxyribose from DNA (108); this acid does not destroy cytosine in most DNA (487). Nevertheless, the disappearance of cytosine-like material from phage DNA was unequivocal in Marshak's work and suggested the desirability of trying other nonoxidizing acids as hydrolytic agents.

The paper of Marshak performed an important service by questioning the validity of our previous "identification." The eventual resolution of the apparent contradictions in this literature performed its usual impressive feat in the history of science, of clarification, and of exciting discovery. It is possible that this method of discovery even fulfills a special educational role, since all the world is titillated by conflict and is pleased to participate, even vicariously, in evaluating its content. The resolution of these contradictions required rigorous and even classical analytical effort prior to the identification of the new base, and both Wyatt and I had been trained, at least, to do this kind of a job. In our earlier analyses we had assumed that cytosine was present in virus DNA as everyone knew cytosine was present in DNA and, finding something like it with a fairly similar chromatographic and spectrophotometric behavior, we called it "cytosine." We now had to know if it was indeed cytosine, and to do the job properly we had to account for all the possible bases.

The Discovery of 5-Hydroxymethylcytosine (HMC)   Initially the hydrolysis of intact phage was repeated with perchloric acid and the bases, amounting to 75% to 80% of the virus P, were separated chromatographically. Small and variable amounts of a compound at the cytosine position were revealed in some solvents; the substance was now seen to have a slightly different spectrophotometric behavior from that of cytosine, and it also migrated a little differently from cytosine in particular solvents. The hydrolysis of phage DNA by formic acid was then studied, and the precise conditions for obtaining a maximal yield of the cytosine-like base were eventually established. It became overwhelmingly clear that cytosine was indeed absent but was replaced by a cytosine-like compound which differed slightly but significantly from cytosine in its chromatographic and spectrophotometric properties. In the first isolations of the pyrimidine during development of the analytical method, only 90% to 91% of the possible bases could be recovered (820, 819). Additional improvements elevated the yield of bases to 95% to 99% of the molar phosphorus content, that is, of the presumed maximum. As the recoveries of the bases improved, the ratios of adenine to thymine and of guanine to cytosine more closely approached unity, paralleling the ratios found earlier by Chargaff and his collaborators (102). This led us to suggest the existence of a DNA structure that required this relationship (821, 409). Indeed, the Watson-Crick model was published (792) after we had committed this hypothesis to writing. I have always felt particularly pleased by the congruency of tradition and result: sound quantitative and qualitative analysis, leading to the recovery of all the components of the sample, is genuinely useful; apparently the analytical training I had obtained at Columbia had some relevance to the exigencies of the real world.

It is not known to this day why perchloric acid is so destructive of HMC nucleotides in phage DNA. Free HMC is not unstable when heated with this acid. It is suspected but as yet unproved that this effect of perchloric acid is mediated through the relatively specific degradation of the glucosyl residues attached to HMC, which were not discovered before 1954.

The careful study of chromatographic solvents had revealed not only solvents for the isolation of the new cytosine-like structure but also the existence of a hydrophilic group (819, 821). Comparisons of its spectrophotometric behavior with that of cytosine and 5-methylcytosine over a wide pH range revealed considerable similarities in spectra and in shifts in absorption with change of pH, which were best interpreted as substitution of cytosine at the 5 position. Since 5-hydroxycytosine showed very different properties from the viral pyrimidine, the 5-hydroxymethyl derivative of cytosine seemed most likely. The elementary analyses of the crystalline base, isolated via the crystalline picrate, supported this hypothesis; the presumed structure of the viral pyrimidine is presented in Fig. 2a.

Synthesis of the Viral Pyrimidine   A most important element in the proof of the structure of the new base was the existence of the sample synthesized at our suggestion by Dr. Charles S. Miller (510). It was identical in every respect with the material isolated from

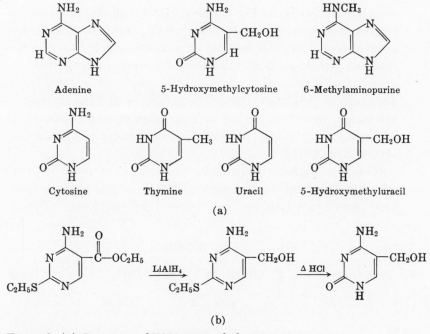

(a)

(b)

Figure 2. (a) Structures of DNA bases of phage nucleic acid. (b) The synthesis of 5-hydroxymethyl-cytosine (510).

phage DNA. Of the two methods of synthesis devised (510), that presented in Fig. 2b has been adapted to the preparation of radioactive HMC (807). Miller also prepared 5-hydroxymethyluracil (HMU) which served as the standard with which we compared the deamination product derived from isolated HMC. Briefly, then, the new virus pyrimidine isolated in the crystalline state was rigorously identified as 5-hydroxymethylcytosine by classical chemical methods. It was a new compound, never having previously been seen to occur naturally or never having been synthesized, and it represented the first instance of a low-molecular-weight compound present in a virus which is not present in a cell.

Some Naturally Occurring Analogues of HMC   The existence of the new virus pyrimidine raised the question whether similar structures were known in biological materials and how these might be synthesized in cells. As Fig. 3 shows, HMC is similar in numerous respects to components of vitamins B_1 and B_6, that is, to the thiamine pyrimidine and to pyridoxamine, respectively. It is known that the thiamine pyrimidine, 2-methyl-4-amino-5-hydroxymethyl pyrimidine (toxopyrimidine), causes convulsions in mice and is actually an antagonist of pyridoxine (762). The prevention and the reversal of this toxicity have been studied in many microorganisms (524). It is of interest that pyridoxal is an inhibitor of thiamine phosphatase in several fungi (437).

Numerous analogues have been prepared, their preparation in part stimulated by the discovery of HMC; several of them have toxic activities which are not reversed by pyridoxine. The 2-

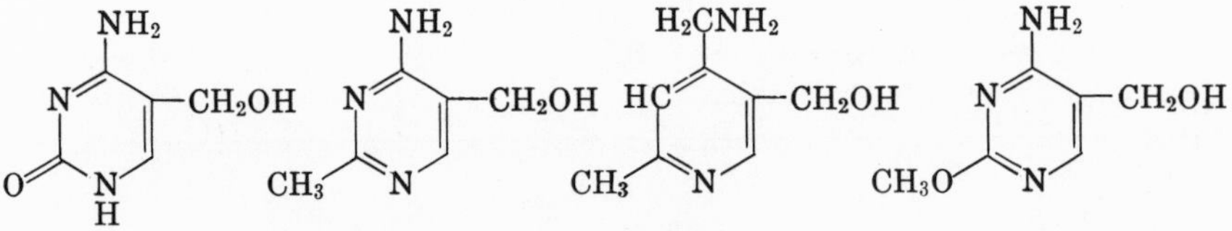

| HMC | Toxopyrimidine | Pyridoxamine | Bacimethrin |

Figure 3. Naturally occurring analogues of 5-hydroxymethylcytosine.

methylthio derivative of HMC, for instance, is highly inhibitory to a strain of *E. coli* which requires the pyrimidine moiety of vitamin B_1 for growth (767). In addition, an antibiotic termed Bacimethrin, inhibitory to some yeasts and bacteria, has been identified as 2-methoxyHMC. This antibiotic, derived initially from a species of *B. megatherium* (734, 733), or now available synthetically (385), is antagonized by either vitamin B_1 or B_6. The medium from which Bacimethrin was isolated was also rich in free thymine. We observed in our later work that HMU and deoxynucleosides of HMC and HMU also inhibit growth of *E. coli*, but we have not studied this further.

It is still not entirely clear how the pyrimidine moiety of thiamine is made; in *E. coli* the biosynthetic pathway appears to be different from that giving rise to uracil, cytosine, and thymine (258). Until recently there were not available biological systems permitting extensive synthesis of the thiamine pyrimidine, apparently because of repression of the biosynthetic route by thiamine pyrophosphate (530). It has recently been found that preincubation of some gram-negative organisms in the presence of high concentrations of adenosine derepresses this pathway to pyrimidine biosynthesis (530). The study of such derepressed organisms has facilitated the dissection of the pathway. In addition, analysis of excretion products from appropriate mutants of *S. typhimurium* has revealed that the thiamine pyrimidine is derived from the purine precursor, 4-aminoimidazole ribonucleotide (531).

Neurospora has been reported to have a thymine 7-hydroxylase which converts thymine into 5-hydroxymethyluracil (Fig. 4) in the presence of glutathione, TPNH, and molecular oxygen (1). Most recently the true requirements have been reported to be Fe^{++}, ascorbate, and α-ketoglutarate (2). A similar enzyme probably exists in rat liver (207). It is conceivable that such a system also oxidizes

Figure 4. The enzymatic conversion of thymine into 5-hydroxymethyluracil.

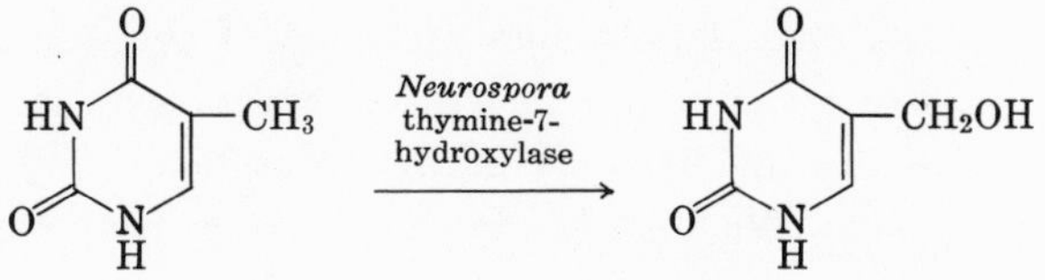

5-methylcytosine, but the specificity of the hydroxylase has not yet been defined. As yet, no evidence has been obtained to suggest that a hydroxymethyluracil is ever converted into a hydroxymethylcytosine (103). Furthermore, from considerations of comparative biochemistry, it may be suggested that a mechanism involving the utilization of molecular oxygen or ascorbate, although possible in eucaryotic cells, would not be expected to be the route used by the procaryotic *E. coli* for such a synthesis.

The early literature was quite confusing about the stability of HMU; this compound has finally been shown by Cline and his colleagues (103) to be quite stable. Free uracil or its nucleosides can be converted into 5-hydroxymethyl derivatives in high yield by simple condensation with formaldehyde in alkaline or acidic media (103). Such a procedure is readily adaptable to the preparation of radioactive HMU, which is also suitable for metabolic experiments. A more recent synthesis of 5-hydroxymethyl-6-azauracil has required the cyclisation of the thiosemicarbazone of hydroxypyruvic acid (62). Ulbricht (766) has recently reviewed the synthetic methods suitable for the preparation of 5-hydroxymethyl pyrimidines and their derivatives, as well as the properties of these compounds. Some of these derivatives, such as 5-mercaptomethyluracil (254), show some interesting antitumor properties.

In a recent review Weiss has referred (805) to the conversion of thymine into HMU by X-rays.

The Analysis of Phage DNA   In analyses of a fairly large sample of T6r+ phage, we estimated that the cytosine present in the DNA was less than 0.2% of the HMC content (821). From a DNA content of about 2.0×10^{-16} g of DNA or about 400,000 deoxyribonucleotides per phage particle, we have estimated the presence of about 68,000 molecules of HMC, or fewer than 130 molecules of cytosine per phage chromosome. The analysis has not yet demonstrated the absolute exclusion of cytosine from the genome. We may ask if complete replacement of cytosine by HMC is essential to the maintenance of the inheritance and multiplication of the phage. We shall see below that the complete, or almost complete, replacement observed is not essential to inheritance but has in itself been one of the mechanisms assisting survival of the phage genome. The addition of the hydroxymethyl group has provided a chemical basis for the evolution of several additional mechanisms which facilitate the survival of virus DNA. Other mechanisms which control the replacement of cystosine by HMC are considered in later chapters.

Contrary to our hopes that many viruses might contain one unusual base or another which could not help but relate to the pathology produced by the viruses, we observed (821) that numerous other phages and some animal viruses, T5, T7, vaccinia, for example, contain the usual bases, including cytosine. The evidence of the years since the early 1950s has shown that the existence of HMC is a biochemical freak. Like cellular nucleic acids, all other viruses except a very few relatives of the T-even phages, such as C16, do contain cytosine (337). A few viruses have been found to contain some other unusual bases, as will be noted below. However, these viruses also represent relatively unusual occurrences; by far the largest proportion of the viruses contain the normal nucleic acid bases, and indeed no plant or animal virus has yet been found to contain an unusual base.

The analyses of the base composition of the T-even phages revealed that their base compositions could not be distinguished with respect to the four major bases. Although these viruses are different in many respects, the gross base analysis is inadequate to distinguish the molecular bases of these numerous differences. The T-even phages contained not only HMC but also a very high disproportion in the ratio of adenine + thymine to guanine + cytosine-like compounds—of the order of 1.9 (821). In *E. coli* this ratio is about 1.0. The DNA of *Rickettsia prowazeki* (818) also has a very high ratio (A + T/G + C = 2.1). Few organisms attain high ratios of these components, and it is of interest that such organisms are frequently virulent parasites. However, although virulent T5 has a fairly high ratio, numerous other virulent phages have AT/GC ratios for DNA very like that of the host they infect (410). Such a result is also frequently found for the temperate phages, whose genomes can become associated rather stably with the bacterial genome.

It had been suggested that this apparent similarity in base composition of temperate phage DNA and bacterial DNA would reflect the homology that must exist in the respective DNA structures, although this need not follow if bacterial DNA proves to be as heterogeneous along its length as we might expect. Indeed, numerous temperate phages have now been found with DNA compositions quite different from those of their bacterial hosts. In any case, because of both the presence of HMC in the phages and the discrepant base ratios between T-even phage DNA and bacterial DNA, no homology of these organisms was suspected. Actually, no evidence of any homology of T-even phage DNA with the DNA of *E. coli* or indeed of any other organism, including T-odd phages (638; however, see 148), has been detected by hybridization techniques. Of course, the sequence homology of one T-even phage DNA with another of the T-even group is quite extensive, although incomplete. At this time the evolutionary origin of a T-even phage is quite obscure.

The Distribution of Odd Bases   The presence of several methylated bases has been recorded in the DNA of some viruses, but at present such bases are unknown in any virus RNA. About 90 molecules of 6-methylaminopurine (180) are present in the DNA per particle of T2 and T4. This base is not present in T6 (239), or in T3 or T5. The presence of this compound in the T2 and T4 viruses results from a methylation of adenine moieties in virus DNA in certain infections only. This base is also known in the DNA of certain strains of *E. coli* (180) as a product of the action of a bacterial methylase (239). The absence of the methylated adenine in T4, which normally has this base, does not detectably affect the multiplication or inheritance of the virus, as tested in an ingenious experiment to be described in a later chapter.

Another methylated base, 5-methylcytosine, has been found in the DNA of the temperate phage λ, grown in several different bacterial strains (421). This base is also known in the DNA of a common host of λ, *E. coli* strain K12, but is not known in the DNA of strain B. It arises from the action of a methylase on the cytosine of DNA, and, as we shall see below, the mechanism differs in many respects from that giving rise to HMC in phage DNA. 5-Methylcytosine is also known to be present in a variety of DNA's from plant and animal sources, being particularly high in the former. Although the DNA isolated from purified mouse polyoma virus had been shown to contain 5-methylcytosine (815), it appears that it is present in the cellular DNA but not in the infectious viral DNA, both of which may be present in purified preparations of polyoma virions (357). The significance of the presence of the base in λ or other organisms is not yet understood. The resistance of messenger RNA, including all viral RNA, to methylation of enzymes which methylate other types of RNA is still another interesting mystery.

The study of phages infecting *B. subtilis* has been undertaken in the past few years since the discovery that, unlike many strains of *E. coli,* the organism can be transformed by exogenous DNA. It appeared particularly useful to have systems in which both isolated bacterial and phage DNA could be assayed for their genetic properties. The numerous *B. subtilis* phages have proved to have numerous interesting features, including the presence of unusual bases. Several classes of these phages have been described; one group is known to contain uracil instead of thymine (721), and another contains 5-hydroxymethyluracil instead of thymine (347). None of these phages is known to contain HMC.

The DNA of the phage PBS2 containing uracil instead of thymine showed an apparent discrepancy in the relation of melting temperature (T_m and buoyant density; this finding prompted chemical analysis which revealed the presence of uracil, base equivalence, and a very high ratio of A + U to G + C. The latter character is unusual in that the phage is a transducing lysogenic phage and possesses a base composition markedly different from that of the host DNA (731). The virus DNA yields an X-ray pattern apparently normal for double-stranded DNA (408).

The group of phages containing HMU instead of thymine, represented by the phage SP8, are considered later in some detail with respect to their metabolic properties, as they provide an interesting comparison with the T-even phages which contain HMC. As in the case of PBS2, the chemical analysis of the DNA of SP8 was prompted by an observed discrepancy between T_m and buoyant density. The presence of 5-hydroxymethyluracil apparently results in a T_m 11° lower than that of a thymine-containing DNA of the same guanine-cytosine content (96). Curiously, hydrolysis with concentrated perchloric acid led to the destruction of the new base; hydrolysis with concentrated formic acid permitted the detection and characterization of HMU instead of thymine. The nature of the deoxyribonucleotide was demonstrated by comparison with the deamination product of the deoxyribonucleotide of HMC (see below). The double-stranded SP8 DNA, unlike that of T-even phage, can be separated easily into the complementary strands by centrifugation in a cesium chloride gradient. The odd bases found in phage DNA are presented in Table 3.

Some Reactivities of Hydroxymethyl Pyrimidines   Hydroxylamine is known to be a mutagen for many viruses and appears to be particularly potent for the T-even phages. The mutagenic effect is largely, if not exclusively, due to its reaction with the pyrimidine ring of cytosine or hydroxymethylcytosine. The reaction of hydroxylamine with cytosine, however, differs from that with HMC or 5-methylcytosine (333). As presented in Fig. 5, HMC gives rise only to the 4-hydroxylamino derivative, while cytosine gives rise initially to an addition product to the 5,6 double bond. The 4-amino group of this cytosine derivative is also subsequently replaced by a

Table 3. Unusual Bases in Some Phages

Base	Virus
5-Hydroxymethylcytosine, replacing cytosine	T2, T4, T6, C16
5-Hydroxymethyluracil, replacing thymine	SP8
Uracil, replacing thymine	PBS2
5-Methylcytosine, derived from DNA-cytosine	λ
6-Methylaminopurine, derived from DNA-adenine	T2, T4

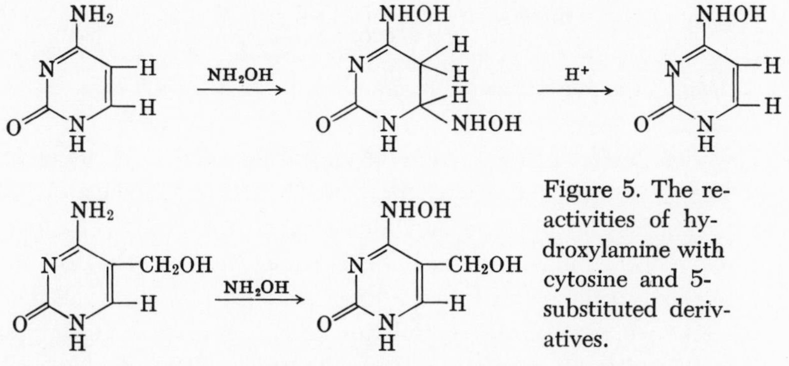

Figure 5. The reactivities of hydroxylamine with cytosine and 5-substituted derivatives.

hydroxylamino group to form the 5,6-dihydro-6-hydroxylamino-N⁴-(hydroxylamino)-cytosine. The first molecule of hydroxylamine added across the double bond can be eliminated quite easily by acid. The effects of introducing these different cytosine derivatives on the template properties of polycytidylate have been discussed recently (814). Fortunately, the chemical changes in HMC systems seem to be a bit simpler, and the reaction leading to C4 substitution may be the major cause of replication error (420).

Phages described as rII mutants, derived from a transition of the r⁺ DNA from the adenine-thymine (AT) pair to a guanine-HMC pair may be reverted to the r⁺ form, presumably containing the original AT pair, by treatment with hydroxylamine. An ingenious test by Levisohn (436) has detected the existence of two classes of such phage revertants; in one class the hydroxylamine-treated HMC was present in the transcribed strand of the rII cistron and hence could grow readily as an r⁺ phage. It appears that hydroxylamine can be used specifically to probe the role of HMC residues in particular cistrons of the T-even phages.

A T-even phage appears to have a lower sensitivity to ultraviolet irradiation than do other phages which contain cytosine. The deoxyribonucleotide containing HMC is reported to be relatively insensitive to ultraviolet irradiation (812). The ability of HMU to dimerize is also significantly lower than that of thymine or uracil (780). It appears therefore that the introduction of hydroxymethyl pyrimidines has altered the sensitivity of phage DNA to a variety of treatments. Nevertheless, it has been observed that complementary strands of SP8 DNA can be "crosslinked" by ultraviolet irradiation, despite the replacement of thymine by HMU (347).

Initial Studies of the Structural and Metabolic Relations of HMC
The Cold Spring Harbor Symposium in 1953 took place one short year after the isolation and identification of the new pyrimidine. Some of the numerous metabolic questions posed by the existence of the compound are indicated in the detailed paper by Wyatt and me (821) which describes its isolation and identification. In that paper we began to attempt to set down all the possible routes with which we eventually became concerned. Our emphasis on possible metabolic precursors was limited to free bases and nucleosides, and leaned heavily to the latter. Our discovery and metabolic problems were formulated before the discovery of the *de novo* route of biosynthesis of pyrimidine nucleotides by Lieberman and his colleagues beginning in 1955 (442), and our approaches were thus conditioned by nutritional data on the effectiveness of pyrimidine nucleosides as metabolic precursors. By contrast, the few studies of the fate of exogenously supplied nucleotides suggested that such nucleotides were not readily metabolized. In retrospect, it is astonishing that we so neglected the nucleotides, but the weakness of the biochemistry of 1952 and 1953 in the isolation and fractionation of nucleotides from DNA undoubtedly influenced these choices. The immediate emphasis of our chemical effort after the discovery of HMC was to isolate its deoxyribonucleoside from DNA for various metabolic experiments. As deoxyribonucleosides were not yet available from commercial sources, these experiments also frequently used the thymidine we had isolated from phage.

In that busy year we prepared the pyrimidine deoxynucleosides from phage and other DNA and began numerous types of experiments designed to test the metabolic origins of HMC in intact infected cells (114). These experiments also required that we obtain stocks of auxotrophic strains of *E. coli,* among which were several different types of pyrimidine-requiring organisms. Despite the existence of a fairly extensive literature on pyrimidine utilization, we soon discovered that suitable organisms were not available in laboratory collections. For example, a strain of *E. coli* having a requirement for cytosine or cytidine has never been found. The common uracil-requiring strains then available did not multiply T-even phages; for example, the W strain, including pyrimidineless derivatives, which had been widely used in the genetic analysis of nutritional deficiencies, was found to adsorb T-even phages and to be killed by these viruses but not to multiply the phages. We eventually isolated our own uracil-auxotroph of *E. coli* strain B. Our inquiries also turned up a single thymine-deficient mutant of strain 15. Our initial efforts to perform experiments with this organism revealed some technical difficulties that led to the discoveries of both "thymineless death" and virus-induced acquisition of metabolic function, which are discussed in a later section.

Parenthetically we note that exogenous thymine is utilized poorly for synthesis of DNA by most bacteria, including *E. coli*. Nevertheless, the presence of exogenous deoxyribonucleosides in the medium of growing cultures of the latter organism has recently been shown to permit the utilization of exogenous thymine (349). Furthermore, infection by T-even phage enables a prototrophic strain to use the free pyrimidine to the level of 15% of the thymine requirement in the absence of exogenous deoxyribonucleoside (350). It is not known if infection has merely made deoxyribosyl donors more readily available, perhaps as a result of degradation of host DNA.

HMC and the Discovery of Glucose   The deoxyribonucleoside of HMC proved to be difficult to isolate by so-called classical methods involving preliminary successive hydrolysis of phage DNA with deoxyribonuclease and alkaline phosphatase. Unlike the release of deoxycytidine from normal DNA, the HMC nucleoside was not released readily after such treatment, but was concentrated within an enzyme-resistant polynucleotide fraction (114). This nucleoside was released from phage DNA more easily after a brief acid hydrolysis of the DNA followed by alkaline phosphatase; its isolation by this method and subsequent characterization were described (114).

These observations were duly noted by Volkin (772), who learned of the presence of glucose in phage DNA from the report of Jesaitis and Goebel (340). Volkin undertook to determine if the presence of glucosylated HMC was not the basis of the enzymatic resistance of the viral DNA. He degraded T4 DNA enzymatically and showed that HMC and glucose were associated in equimolar amounts in a number of separated DNA fragments. He also isolated a mononucleotide containing a mole of HMC and a mole of glucose, which he tentatively allocated to the 5-hydroxymethyl group. Almost simultaneously Sinsheimer described the presence of a monoglucosylated and a nonglucosylated deoxyribonucleotide of HMC (668) in digests of T2 DNA prepared by successive treatment with DNase and phosphodiesterase. Sinsheimer apparently came to this discovery by the extension to T2 DNA of his procedure for the isolation and characterization of DNA nucleotides following enzymatic digestion. Jesaitis, developing the work he had begun with Goebel, went on to describe diglucosylated HMC in T6 DNA (336). Loeb and I have also described the isolation of diglucosylated hydroxymethyldeoxycytidine from T6 DNA (453). The differences in glucose distribution of the phages, to be explored so intensively by many workers, including ourselves, are considered later in greater detail.

At this point I note ruefully that in my first paper on phage, published in 1946 with Anderson, we recorded the presence of a significant amount of an aldohexose in T2 (122). I had completely forgotten this observation, which was rediscovered independently by Jesaitis and Goebel and intensively exploited by Volkin.

The acid hydrolysis that I used to sensitize the enzyme-resistant fraction to phosphatase obviously cleaved the glucose from the HMC and also removed the purines. The resulting apurinic polynucleotides were then cleaved to the 3',5'-diphosphates of the pyrimidine deoxyribonucleosides. The immediate precursor of 5-hydroxymethyldeoxycytidine, in our procedure of acid hydrolysis and alkaline phosphatase, is presumed to be the 3',5'-diphosphate of this nucleoside. This compound was isolated by Weed and Courtenay (795) after a comparable acid hydrolysis.

HMC does exist in a typical hydrogen-bonded double-stranded DNA structure, despite the presence of glucose (283). This finding has been affirmed not only by the ratio of guanine to HMC and the X-ray analysis, but more particularly by the lack of binding of formaldehyde to amino groups of HMC until after heat denaturation of the DNA (272). Glucose is believed to be located in the wide groove of the B form of virus DNA (514).

That glucosylated HMC nevertheless presents some unusual structural features is stressed by the discoveries of Levine and his collaborators. They showed that T-even phage DNA is antigenic in rabbits, that the sites reactive with antibody are revealed when the DNA is single-stranded, and that these sites contain glucosylated HMC (432, 521). Thus specific antisera are now available for T-even phage DNA in its denatured state (522). Formaldehyde binding and immunochemical reactivities fall on identical curves during thermal denaturation (272). Most recently it has been shown that such antisera do not react with nonglucosylated phage DNA but only with the glucosylated DNA (514).

These unusual discoveries, dependent initially on the discovery of the unusual antigenic activity of glucosylated HMC in denatured DNA, have led to renewed interest in the possible antigenicity of other nucleic acid bases. Thus antibodies in the sera of persons with lupus erythrematosus have been found to react with single-stranded DNA also, but these include unheated DNA of ϕX174 or heated DNA of other cytosine-containing organisms (702). Some of these sera react with small polynucleotides such as tri- and tetrathymidylate better than with comparable nucleotides containing cytosine (701). Such sera also inhibit DNA polymerase activity *in vitro* (813). These studies have led to the synthesis of new series of antigens whose determinants contain purinoyl (88) and pyrimidyl residues (735) as well as ribonucleosides and ribonucleotides (198). Such antigens stimulate the production of antibodies possessing considerable specificity for these determinants and perhaps present the perspective of new sets of reagents for the exploration of nucleic acid structure.

Some Properties of 5-Hydroxymethyl Pyrimidine Nucleosides
The enzymatic deamination of 5-hydroxymethyldeoxycytidine by
the deoxycytidine deaminase of *E. coli* proceeds at a rate only 2%
to 4% that by deoxycytidine (114) or 5-methyldeoxycytidine (126).
The resulting deoxyribosyl HMU was isolated (114); in its turn
it appears to be very slowly cleaved by bacterial nucleoside phosphorylase. It may be noted that HMC is not deaminated at an appreciable rate by the cytosine deaminase of *E. coli* or of yeast (114),
although the latter enzyme readily deaminates 5-methylcytosine.
Thus the hydroxymethyl group significantly modifies the sensitivity
of various pyrimidines and their derivatives to a number of enzymes;
with the exception of the studies with Bacimethrin and related free
pyrimidines described earlier, this property has not yet been exploited extensively in the study of possible nucleoside inhibitors.
The 5-hydroxymethyl derivatives of 6-azadeoxyuridine and 6-azade-
oxycytidine are reported (62) to be uninhibitory to the growth and
multiplication of *E. coli* or T4.

Having isolated the sought-after test compounds, we then found
that they were essentially inert in supporting growth of the available mutants. Nor were they precursors in the multiplication of
phages in several test systems (114).

Synthesis of 5-Hydroxymethyl Pyrimidine Nucleosides   A synthesis of 5-hydroxymethyldeoxycytidine has been described (Fig. 6)
(79); it involves the formation of 5-benzyloxymethylcytosine which
is then benzoylated. The mercury salt of this base was condensed
with 3,5-di-*p*-toluyl-2-deoxyribofuranosyl chloride to yield an
anomeric mixture, which was separated into α- and β-anomers. The
conversion of the β-anomer into the β-anomer of thymidine, via a
deamination and a reduction described in our laboratory (265), is
taken as proof of structure of this derivative. This proof of structure is also one we used in 1956 to define the β configuration of
natural 5-hydroxymethyldeoxycytidine (133). A similar route has
been used for the production of an anomeric mixture of the 5-hy-
droxymethyldeoxyuridine from which the β-anomer was isolated

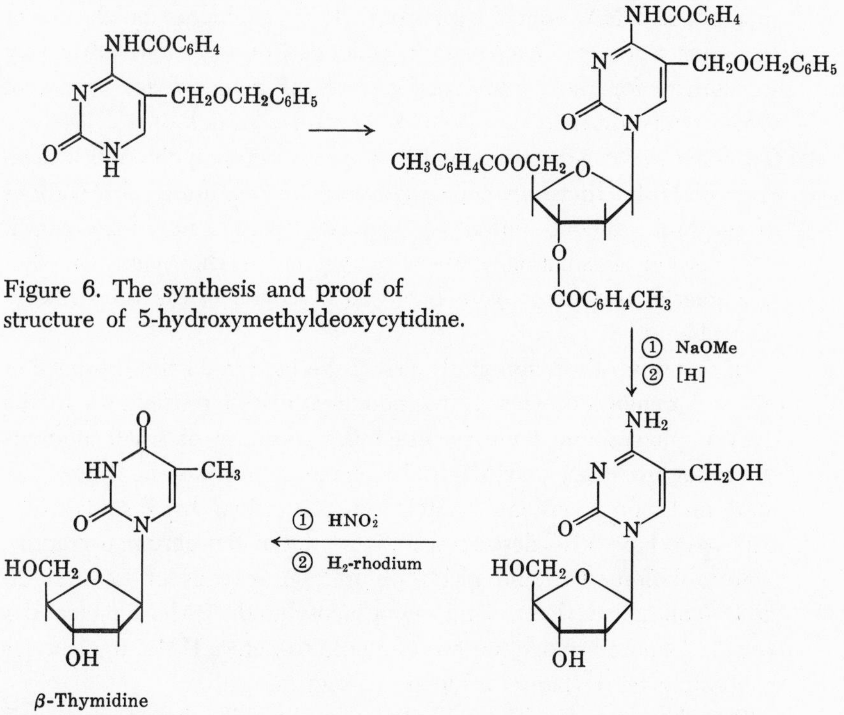

Figure 6. The synthesis and proof of structure of 5-hydroxymethyldeoxycytidine.

β-Thymidine

(80). Both ribosyl and deoxyribosyl derivatives of HMC and HMU have been synthesized (81, 587).

The impetus for the most recent studies of HMU appears to have been the discovery of HMU in the DNA of the *B. subtilis* phage, SP8. Alegria has recently described the synthesis and properties of 5-hydroxymethyl derivatives of the 5′-mononucleotides of uracil and cytosine in both the ribose and deoxyribose series (4a). The syntheses involve a direct coupling of formaldehyde to the pyrimidine, catalyzed by base in these instances.

On Glucosylated Nucleotides In the course of characterizing numerous preparations of phage and phage DNA, we had observed that our preparations of r strains were rich in glucose. The apparent correlation of "r ness" and increased glucose content of the DNA, of r phage DNA, which I reported (117), could not be confirmed by other workers. This led to a prolonged effort in our laboratory to analyze for the content and variety of glucosyl derivatives of HMC nucleotides in the DNA of r^+ and r strains of T2, T4, and T6 phages. We were then unable to detect the polyglucosyl derivatives of HMC that had been suggested by our initial observations of the high glucose content of r phages (441). I now believe that our method of isolation of these phages led to the inclusion either of bacterial fragments or of bacterial glycogen in the preparations of r phages.

In our more thorough study (441) we confirmed the presence of di- and monoglucosylated and nonglucosylated nucleotides in the T-even phages and have recorded the presence of small amounts of monoglucosylated dHMP in T6 phage, as well as the diglucosylated and nonglucosylated nucleotide described by Jesaitis (335, 336). We have also described in some detail the chromatographic, spectrophotometric, and electrophoretic properties of isolated di- and monoglucosylated and nonglucosylated HMC nucleotides (441). As noted above, we were unable to detect HMC nucleotides containing more than two glucosyl residues.

We also extended our early data on the difficulty of enzymatic degradation of phage DNA containing glucosylated HMC to the isolation of all the HMC nucleotides. Although the rate of degradation of phage DNA by pancreatic DNase is markedly slower than with DNA of calf thymus or *E. coli,* the average sizes of the terminal fragments in all of these cases are of the same order of magnitude.

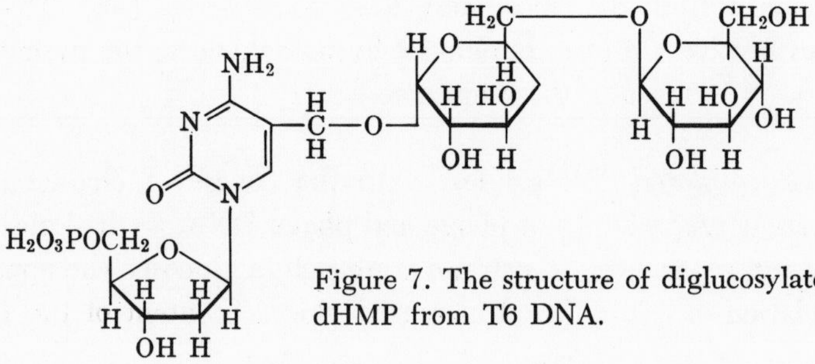

Figure 7. The structure of diglucosylated dHMP from T6 DNA.

Table 4. Nature and Distribution of Glucosylated dHMP in T-Even Phage †

	Percentage of Total Nucleotide		
	T2	T4	T6
Nonglucosylated	25	0	25
α-Glucosyl	70	70	3
β-Glucosyl	0	30	0
β-Glucosyl-α-glucosyl (gentiobiosyl)	5	0	72

† Taken from (389).

Also, as Volkin had described in his detection of the 1:1 correlation of glucose and HMC in T4 (772), a purified venom phosphodiesterase gave a poor yield of HMC mononucleotides, glucosylated or otherwise. Our studies on the distribution of glucosylated HMC nucleotides were thus limited by the incompleteness of release of all of the nucleotides (441). We have shown that the presence of the hydroxymethyl group on dHMP markedly inhibits the dephosphorylation of the nucleotide by the alkaline phosphatase of *E. coli* as compared to the rate on dCMP, and the presence of glucosyl moieties increases this inhibition even more.

The problem of the complete distribution of these nucleotides in phage DNA required the isolation of a phosphodiesterase which completely degraded a phage DNA, that is, DNA containing glucosylated nucleotides. Such an enzyme, isolated from *E. coli* (423), was used by Lehman and Pratt for an analysis of this kind (424). Studies with α- and β-glucosidases revealed the existence of both configurations in phage DNA (424). The diglucosyl substituent present in T6 was found to be gentiobiose, a 1,6 β-linked disaccharide shown in Fig. 7 (404). The distribution of the dHMP nucleotides is presented in Table 4.

Some Biological and Chemical Properties of Glucosylated and Nonglucosylated DNA Cocito and Hershey (104) have demonstrated that parental DNA-glucose is transferred to progeny with an efficiency equivalent to that of parental adenine, indicating that the parental DNA participates in replication in the glucosylated condition. Differences in glucosylation among the T-even phages, as summarized in Table 4, have led to numerous studies of the possible role of glucose in mechanisms of inheritance of these phages. For example, Sinsheimer (669) showed that, in T2 derived from T2 and T4 crosses, inheritance of the ability to glucosylate all HMC nucleotides, as in T4, was unrelated to the r, h, or w markers. Jesaitis pursued this particularly in crosses of T2 and T6 with strains whose glucose contents were markedly different. No correlation could be found between serological specificity of viral proteins and glucose content. Among the hybrids containing segments of both parental nucleic acids, Jesaitis found only strains that had the glucose content of one phage or the other. Thus in this study a particular limited segment of a phage nucleic acid controlled the degree and specificity of glucosylation (338, 339).

In some hybrids derived from T2 and T4 and possessing the host range of T2, however, the glucose content was observed to be intermediate between the two. As will be described in a later section, the α-glucosyl transferases induced by T2 and T4 are different, and T4 also induces a β-glucosyl transferase. Thus at least two T4 genes can control glucosylation of the DNA of hybrids derived from T2 and T4, and only one of the T4 genes appears to have been present in the T2 of the intermediate glucose content.

Numerous studies have been made of crosses of T2 and T4 stocks. A correlation was found between glucose content and the efficiency of plating (the ability to form a plaque on a bacterial lawn) of a T-even virus, since T2 strains, possessing a glucose content characteristic of T4, had now increased their efficiency of plating to a level comparable to that of T4 (710). This change of property appears to relate to the disappearance of nonglucosylated HMC residues in the DNA chain, residues which determine the increased sensitivity to the nucleases of infected cells of T2 DNA as compared to T4 DNA. Barner and I had observed differences in sensitivity of phage DNA's in studies with pancreatic DNase (116).

I had suggested (114), as a result of our early difficulties in isolating nucleotides and nucleosides of HMC after enzymatic hydrolysis, that the survival of phage DNA within the bacterium was possibly related to the apparent resistance of phage DNA to degradative enzymes. The correlation between efficiency of plating, glucose content, and relative resistance of phage DNA to DNase tended to support this hypothesis. Recent studies of certain host-induced modifications of T-even phages have indeed indicated the relation of glucosylation to the survival and multiplication of these phages. Some bacterial strains, deficient in uridine disphosphoglucose (UDPG) pyrophosphorylase (231), are low in UDPG, the coenzyme that transfers glucose to HMC in phage DNA. Such strains produce T-even phages which are very low in glucose (290). These glucose-deficient phages cannot grow on *E. coli* strain K12 or B, restricting hosts, but multiply readily on strains of *Shigella dysenteriae*, a permissive host (290, 232, 466). Similar results have been obtained in several laboratories (655, 725).

It has been shown that the nonglucosylated DNA is broken down to acid-soluble fragments by deoxyribonucleases early in infection in the restricting bacteria, but not in permissive strains (289). Khesin has reported that nucleases present in extracts of T2-infected *E. coli* degrade nonglucosylated T2 DNA but not glucosylated T2 DNA (514). Thus glucosylation does appear to facilitate survival of the viral chromosome among degradative cellular enzymes, as we had suspected in studies of the resistance to enzymes of HMC-containing units. As noted above, the mere presence of the hydroxymethyl group also has a protective effect on nucleosides and nucleotides (114). An additional important conclusion to be drawn from these studies is that glucosyl residues do not alter genetic information; this appears to be fully encoded within the nonglucosylated DNA which can multiply in Shigella.

Despite the presence of different amounts of glucose bound to HMC, the T_m's of T2, T4, and T6 DNA are very similar and correspond to the T_m of a molecule with a G-C content of 34% (637). Since this value is also the G-HMC content, it appears that the presence of the hydroxymethyl group does not affect this aspect of secondary structure (727). This result is in contrast to the considerable effect on T_m of hydroxymethyluracil in replacing thymine in the SP8 DNA (96).

Variously glucosylated DNA's can be separated readily in density gradients made with $CsSO_4$ despite the gross identity of their base compositions. Using this method, Erikson and Szybalski (197) have observed the intracellular development of nonglucosylated phage DNA until the ninth minute after T6 infection. After this time there is a gradual transformation of this DNA to fully glucosylated T6 DNA in wild type bacteria but not in restrictive strains. Comparisons of the sedimentation behavior of such DNA's have been described (155).

The optical rotation of T-even phage DNA is also modified by the degree of glucosylation (473, 474). After correction for its glucosyl content, the rotation of T-even phage DNA at 290 mμ was calculated to be essentially identical with that of other DNA (473). Recent comparison of the T-even viruses and their nonglucosylated forms has revealed some quantitative discrepancies, which have not yet been clarified (474). As determined by X-ray analysis (514), nonglucosylated T2 DNA can assume both A and B configurations, while normal T2 and T4 DNA exist only in the B form.

Polynucleotide Sequence and Glucosylation   Several groups of workers have begun the very difficult study of polynucleotide sequence in DNA. Burton and his collaborators have explored this problem with T-even phage DNA (458, 87). They have concentrated on sequences of pyrimidine oligonucleotides isolated after degradation of T2 DNA with 2% diphenylamine in 67% formic acid, a reagent which does not remove glucose from HMC residues. The procedure destroys deoxyribosyl purine linkages and, via a series of β-elimination reactions, labilizes phosphodiester bonds involving these deoxyribosyl moieties. The shorter products have been separated on ion-exchange columns, and a series of techniques for the characterization of these sequences has been devised.

The α-glucosyl residues of T2 are not distributed in a random fashion among the HMC residues of T2 DNA. For example, in sequences containing two or three adjacent HMC nucleotides, originally terminated at both ends by purine nucleotides, only one glucose has been found attached to the HMC containing a free 5'-phosphate. Some unglucosylated residues are also found in sequences comprised entirely of HMC and thymine. The presence of a purine nucleotide on both sides of HMC residues restricts glucosylation more than a purine on one side; the presence of a purine nucleotide on the 3'-phosphate side of the HMC nucleotide is more restrictive than on the 5'-phosphate side. Although it was thought at first that guanine was more restrictive than adenine in glucosylation of HMC in the sequence $\overset{3-5}{\text{p}}$ HMC $\overset{3-5}{\text{p}}$ Purine p, evidence has not been found for this in the dinucleotides isolated after DNase digestion (460). Patterns of glucosylation in some nucleotide sequences, which bear on the specificity of the T2-induced α-glucosyl transferase, are presented in Table 5.

Such analyses have also been extended to T6 and a number of mutant strains. HMC nucleotides bearing gentiobiosyl groups are not randomly distributed either (459). It is evident that the task of defining the structural and functional significance of glucosylation on the DNA chain has barely begun.

At one time it was considered that the DNA of a single phage particle, T2 for example, comprised several molecules which could be separated chromatographically and distinguished by the glucose contents of the HMC of each piece (82). Some biological support for such a possibility had been obtained initially by means of the

Table 5. Degrees of Glucosylation in Certain Nucleotide Sequences in T2 DNA †

Sequences	Glucose/HMC
Pu-p-HMC-p-Pu	0.67
Pu-p-T-p-HMC-p-Pu	0.80
Pu-p-HMC-p-T-p-Pu	0.94–1.0
Pu-p-HMC-p-HMC *-p-Pu	0.50
Pu-p-HMC-p-HMC *-p-HMC *-p-Pu	0.32

† Taken from (87, 460).
* Nonglucosylated.

molecular autoradiographic technique (435). In 1961, however, the
DNA of a single T2 particle was shown to be a single molecule
(157, 84, 373). Nevertheless, it is not yet known whether T2 DNA
can be fragmented readily into glucose-rich and glucose-poor regions.

Pyrimidine Precursors of the Deoxyribonucleotides in Intact Cells
As noted earlier, we began our metabolic studies with nucleosides
in 1953 and 1954. At that time they were easier to prepare than
nucleotides, and pyrimidine nucleotides had not yet been implicated
as intermediates in pathways of *de novo* biosynthesis. Nucleosides
would enter cells, and rumor and a few experiments indicated that
nucleotides would not. I thought that, if we began with nucleotides, it would be necessary to do enzymatic experiments exclusively. If we began with nucleosides and these substances were active precursors or intermediates, we might also confirm the initial
intact cell experiments with enzymatic experiments. After numerous experiments to be summarized below, it became clear that we
had excluded a possible role for any nucleosides in *de novo* paths
of HMC and thymine biosynthesis. We therefore, and perhaps be-
latedly, turned to nucleotides and the experimental consequence,
enzymology, after we had disproved our initial hypotheses. It has
been remarked in hindsight that it might have been expected that
nucleosides would not be major intermediates in biosynthesis and
conversion. The interaction of an enzyme with compounds containing a carboxyl or a phosphate appears to have been a useful
and conserved feature in innumerable steps of intermediary metabolism. Nevertheless, I have not regretted the experiments with
nucleosides and free bases and certain dihydroderivatives, because
the results, although negative, were among the most conclusive and
therefore the most satisfying we have ever had.

A study with Weed (142) had shown that the thymine and
cytosine of bacterial DNA could serve as precursors of thymine and
HMC, respectively, in viral DNA. In the same study it appeared
that the moiety at the hydroxymethyl level, the β-carbon of serine,
could serve as the precursor of the formyl of purines, the hydroxy-

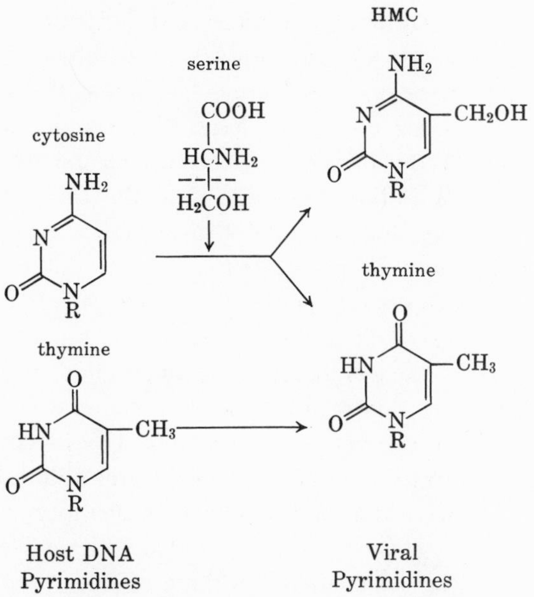

Figure 8. Relationships of host DNA pyrimidines and viral pyrimidines.

methyl of HMC, and the methyl of thymine, as presented in Fig. 8. Subsequent experiments with Green (266) made it evident that the methyl of methionine could not fill either of these roles for the DNA pyrimidines. Since at that time a mechanism for C-methylation to an unsaturated ring was unknown (and therefore thought to be unlikely), and we were hoping for a single route for the biosynthesis of 5-substituted pyrimidines, a hypothesis was formulated involving the intermediate formation of dihydrohydroxymethyl pyrimidines. At that time the possibility of thymine synthesis via the conversion of a hydroxymethylated pyrimidine, which might be rearranged at the level of hydroxymethylated dihydropyrimidine, did not seem too unlikely, to me anyway.[7]

[7] Recent developments in the intermediary metabolism of the nucleic acids have introduced additional complexities, which I am pleased not to have known. It is now known that uracil and cytosine in amino acid transfer RNA (tRNA) can be C-methylated by the methyl of methionine via S-adenosylmethionine to form thymine and 5-methylcytosine, respectively. It is not known at this time whether the ribosylthymine nucleotide thereby produced can serve as a minor precursor for DNA thymine, although this is a real possibility in some instances. Furthermore, dihydrouridylic acid has been found in tRNA and the mechanism of its formation is quite unknown.

Dihydropyrimidines and their nucleosides were synthesized (267, 268, 136) and tested as metabolic precursors, as were the natural bases and nucleosides, including the 5-hydroxymethyl compounds. These tests were designed as competition experiments to determine if the presence of the test compounds reduced the incorporation of radioactive uracil into the thymine of bacterial DNA or the thymine or HMC of phage DNA. Although hydroxymethyl nucleosides did penetrate the bacteria and dihydrodeoxyuridine was phosphorylated, neither the hydroxymethyl nor the dihydropyrimidines nor their deoxyribonucleosides served as intermediates in the formation of bacterial thymine or of viral thymine or HMC.[8] Pressing this work to the very end, we isolated dihydrohydroxymethyl derivatives. They were not only inactive in supporting pyrimidine synthesis (265) but also were inhibitory in bacterial syntheses, as were the hydroxymethyl nucleosides.

This work was concluded with the view that, all other routes having been excluded, these reactions probably went on at the level of the nucleotide. As described below, having no other path available, we then went on to explore the biosyntheses of HMC and thymine at the level of reactions of deoxycytidylate and deoxyuridylate. I am happy to be able to record that these reactions were found to proceed at the level of the 5′-monophosphate rather than that of the di- or triphosphates.

Precursors of Phage Carbohydrates   The main sugar of phage nucleic acid is D-2-deoxyribose; the existence of D-glucosyl residues in the T-even phages is a biochemical curiosity, like that of HMC, and would be impossible without this pyrimidine. As noted in Chapter 1, I have sought the origins of deoxyribose since 1947. In our earliest hypotheses we had considered the reaction catalysed by deoxyribose phosphate aldolase as a possible biosynthetic route

---

[8] Weygand et al. (808) have reported that a small amount of radioactivity from labeled 2-14C-HMC appears in the thymine of DNA of lactobacilli and of *E. coli*. They stated that in strains of the latter organisms the labeled pyrimidine also appears in the DNA as the deoxyribonucleoside of HMC. At this time I know of no metabolic pathways in these organisms that can account for these results.

(Fig. 9a). In 1955 Lanning and I (413, 414) had excluded the biosynthetic role of this enzyme in the formation of bacterial deoxyribose, a result confirmed and extended in the later studies with Loeb (452, 453).

The concept that ribose is the source of deoxyribose stems primarily from the study of Rose and Schweigert in 1953 (614). The work of Loeb on the metabolic origins of deoxyribose clearly implied that the deoxyribose of all of the nucleotides in the DNA of bacteria or virus was derived from ribose. The route was presumably that of the conversion of a ribose nucleotide into a deoxyribonucleotide. The work of Lanning and then of Loeb, and its extension by various workers, strengthened significantly the hypothesis of Rose and Schweigert, which has now been placed on a more rigorous basis by recent enzymology. Two routes for the conversion of ribose into deoxyribose are known to exist (Fig. 9b).

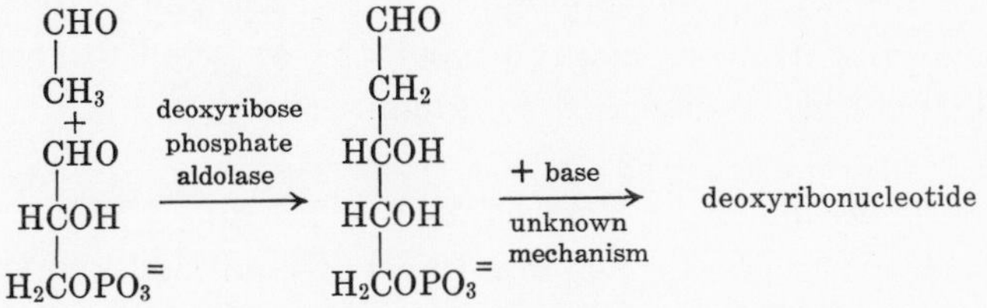

$$
\begin{array}{c}
\text{CHO} \\
| \\
\text{CH}_3 \\
+ \\
\text{CHO} \\
| \\
\text{HCOH} \\
| \\
\text{H}_2\text{COPO}_3^=
\end{array}
\quad
\overset{\text{deoxyribose phosphate aldolase}}{\longrightarrow}
\quad
\begin{array}{c}
\text{CHO} \\
| \\
\text{CH}_2 \\
| \\
\text{HCOH} \\
| \\
\text{HCOH} \\
| \\
\text{H}_2\text{COPO}_3^=
\end{array}
\quad
\overset{+\ \text{base}}{\underset{\substack{\text{unknown} \\ \text{mechanism}}}{\longrightarrow}}
\quad
\text{deoxyribonucleotide}
$$

(a)

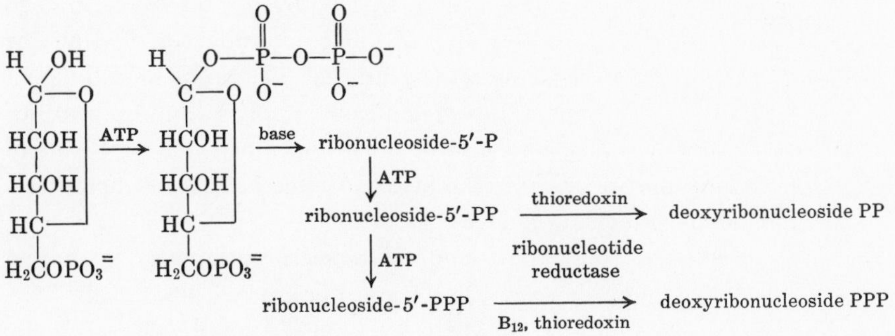

$$
\begin{array}{c}
\text{H}\quad\text{OH} \\
\diagdown\diagup \\
\text{C}\!-\!\text{O} \\
| \\
\text{HCOH} \\
| \\
\text{HCOH} \\
| \\
\text{HC}\!-\!\rule{1em}{0.5pt} \\
| \\
\text{H}_2\text{COPO}_3^=
\end{array}
\quad
\overset{\text{ATP}}{\longrightarrow}
\quad
\begin{array}{c}
\text{H}\quad\text{O}\!-\!\overset{\overset{\text{O}}{\|}}{\text{P}}\!-\!\text{O}\!-\!\overset{\overset{\text{O}}{\|}}{\text{P}}\!-\!\text{O}^- \\
\diagdown\diagup\qquad\ \ |\qquad\quad | \\
\text{C}\!-\!\text{O}\quad \text{O}^-\qquad \text{O}^- \\
| \\
\text{HCOH} \\
| \\
\text{HCOH} \\
| \\
\text{HC}\!-\!\rule{1em}{0.5pt} \\
| \\
\text{H}_2\text{COPO}_3^=
\end{array}
\quad
\overset{\text{base}}{\longrightarrow}
\quad \text{ribonucleoside-5'-P}
$$

$$\downarrow \text{ATP}$$

ribonucleoside-5'-PP $\xrightarrow{\substack{\text{thioredoxin} \\ \text{ribonucleotide} \\ \text{reductase}}}$ deoxyribonucleoside PP

$$\downarrow \text{ATP}$$

ribonucleoside-5'-PPP $\xrightarrow{\text{B}_{12},\ \text{thioredoxin}}$ deoxyribonucleoside PPP

(b)

Figure 9. Postulates on the origin of deoxyribose.

One operating at the level of ribonucleoside diphosphates has been described for *E. coli* (417), a second operating via vitamin B12 at the level of triphosphates has been recorded for some lactobacilli (60, 3, 41, 61). I do not know if the latter route has been rigorously excluded from *E. coli* grown in the presence of vitamin B12, a situation which might exist in the human bowel.

The study with Loeb (453) also provided some information concerning the precursors of glucose in T6r+ DNA. One procedure developed for the characterization of the deoxyribose of HMC nucleotides resulted in the isolation of the diglucosyl derivative of 5-hydroxymethyldeoxycytidine. These glucose residues were identical in specific radioactivity with that of the radioactive glucose supplied in the medium. The converse of this experiment also showed the absence of host precursors for the glucose present in phage DNA. These findings are consistent with the enzymatic mechanisms to be described later, in which a nonglucosylated virus DNA is glucosylated by uridine diphosphoglucose. The glucose of this coenzyme present in the bacteria would be expected to equilibrate rapidly with the glucose of the medium.

On the Penetrability of Nucleotides into E. coli   We wished to know if enzymatic mechanisms involving nucleotides could be proved to be operative in intact virus-infected bacteria. This raised the problem of the entrance of nucleotides into intact cells, a question which was posed even more sharply by our discovery in 1958 that fluorodeoxyuridylate was probably responsible for the thymine deficiency provoked by fluorodeoxyuridine. The problem of the penetrability of nucleotides is a general one, applying not only to our metabolic questions; it is also of great concern to the problems of increasing the specificity, stability, and effectiveness of chemotherapeutically promising nucleosides.

We studied ^{14}C-labeled and ^{32}P-labeled nucleotides, including dCMP. Although deoxycytidine is used nonspecifically for all DNA and RNA pyrimidines, dCMP is metabolized relatively specifically to thymidylate (440). Nevertheless, deoxycytidylate is dephosphorylated before entrance into the cell (440). The dephosphorylated nucleoside is evidently dripped into the cell at a rate determined by the dephosphorylating enzyme.[9] Despite this evidence of the impenetrability of exogenous nucleoside monophosphates, the startling differences between the fates of exogenously supplied nucleosides and nucleotides with such bacteria suggest that similar experiments ought to be repeated with animal cells, as these results may have some therapeutic interest.

In growing *E. coli*, dTMP is used very effectively as a precursor of the thymidylate of bacterial DNA, although in the course of such utilization the phosphate of the exogenously supplied nucleotide is removed and the remaining uncleaved nucleoside is rephosphorylated. Thymidine phosphorylase has recently been found to be localized between cell membrane and cell wall (349), and the dephosphorylation product of dTMP has somehow evaded this compartmentalized enzyme. On the other hand, in infected *E. coli* the thymidine of exogenous dTMP is not used (440). It appears that growing *E. coli* contains a very active specific dTMPase which disappears very quickly after infection (12a). The nature of this unusual phenomenon awaits clarification.[*]

Thymineless Death and the Discovery of Virus-Induced Acquisition of Function

As described earlier, we were given a thymine-requiring auxotroph, *E. coli* strain 15T⁻ (611), whose genetic history and whose multiple biochemical lesions are only now being clarified (610, 71, 72). We wished to test the ability of a hydroxymethyl pyrimidine to satisfy a thymine requirement and, following our routine for such tests, undertook to correlate turbidity with

---

[9] According to recent reports some difficultly penetrable substances, such as actinomycin D (427) and even nucleoside triphosphates (89), are facilitated in their entrance into *E. coli* by certain pretreatments of the cell. The nature of the exclusion mechanisms and of their breakdown in various cells warrants much effort and presumably awaits clarification of the structure and properties of cellular walls and membranes.

[*] NOTE ADDED IN PROOF: T2 and T4 infection have recently been reported to induce a new thymidine kinase more heat-labile than the bacterial kinase (310a). Since the level of this enzyme had previously been stated not to increase after infection (549a), this matter also warrants further study.

viable count at various levels of thymine in the medium. The gross variability of these attempted correlations led us to the notion that viability decreased on incubation in the absence of thymine; testing this hypothesis, we discovered "thymineless death" (32). This superficial analysis of our experimental difficulty eventually permitted the development of useful turbidity-viable count curves in the presence of excess exogenous thymine. We were then able to show that the hydroxymethyl compounds did not replace thymine in supporting the growth and multiplication of the organism (114, 32). Of course, we have used thymineless strains in the study of many other problems.

Although until 1957 we made numerous studies of problems relating to thymineless death which led us to formulate the concept of unbalanced growth (125), our pursuit of virus-induced enzymes led us away from these particular problems. It is not appropriate to discuss here in detail the extensive and frequently inconclusive developments on unbalanced growth and thymineless death. Nevertheless, it does appear relevant to mention some findings about the possible mechanism of thymineless death. Among other effects, thymine deficiency induces lysogenic bacteria to produce phage by a mechanism as yet unknown (508). It is known that *E. coli* strain 15T⁻ contains a defective prophage whose development is launched during thymineless death (662). Although it is tempting to ascribe the killing provoked by thymine deficiency in general to the induction of a virus, some organisms are believed to die as a result of this deficiency without apparently carrying a virus (467, 152).

Despite our negative result on the feeding of *E. coli* strain 15T⁻ with hydroxymethyl pyrimidines in 1953, we decided to do a few additional experiments on infection with the organism (114, 32). In those days we liked to test the ability of new strains to make DNA on infection; the experiment always brought back fond memories of the first time we had done this with strain B. This test became somewhat tricky with strain 15T⁻ because of difficulties of adsorption of T2, to which it alone is sensitive. After learning how to handle this technical problem, we finally did our experiment on infection in the presence and absence of thymine. To our surprise and delight, the infected organism made as much virus DNA in the absence of exogenous thymine as in its presence. Infected 15T⁻ was shown to be able to accomplish a net synthesis of thymine (32), demonstrating unexpectedly a clear instance of a virus-induced acquisition of metabolic function. As a slightly exotic note we also reported that "dead" cells unable to multiply as a result of prolonged thymine deficiency were nonetheless capable of synthesizing virus DNA and thymine after infection.

The ability of an auxotrophic bacterium to develop phage on infection in the absence of the previously required nutrient provides an interesting indication of the new activities induced by the virus. Using this criterion, we found that T5 infection similarly induced the ability to synthesize thymine in *E. coli* strain B_{T^-} (149). Neither the T phages in *E. coli* nor PBS1 in *B. subtilis* (584) is produced in auxotrophs deprived of an amino acid, such as tryptophan—an indication that these viruses do not induce the ability to synthesize this amino acid.

In Retrospect   With these discoveries in 1953, we stated that the synthesis of virus pyrimidines can result entirely from induced acquisitions of function (32). In addition, we referred to the possible similarity between this phenomenon in T-even phage infection and the inheritable changes effected by transduction, transformation, or "even a sexual process." We formulated the possibility that the T-even phage introduced genes for the control of such functions. Since this was only one possibility among others, we also asked if the enzymes were the consequence of existing synthesis distorted by infection, alluding to toxin production in lysogenic corynebacteria, a process which is still not understood. We also referred to the possibility of induction by a low-molecular-weight inducer contained in the phage. In addition, we posed the hypotheses that infection stimulated a previously existing relatively inactive system, and even introduced the enzymes which might be contained in the virus. To be tested, the latter two possibilities required knowledge of the enzymatic mechanisms involved, and after our clarification of these mechanisms in 1957 we did test and exclude these hypotheses. It may be asked, however, why the consequences of the hypothesis of the insertion of new genetic elements were not explored in terms of a search for thymineless or HMC-less phage mutants, for example. Despite knowledge of the existence of the T2-infected 15T⁻ system in 1953, such important questions were not posed by anyone, biochemist or geneticist, until many years later. Such experimental approaches and perceptions existed in the phage community only after the clarification of the biochemistry of the phenomena, the development of the view of the generality of the phenomenon of virus-induced acquisition of function, and the dissection of the phage genome into numerous genes were well advanced.

To summarize, we can say that, although we demonstrated virus-induced acquisition of function in 1953, our laboratory did not pursue its consequences until after we had clarified the biochemistry of biosynthesis of virus pyrimidines in 1957. By 1955 we had excluded the possible role of free bases and nucleosides as intermediates in the virus-induced synthesis of HMC and thymine, and sought other possibilities. In 1956 Friedkin and Kornberg described an enzymatic synthesis of thymidylate in extracts of *E. coli* (228). Lacking other experimental choices, we prepared to work with nucleotides and bacterial extracts. Beginning another new phase of the work, J. Flaks and I confirmed the existence of thymidylate synthetase in extracts of normal bacteria and found much larger amounts of this enzyme in extracts of infected bacteria. At the same time we also discovered a new enzyme, the deoxycytidylate hydroxymethylase, in extracts of virus-infected bacteria (208).

One lives with a few familiar ideas. Two or three. In one's chance
encounters with men and worlds, one polishes these ideas, one
transforms them. It takes ten years to have an idea really one's
own—about which one can talk. Naturally, it is a little discouraging.

ALBERT CAMUS

Chapter 3

DEOXYCYTIDYLATE HYDROXYMETHYLASE AND THYMIDYLATE SYNTHETASE, TWO VIRUS-INDUCED ENZYMES

As indicated briefly in Chapter 2, enzymes were found in extracts of infected bacteria which catalysed reactions generating the two virus pyrimidines, thymine and HMC, as deoxyribonucleotides. Prior to these findings, competition experiments had shown that these pyrimidines were not synthesized in the cells as the free bases or as nucleosides. It was demonstrated also, although somewhat later, that possible nucleotide precursors would not penetrate intact cells. The enzymology of extracts had become the sole possible route of continuing study. Immediately on adoption of this methodology in 1957 we were able to solve the problems of the mechanism of synthesis of these pyrimidines as components of nucleotides.

In considering the history of this discovery it might appear that, if we had chosen this methodology before the ones we did choose, we might have discovered the hydroxymethylase one or two years earlier. Actually, new knowledge acquired in obtaining and handling tetrahydrofolate (THFA), the active conenzyme in the transfer of the one-carbon fragments involved in these reactions, had helped to make our enzymatic studies possible only one or two years before we did them. The availability of this coenzyme undoubtedly helped greatly in obtaining the final unequivocal results. After all, the reduction procedure we had used for the preparation of tetrahydrofolate was not published until 1957 (370). Nevertheless, despite all the good reasons I might present for doing our experiment when we did, the fact seems to be that I tend to avoid enzymology if I think another approach is feasible. I attribute this reluctance in some measure to a deficiency in my training; and I ask if this is not a fairly widespread phenomenon: do not my colleagues also work mainly with the skills they acquired early, and do they tend not to feel too comfortable with a methodology learned fairly late in their scientific development? Of course, this does not apply to physicists, who now do genetics or biochemistry; and occasionally even aging biochemists can and do learn new tricks, but I wonder if the phenomenon may not be significant in the history of biochemical discovery.[10]

Enzymatic Reactions of Pyrimidine Biosynthesis Involving Formaldehyde   The β-carbon of serine may serve as the one carbon fragment which forms the hydroxymethyl group of HMC and the methyl group of thymine (see Fig. 8). Serine is cleaved reversibly to glycine plus formaldehyde by serine hydroxymethylase, which contains pyridoxal phosphate. Free formaldehyde can react chemically with tetrahydrofolate to form N^5,N^{10}-methylene-tetrahydrofolate, as in the sequence.

$$\text{L-serine} \rightleftharpoons \text{glycine} + \text{HCHO}$$

$$\text{HCHO} + \text{tetrahydrofolate} \rightleftharpoons N^5,N^{10}\text{-methylene-tetrahydrofolate} + H_2O$$

[10] The phenomenon, if real, might be of particular interest in defining the nature of training in molecular biology. It is quite relevant, I think, to ask if a young investigator trained recently in "molecular biology," a branch of knowledge which lays claim to some acquaintance with enzymes, would ever undertake to prepare triphosphopyridine nucleotide, tetrahydrofolate, or any recently characterized but commercially unavailable coenzyme thought to be crucial in a reaction under investigation.

Serine hydroxymethylase is believed to be in excess in *E. coli* and does not appear to be increased during infection by T-even viruses (571).

As noted earlier, Friedkin and Kornberg had demonstrated the presence of an enzyme in extracts of uninfected *E. coli* which catalysed the fixation of radioactive formaldehyde to deoxyuridylate in the presence of tetrahydrofolate to form thymidylate (228). The source of the hydrogen atoms to form the methyl of thymine was eventually shown by Friedkin to be the hydrogen atoms of THFA itself, which was thereby converted into dihydrofolate (DHFA) (226). This overall reaction is represented in Fig. 10a. It was suggested that the actual donor of the one carbon fragment to form thymine is N^5,N^{10}-methylene-tetrahydrofolate.

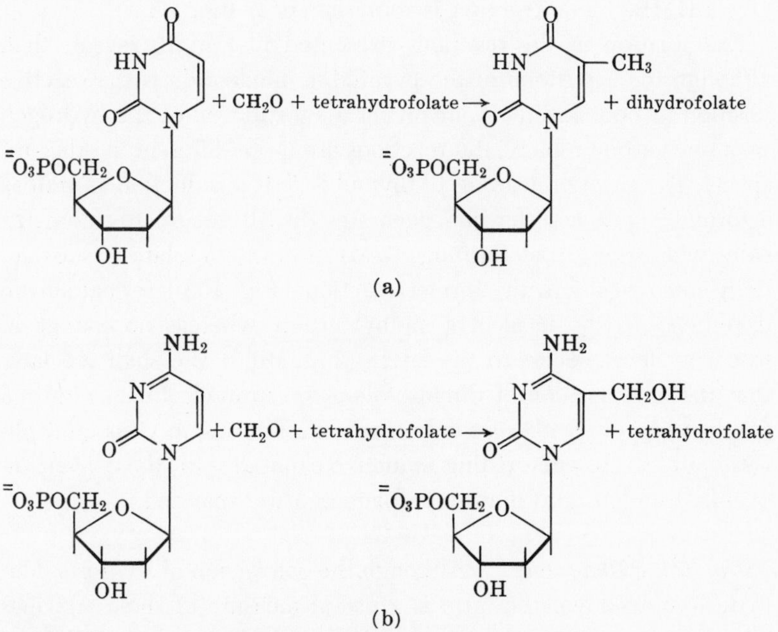

(a)

(b)

Figure 10. (a) The synthesis of dTMP, the reaction catalysed by thymidylate synthetase. (b) The synthesis of dHMP, the reaction catalysed by deoxycytidylate hydroxymethylase.

Flaks and I undertook to confirm the presence of this enzyme, thymidylate synthetase, in extracts of normal and phage-infected bacteria by studying the conversion of ^{14}C-formaldehyde into a nonvolatile acid-stable form in the presence of dUMP and THFA. The activity was indeed present in normal bacteria, but we also found it at a level several times higher in extracts of infected bacteria; the product with both types of extract was thymidylate (208).

This result encouraged us to try deoxycytidylate as a substrate, and we were unable to demonstrate fixation of the radioactive formaldehyde with extracts of uninfected bacteria. With extracts of infected bacteria, however, we could do so readily. In the latter instance the nucleotide product, containing radioactive ^{14}C and separated from deoxycytidylate by chromatography on an anion-exchange resin, was shown to be the 5-hydroxymethyldeoxycytidylate (dHMP). This reaction is represented in Fig. 10b.

Examination of the reactions presented in Fig. 10 reveals that, although the 5 position of the pyrimidine nucleotide is the reactive position in both instances, involving a substitution of the hydrogen by a one-carbon moiety, the reactions are quite different in other respects. The reaction leading to thymidylate is a reduction as well as a formaldehyde transfer and generates dihydrofolate stoichiometrically whereas, in that forming dHMP, tetrahydrofolate is substantially unchanged. In the former reaction (Fig. 10A) formaldehyde is reduced to the level of a methyl group, whereas no change in oxidation level occurs in the latter (Fig. 10B). We shall see later that the regeneration of dihydrofolate to tetrahydrofolate required for thymidylate synthesis can become rate-limiting in virus multiplication unless the pre-existing reductive capability for the conversion of dihydrofolate into tetrahydrofolate is also expanded.

Assay of the Reactions   Although the conversion of ^{14}C-formaldehyde into a nonvolatile form is a useful measure of these enzymes when they are present in large amounts, the fixation of HCHO to compounds as yet undefined is significant although low in extracts lacking these activities. Therefore this assay method is not satisfactory when low levels of these enzymes are present. In the study of deoxycytidylate hydroxymethylase, Somerville and his co-workers showed (684) that dHMP and dCMP can be separated easily and completely on a cation-exchange column in acid solution at pH 1 to 2. The radioactivity of aliquots of an eluate containing the purified dHMP can then be assayed easily. This method of assay is slow but quite reliable at the usual assay levels of radioactivity (575). With very high levels of radioactive formaldehyde, as in our experiments designed to attempt to demonstrate the absence of an enzyme, we have been compelled to purify successively carrier nucleotide, nucleoside, and free bases.

In the assay of thymidylate synthetase numerous methods have been tried. Using labeled HCHO, we can also examine radioactivity adsorbable to charcoal, presumably on a nucleotide (228). Friedkin has used labeled dUMP, separating labeled thymidylate produced from the dUMP in the reaction mixture (226).

The spectrophotometric procedure of Wahba and Friedkin (783) followed the disappearance of THFA at 338 mμ ($\Delta a_M = +6600$ $M^{-1} cm^{-1}$) and indeed provided the first evidence of the simultaneous formation of dihydrofolate. This method is clearly useful only in the absence of gross impurities, that is, at high levels of enzyme in crude extracts or with purified enzyme. It is also best suited for the estimation of initial reaction rates for the estimation of various kinetic constants.

More recently Smith and Greenberg have developed an assay of thymidylate synthetase based on the release of the tritium atom of deoxyuridylate-5-³H as a proton during the formation of thymidylate. This proton is exchangeable with that in water, and the radioactivity of the water can be assayed after adsorption of the nucleotide on charcoal (681, 682). Analysis of the method (682, 348) has revealed, however, that the maximal apparent enzyme activity by this method is only 37% that in the spectrophotometric assay. It was suggested that the discrepancy in rates may result from an isotope effect (348).

Yeh and Greenberg have recently demonstrated that the dCMP hydroxymethylase also catalyses a specific exchange between the tritium atom on carbon 5 of dCMP-5-³H and water. They have adapted this reaction to a sensitive assay for this enzyme, measuring either the tritium released into the water or that retained in the nucleotide, adsorbed on charcoal (823).

To show that the reactions studied are not complicated by substances such as activators or inhibitors present in extracts or by the existence of unsuspected coupled enzymes, cofactors, or other reactants, it is customary to estimate reaction rate as a function of variation in the amount of extract. The rate of fixation of formaldehyde to dCMP was proportional to the amount of the extract (210), as was that of tritium release from dCMP-³H (823). A linear dependence of reaction rate on concentration of the extract has also been seen for thymidylate synthetase (211, 682). However, the presence of undefined substances inhibitory for dihydrofolate reductase has been detected in extracts of *E. coli* (499, 227, 501).

We also followed the dependence of rate on time in the hydroxymethylase reaction carried out at 37° and noted that the rate usually fell off after 20 minutes. It was shown that the presence of mercaptoethanol maintained the initial rate for longer periods, and we have suggested that mercaptoethanol protects the THFA from oxidation. The decrease in reaction rate with time, however, is also due to inhibition by the production of dHMP, which was shown to be inhibitory on the ³H-exchange reaction as well (823).

Mechanisms of the Reactions   In our early studies of the reaction products derived from dCMP in reaction mixtures containing crude extracts and radioactive HCHO, the bulk of the ¹⁴C fixed was isolated in dHMP (208, 210). Traces of other radioactive compounds were also separated, including traces of 5-hydroxymethyldeoxyuridylate, containing 1% of the isotope fixed. These are clearly products of side reactions due to contaminating enzymes, which are discussed in Chapter 4. The hydroxymethylase activity in uninfected cells was less than 1/200 of the activity in infected cells; as will be seen below, it was shown eventually that there is actually no dCMP hydroxymethylase at all in uninfected cells.

In our early studies it was not at all clear that the initial product of the thymidylate synthetase in crude extracts was not the hydroxymethyldeoxyuridylate. To test this, the latter compound was prepared in the labeled form, but it was not converted into thymidylate in the active system. Although this substance was slightly inhibitory to thymidylate synthesis, its presence in the unlabeled form in reaction mixtures did not markedly affect the incorporation of formaldehyde into thymidylate. Thus, free 5-hydroxymethyldeoxyuridylate is not an intermediary in the formation of thymidylate (211). A mechanism of this reaction with particular reference to the contribution of a hydrogen atom by the reduced pterin in THFA has been postulated by Friedkin (225). A reaction sequence indicating the dissociation of hydrogen at carbon 5 and the hydrogen donation from N^5,N^{10}-methylene-THFA is presented in Fig. 11.

Although it was originally supposed that N^5,N^{10}-methylene-tetrahydrofolate was a reactant in both reactions, the study of the requirements for catalytic exchange of the hydrogen atoms on carbon

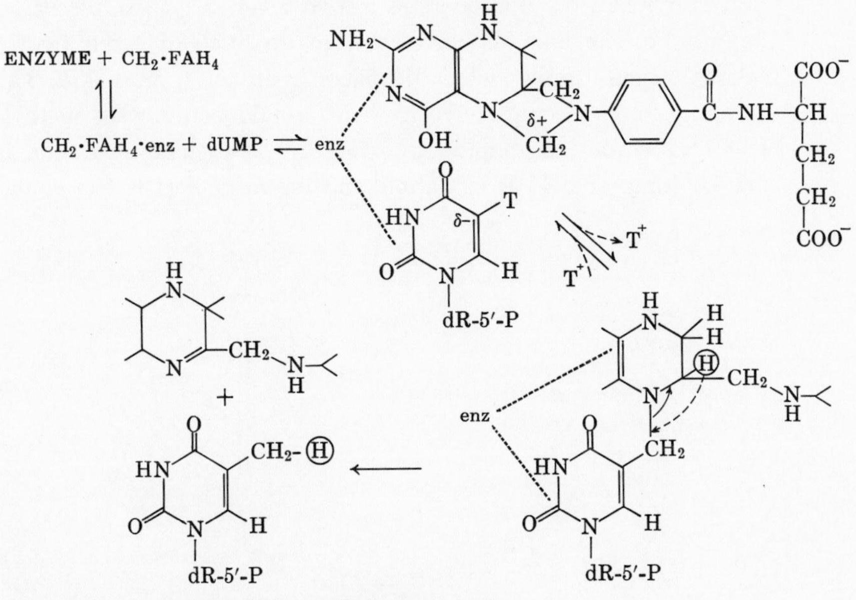

Figure 11. The origin of the methyl group in the thymidylate synthetase reaction (683). $CH_2 =$ FAH_4 (N^5, N^{10}-methylene tetrahydrofolate).

5 of the nucleotide substrates has revealed marked differences in the mechanisms of the two systems. In the case of thymidylate synthetase, the exchange rate is maximal when all components of the system are present (683). Although the exchange had an absolute requirement for tetrahydrofolate, as did the binding of deoxyuridylate to the enzyme, omission of formaldehyde decreased the exchange to no more than 22% to 29% of that in the complete systems. Even this low exchange rate may have been caused by the presence of traces of formaldehyde in THFA preparations. The mechanism in Fig. 11 supposes that N^5,N^{10}-methylene-tetrahydrofolate is an obligate reactant for both hydrogen exchange and methyl formation by thymidylate synthetase.

On the other hand, the exchange of hydrogen from dCMP by the hydroxymethylase, although requiring tetrahydrofolate, was even more active in the absence of formaldehyde than in its presence (823). Yeh and Greenberg have demonstrated that the dCMP hydroxymethylase reaction operates in two reversible steps, presented in Fig. 12. The first step involves the formation of a tetrahydrofolate-enzyme complex which displaces hydrogen from dCMP. The resulting ternary complex reacts with formaldehyde or the methylene-tetrahydrofolate to produce dHMP. The exchange reaction is rate-limiting for dHMP formation, and the ratio of $H^{14}CHO$ bound

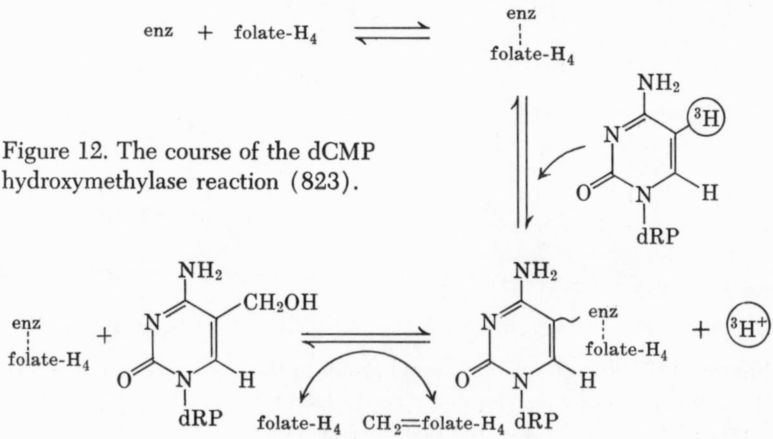

Figure 12. The course of the dCMP hydroxymethylase reaction (823).

to ^{3}H released approaches 1.0 throughout various stages of enzyme purification.

The reversibility of the dCMP hydroxymethylase reaction can be demonstrated by coupling it to the synthetase reaction, removing formaldehyde from dHMP to form the methyl group in dTMP. In such a reaction, tetrahydrofolate is also converted into dihydrofolate.

Some Properties of the dCMP Hydroxymethylase   A significant purification of the dCMP hydroxymethylase, to be discussed later, permitted the estimation of a number of kinetic constants for the enzyme (574). After a 40-fold purification the enzyme preparation was free of the thymidylate synthetase but still contained some bacterial protein. The enzyme behaved as a typical protein, being fairly stable at neutral pH and maximally active in the range pH 6.5 to 8 when assayed in phosphate buffer at 37°. No significant requirement for metal ions was detected. The enzyme is completely inactive on CMP; however, the arabinonucleotide, araCMP, appears to be about 0.6% as active as dCMP in the standard assay (572). The K_m's determined for THFA, dCMP, and HCHO were $1 \times 10^{-4}\,M$, $6 \times 10^{-4}\,M$, and $1.5 \times 10^{-3}\,M$, respectively, in order of decreasing affinity for the enzyme. As we shall see later, the presence of dCMP or dHMP stabilizes the enzyme (810); this fact suggests the possible use of dCMP in some purification steps. The reaction product, dHMP, is inhibitory to the enzyme in a competitive manner with K_i of $1 \times 10^{-4}\,M$ (574). The reaction product, then, has a greater affinity for the enzyme than does the substrate, deoxycytidylate.

Although important inhibitors have been found for thymidylate synthetase or dihydrofolate reductase, to be discussed below, a powerful inhibitor other than dHMP has not been found for the dCMP hydroxymethylase. Imidazole as a buffer in the reaction mixture is somewhat inhibitory. Neither araCMP, CMP, nor 5-fluorodeoxycytidylate was inhibitory when added with dCMP or preincubated alone with the enzyme. Purified enzyme, injected into rabbits, yielded antisera which completely inactivated the enzyme (574).

By 1961, despite a considerable effort in purification of the enzyme, it was clear from serological and metabolic studies that the enzyme preparation still contained significant amounts of bacterial proteins (574). It is of methodological interest that at this stage these gross impurities were not revealed by sedimentation or electrophoretic analysis. Nevertheless, a molecular weight (MW) was obtained for the particle bearing enzymatic activity. A sedimentation rate constant ($S_{20,w} = 4.29 \times 10^{-13}$ cm/sec) was obtained by means of the transport method with the fixed partition cell (753), and a diffusion constant ($D_{20,w} = 6.10 \times 10^{-7}$ cm²/sec) was estimated with the porous disc diffusion cell (539). From the relation $MW = RTS/D \ (1 - \bar{v}\rho)$, a partial specific volume of 0.75 being assumed, a molecular weight of $68,500 \pm 4000$ has been calculated for the enzyme from the data.

Some Remarks on the Discovery of a Virus-Induced Enzyme   For several reasons the purification of the dCMP hydroxymethylase was developed until it was essentially free of bacterial proteins (497). The enzyme still behaves as a protein and contains amino acids incorporated totally after virus infection. The proof of the *de novo* origin of this enzyme took about seven years of effort in our laboratory. These points are mentioned in view of the significance assigned by Stent (693) to the work of Sertic in 1929 (648) on a soluble lysin liberated by phage-infected cells. Stent believes that Sertic was the first to discover a phage-induced enzyme. Without minimizing in any way Sertic's significant contribution, I wish to examine this view.

An enzyme is defined generally as a protein catalyst, and a catalyst is understood to lower the energy of activation of a reaction: Such a definition has been accepted for many decades. The discovery of the existence of an enzyme would then seem to warrant the definition of the catalysed reaction, including the substrates and products, as well as its stoichiometry. Furthermore, some evidence concerning the protein nature of the particle bearing the catalytic activity is required in view of the catalytic activity of numerous small molecules. These considerations, which are elementary in modern biochemistry and were so even at the time of Sertic's discovery of the existence of a lysin in phage plaques, are not part of Stent's frame of reference in his appraisal of Sertic's work. Stent alludes to Sertic's antigenic tests and to differences in heat sensitivity among phage-induced lysins, which Stent freely categorizes as "lysozyme." Lysozyme has been exactly defined for some years as a muramidase, as we shall see later. Many lysins other than lysozyme are known as products of phage infection; there is a very good chance that the activity observed by Sertic was not that of a muramidase. It is easy to imagine situations in which serology would fail to reveal the presence of a protein in a normal cell or in which heat sensitivity of activities would be modified by substances present in nondialysed extracts. In short, Sertic had not defined the reaction thought to be catalysed, nor had he satisfactorily characterized the presumed catalysts.

One distinction it seems important to make is that between the discovery of an activity and its biochemical characterization. Dalton postulated the existence of atoms from data on stoichiometry; he did not discover the existence of atoms. It must also be said that Sertic's formulation of his conclusion concerning the origin of the lysin is not so unequivocal as the interpretation of it by Stent. As I have indicated above, this interpretation has not yet been supported by the experimental data.

From the preceding remarks it appears that data on only a few enzymes found in virus-infected cells have met the simple, if rigorous, criteria for the claim of discovery of a virus-induced enzyme, criteria which would satisfy a biochemist writing in the 1960s. The clarification of the nature and origin of the deoxyribonuclease activity, which increases during infection, to which Stent also referred, took about fifteen years, of which the last three have been decisive; this topic is discussed in Chapter 4. Indeed, the problem of meeting these criteria for the nature and origin of numerous such enzymes has proved to be one of the most difficult and pressing tasks in plant and animal virus systems, as well as in bacteriophagy.

Physiological Control of dCMP Hydroxymethylase (209, 212)
After discovery of this new activity in infected cells, we raised
various questions concerning the origin of the enzyme. Was it inserted into the bacterium by the virus? It was not possible to detect the enzyme in large quantities of disrupted virus. Was the
enzyme present in an inhibited state in uninfected cells? No excess
of such an inhibitor could be detected in the uninfected cells, since
mixing of extracts of uninfected and infected cells did not reduce
the activity. Was the production of the enzyme characteristic of T-
even phage infection? Yes, since multiplication of T1, T5, and λ
phage in *E. coli* did not elicit the appearance of the enzyme. A T-
even phage particle, which has lost its internal contents as a result
of osmotic shock but is capable of adsorbing to the bacteria and of
affecting bacterial metabolism, cannot induce the production of the
enzyme. The contents of a T-even phage head, then, are essential
for the appearance of the enzyme. In addition to the viral DNA,
small amounts of a specific internal protein (432), polypeptides
(305), and polyamines (305, 7) are also lost from the phage by
osmotic shock, but the replacement of the polyamines by other cations is reported to be without effect on phage viability (6). The
phage head does not contain free pyrimidine deoxyribonucleotides,
which, it might be imagined, induce the biosynthesis of the hydroxymethylase (212). In short, it might be inferred that the insertion
of a specific virus DNA initiates and determines enzyme synthesis.

When a culture of prototrophic *E. coli* strain B has been infected
in the exponential phase of growth at 2 to 4×10^8 bacteria per ml
with T-even phage and aliquots have been assayed for enzyme content at various intervals, the appearance of enzyme can be detected
within 2 minutes, the earliest point taken by us. Somerville and his
colleagues (684) have recorded the detection of enzyme within 1
minute, and a report from Kornberg's laboratory (390) indicates a
similar finding. On the other hand, Buchanan's laboratory reports
that an enzyme such as the dCMP hydroxymethylase appears at
least 3 minutes after infection (274). It is impossible to determine
from the published papers of the latter group precisely how most
of the experiments were done; it is stated in an early paper (172)

that cells were grown to 1×10^9, chilled, warmed for 1 minute at 37°, and then infected. Since the cells were probably no longer in their exponential phase, it is perhaps not surprising that these workers observe a lag in the appearance of enzyme. On the other hand, it is quite clear that under most conditions of infection there is a delay of several minutes in the appearance of the thymidylate synthetase (211, 644) as compared to that of the dCMP hydroxymethylase. The possible significance of both of these observations is discussed in Chapter 6.

After the initiation of increase of the dCMP hydroxymethylase, the rate of increase is often fairly constant for 10 to 15 minutes. It is of interest that at the time DNA synthesis begins (at about 7 minutes) the hydroxymethylase content of the cell can maintain a rate of dHMP synthesis sufficient to produce 120 T2 virus particles per cell, if synthesis is continued for 14 minutes. This value is close to that of a typical yield of T-even phage per cell in a one-step growth experiment in the glucose-salts medium used.

A plateau in enzyme level is attained between 15 and 20 minutes (211). This apparent arrest of synthesis of the hydroxymethylase is obtained shortly after DNA synthesis has begun. Such a result has been obtained for all enzymes produced early in infection; the paper of Kornberg and his co-workers indicates the generality of this phenomenon (390). Only the virus internal protein, to be discussed later, is synthesized both early and late throughout the multiplication cycle (511). We return to these phenomena in some detail later, but some of the questions posed may be at least noted at this point: Does the synthesis of early enzymes actually stop? Assuming that the arrest of synthesis of early enzymes is real, how is it controlled? Recalling that the virus structural proteins appear late, we can ask also about the nature of the switch that turns off synthesis of early proteins and turns on the synthesis of the late proteins.

As an approach to the problem of the role of virus DNA in determining enzyme production, we irradiated virus with lethal doses of ultraviolet light. After infection with such killed virus, under conditions in which neither DNA synthesis nor virus multiplication occurred, hydroxymethylase production was not reduced (209, 212). In fact, as reported by Delihas (160, 161) and subsequently by Dirksen and her colleagues (172), under these conditions enzyme appearance continues long after the time at which the switchoff should have occurred and can attain a level several times greater than that attained normally (172).

A similar result on the continuation of synthesis of the hydroxymethylase and other early enzymes was obtained with certain phage mutants, termed "amber," which are incapable of synthesis of virus DNA (811). The significance of these observations and of these mutants is discussed later in greater detail; for the present it may be noted that infection with irradiated phage or certain phage mutants can, by increasing the specific activity of an extract, facilitate the isolation of a virus-induced enzyme.

In a third method of removing the control of enzyme synthesis, Mosig and Revel (520) used particles isolated from T4 populations which contain a single DNA fragment about two-thirds as long as normal T4 DNA. Although such deficient particles cannot multiply under conditions of single infection, they do not all contain the same piece of DNA but appear to contain continuous random segments of the genome. In single infection they produce both dCMP hydroxymethylase and dTMP synthetase and, as with irradiated or amber particles, enzyme synthesis does not turn off at the usual time. On the other hand, in multiple infection, although progeny do not appear in 40% of the cells, enzyme synthesis is stopped at 15 minutes.

Of course, application of relatively large amounts of ultraviolet irradiation to the virus reduces the ability to produce the dCMP hydroxymethylase. About 19 phage-lethal hits reduce the induced activity to 37% of the unirradiated control; that is, the sensitivity of the site in the DNA controlling this activity is about 5% that of infectivity, or the totality of sites determining the ability to multiply (161). On the other hand, the sensitivity of the site to electrons (161) and ^{32}P decay (184) are 34% and 40% that of infectivity, respectively. Although the data on sensitivity to ultraviolet light suggest a site of the order of size ascribed to various individual cistrons, the data on sensitivity to electrons and ^{32}P decay suggest the participation of a rather large subunit of the phage DNA in the phenotypic expression of a phage gene. As we shall see later, the cistron for thymidylate synthetase is believed to be in a different part of the phage chromosome from that containing the cistron for the hydroxymethylase. It is possible that these cistrons may show similar sensitivities to ultraviolet radiation but very different sensitivities to the other treatments.

As a byproduct of the study by Delihas (161) it was determined that the rate of development of the hydroxymethylase was independent of the multiplicity of infection. This result was also obtained later for two T-even phage-induced enzymes, deoxycytidine triphosphatase (556) and DNA methylase (294).

Enzyme Appearance and Protein Synthesis   Previous formulations of the phenomena employed "appearance," "production," and "synthesis," but it was possible that these terms should not be used interchangeably. As a first approach to defining the nature of the events involved, we wished to see if appearance of the enzyme had an amino acid requirement, that is, required protein synthesis. As described earlier, inhibition of virus multiplication and DNA synthesis by 5-methyltryptophan, added early in infection of *E. coli* strain B, was reversed by simultaneous or subsequent addition of trytophan (109, 110, 130). Extending these results, we showed that enzyme appearance was prevented by 5-methyltryptophan in the absence of tryptophan. The presence of the natural amino acid, if added immediately with the analogue or even after a period of inhibition of 15 minutes, permitted an immediate synthesis of the hydroxymethylase (212). An essentially identical result, an amino acid requirement for enzyme appearance, has been obtained in the infection of amino acid-requiring auxotrophs, such as the tryptophan- or methionine-requiring mutants of *E. coli* strain B (212, 573). The conclusion has been generally accepted that the appearance of this enzyme does involve protein synthesis.

It is common these days to use chloramphenicol to demonstrate a requirement for protein synthesis in this (499) and numerous other developmental phenomena, as indeed it was used earlier to show the need for protein synthesis as a prerequisite to the synthesis of phage DNA (86, 756, 309). Recent experiences with this antibiotic, however, suggest that it may have other roles in addition to that of inhibiting polypeptide synthesis. Some caution is therefore warranted at this time about forming conclusions after its use. Indeed, in some instances, caution is also warranted in interpreting results with some amino acid requirements; for example, methionine fulfills several metabolic roles. Nevertheless, the results in infection of a tryptophan-requiring organism by T2 in the presence and absence of tryptophan appear unequivocal at present. These results suggest that we have solved the problem of the nature of the requirement for synthesis of nonviral proteins in producing virus DNA. The requirement is clearly that of permitting the appearance of the early enzymes, such as the dCMP hydroxymethylase, which are essential for the production of components of viral DNA.

Enzyme Appearance and RNA Synthesis   As the synthesis of proteins in bacteria is dependent for the most part on a previous synthesis of RNA, it would be important to be able to show that an RNA component is essential for enzyme production. Despite the lack of accumulation of RNA in infection (109, 110), it had in fact been shown that RNA bases and the synthesis of RNA were essential to the production of phage (774, 561). It is difficult, however, to establish a requirement in these systems for an RNA component, such as uracil. The turnover of RNA, which supplies uracil nucleotides to the intracellular pool, usually permits enzyme production after only a slight delay, as in the case of the uracil-less *E. coli* strain THU infected by T6 in the absence of uracil (644). However, in infection by T6 of the unusual uracil-requiring *E. coli* strain W_{c^-}, which produces hydroxymethylase but not virus DNA, the appearance of hydroxymethylase was almost completely dependent on exogenous uracil (573). At this level of the analysis, then, the physiological results suggested that the appearance of enzyme required synthesis of both RNA and protein, syntheses which were determined by the injection of viral DNA.

The Absence of Active dCMP Hydroxymethylase in Normal E. coli

To approach the proof that the enzyme is determined entirely by the viral genome and synthesized entirely after infection, we wish to be sure that the bacterial genome does not store the information for even a single molecule of the enzyme. We cannot solve this problem directly at this time, but we can ask if any molecules of active enzyme can be detected in the uninfected cell. It will be recalled that in the usual induction of enzyme synthesis by small molecules, enzymes determined within the cellular genome, small but nevertheless significant base levels of active enzyme can always be detected.

To determine if there is not even one active molecule per cell, we had to know the approximate turnover number of the enzyme

Table 6. Exclusion of Active dCMP Hydroxymethylase in Uninfected E. coli

	Chromatography			
	Nucleotide	Free Base		
Assay Tube (mg protein) †	Isobutyrate-NH₄OH	Butanol-NH₄OH	Isopropanol-HCl	Expected cpm for 1 Molecule Enzyme per Cell †
	cpm per 0.55 μmole			
0	9900	890	22	0
1.56	5050	440	15.4	652
3.12	4450	288	3.7	1304
4.68	2800	332	6.4	1956
3.12 + 0 dCMP	1430	120	0.5	0

† One milligram of protein = 5.6×10^9 cells. One molecule of enzyme of molecular weight 68,000 would produce 1.07×10^{-14} μmoles dHMP per 20 minutes.‡ ¹⁴C-Formaldehyde was used at 7×10^6 cpm/μmole.

‡ In a paper written in 1961 (118) the calculation given was based on a lower specific activity of enzyme than was obtained in later work. As described by Mathews, Brown, and me (497), the most active enzyme obtained had a specific activity of 9500 units per mg of protein, a value markedly higher than that used in the early calculation. A unit of enzyme is defined as that amount which adds 0.01 μmole of formaldehyde to form dHMP in 20 minutes. The turnover number of the enzyme has been calculated to be 320 molecules of substrate per minute per molecule of enzyme.

molecule, that is, the number of molecules of substrate used per minute per enzyme, and to devise a test involving a sufficient number of cells over a sufficient length of time to permit the detection of the product of activity of one enzyme molecule per cell. In this instance the calculation compelled us to use a very sensitive assay method which, in our hands at that stage of the technical development, meant that we had to use HCHO of fairly high ^{14}C content. In the actual experiment performed by Dr. L. I. Pizer (see 118), unlabeled carrier dHMP added to the different reaction mixtures containing various levels of cell extract, or lacking substrate, was not readily freed of label. After purification of the free base derived from this dHMP, it was shown finally (Table 6) that there was present in the HMC far less radioactivity than would be present if an extract contained the equivalent of 1 molecule of enzyme per cell. It appears, then, that a normal cell does not contain a single molecule of active enzyme before infection.

On infection with a T-even phage, as a consequence of protein synthesis, a bacterium develops about 6000 molecules of enzyme in about 20 minutes. Is this enzyme the newly synthesized protein, as we might suspect? Before we answer this question, let us survey the data on thymidylate synthetase.

Thymidylate Synthetase   In contrast to the dCMP hydroxymethylase, which increases in amount from zero activity to some finite number of isolable enzyme molecules, a significant level of thymidylate synthetase is present in all but a few thymine-requiring strains. The presence of such an enzyme is of course consistent with the presence of thymine in most DNA. On infection of a prototrophic *E. coli* with a T-even phage the increase of synthetase activity presented in Fig. 13, starts at a finite level and increases about 5-fold before reaching a plateau between 15 and 20 minutes (211). Does this increase in a pre-existing activity represent the formation of a completely new polypeptide determined by a viral gene, or is it due to depression of an existing bacterial gene?

The dTMP synthetase should not be confused with the dCMP hydroxymethylase. Not only can dTMP synthetase be separated

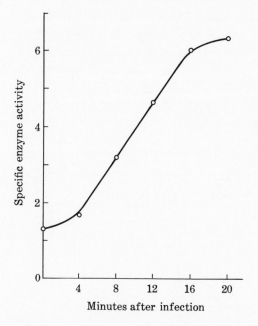

Figure 13. The time course of increase in thymidylate synthetase activity of cells infected with T2r+ (211).

physically from the latter, but indeed it appears a bit later in time in a T-even phage infection. In a T5 infection the dTMP synthetase is synthesized without any appearance of the hydroxymethylase (33). On the other hand, neither enzyme is produced in infection with T1 or with T-even phage ghosts. These data strongly suggest, but do not prove, that the virus genome determines whether the synthetase is formed. It will be recalled that the appearance of thymine synthesis in a thymineless auxotroph was our first indication for a virus-induced function. Although our failure to find evidence for the existence of this synthetase in *E. coli* strain 15T⁻ before infection (33) suggests a determining role for the virus genome, other commonly used thymineless strains such as *E. coli* strain B_{T-}, for example, B_3, do contain low levels of the enzyme. Therefore the possibility of depression cannot be easily excluded with such organisms. The production of the enzyme required tryptophan in an infected auxotroph, but this result would be expected for either mechanism.

Greenberg and his collaborators (271) were the first to show that an extract of an infected prototroph contains two separable fractions of thymidylate synthetase, in contrast to extracts of normal cells which contain only one. This result is presented in Fig. 14. Rechromatography of the new fraction appearing after infection did not affect its characteristic elution profile. Analysis of infected thymineless bacteria revealed only a single fraction of thymidylate synthetase; in the elution pattern it was in the position characteristic of the new peak appearing on virus infection of a prototroph (271). Kinetic constants for the bacterial and phage-induced synthetases showed some differences. Although the K_m values for dUMP

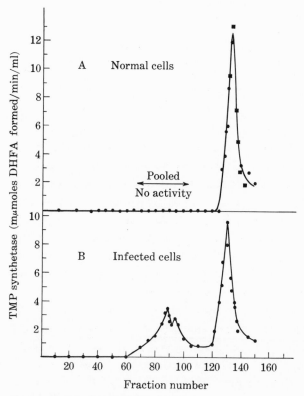

Figure 14. The thymidylate synthetases of normal and T2r$^+$-infected *E. coli* (271).

with both enzymes were similar, the K_m values for THFA were significantly different (271). This evidence suggests most strongly that the increase in this activity is effected by the synthesis of a completely new protein, and it would be supposed that its polypeptide sequence would not be represented in the host genome. Greenberg and his colleagues (271) have described the marked lability of the virus-induced enzyme, a property which has tended to minimize work on its purification, work which is needed to confirm these inferences unequivocally. Nevertheless, other data have provided evidence for the control of synthesis of the enzyme by virus genes. Some of these data stemmed originally from our studies of cell death as a result of thymine deficiency.

Some Studies with 5-Fluorouracil   I have described our experiences with thymineless death in Chapter 2 and have shown in the preceding section how the requirement for thymine in certain thymineless strains results from a deficiency of thymidylate synthetase. In 1954 Heidelberger and Duschinsky and their collaborators (182, 299, 68, 636) showed that 5-fluorouracil, and particularly its deoxyribonucleoside, possess unusual antitumor activity and that these compounds affect the biosynthesis of thymine in bacterial and tumor systems (299, 68, 636). These workers invited our laboratory to participate in the study of the effects of these compounds in bacterial systems. Our earlier experience with pyrimidine nucleosides had even permitted us to develop a useful enzymatic procedure for the synthesis of fluorodeoxyuridine (129).

The study of these compounds in growing bacteria made it possible to show that free fluorouracil or its ribonucleoside was mainly bacteriostatic, the inhibition being extensively reversible by uracil (129). These results suggested that these compounds mainly affect RNA metabolism, and indeed it has been shown that fluorouracil ribonucleotides can enter the RNA of many kinds of cell and even produce aberrant messages. Fluorodeoxyuridine was quite bactericidal, however (129). That the bactericidal effect is readily prevented by the presence of thymine but not uracil emphasizes the effect on DNA synthesis. We have concluded that the presence of the deoxyribonucleoside produces thymineless death, and it is generally believed that a similar mechanism operates in the effect of this substance in killing tumor cells and in restricting tumor growth. Fluorouracil and its deoxyribonucleoside do not enter DNA, although fluorodeoxyuridine can be phosphorylated to fluorodeoxyuridylate (F-dUMP) (129). Both F-dUTP and dUTP are incorporated into DNA *in vitro* by the *E. coli* DNA polymerase (389). It appears that significant levels of F-dUTP and dUTP do not accumulate *in vivo*. The latter, at least, is actively dephosphorylated (270, 54); thus its exclusion from normal DNA is completely explained.

With the high levels of thymidylate synthetase present in extracts of infected cells, we were able to show that fluorodeoxyuridylate inhibited this reaction quite specifically (129). The D-arabinonucleotide of 5-fluorouracil has about 1/100 of this inhibitory activity, whereas the inhibitory activity of the ribonucleotide is only about 10^{-4} that of F-dUMP (118). Preincubation of the enzyme with F-dUMP seemed to inactivate the enzyme irreversibly (129, 211). Estimating initial reaction rates by spectrophotometric methods, we showed that the enzyme can be essentially titrated with this nucleotide; during preincubation in the absence of substrates there appears to be a stoichiometric reaction between enzyme and inhibitor (498). On the other hand, when F-dUMP and dUMP are added simultaneously, the substrate competes with the inhibitor for binding sites (498). Although large amounts of substrate can no longer release the inhibition observed with enzyme preincubated with F-dUMP, it appears that the inactive enzyme-F-dUMP complex can be reactivated by dialysis or Sephadex chromatography (496).

A number of kinetic constants were determined for the thymidylate synthetase induced by T2 and T6 in different bacteria (498). Table 7 shows that the K_m for dUMP and the K_i for F-dUMP were considerably different for the T2- and T6-induced enzymes. These values for the T2 enzyme were the same in two different hosts. Although T6 does not infect *E. coli* 15T$^-$, the *E. coli* strain 15 THU does support T6. The synthetase induced in T6-THU has properties similar to that induced in *E. coli* strain B. Briefly, then, different

Table 7. Properties of Thymidylate Synthetase
Preparations (498)

Enzyme Source	K_m for dUMP $(M \times 10^5)$	K_i for F-dUMP $(M \times 10^8)$	F-dUMP Concentration Giving 50% Inhibition $(M \times 10^8)$
T2-15T⁻	1.8 ± 0.1	2.9 ± 0.4	3.9
T2-B	1.7 ± 0.1	2.8 ± 0.1	3.7
T6-B	3.0 ± 0.3	7.3 ± 0.1	8.7

viruses infecting the same host produce different enzymes, and this conclusion suggests that the phage genome determines the primary structure of the enzyme.

The thymidylate synthetase of uninfected *E. coli* strain B has recently been isolated, and various kinetic constants for the inhibition of the enzyme by pterin derivatives have been reported (677).

The Physiological Role of Phage-Induced Thymidylate Synthetase
We had suggested that the expansion of this activity facilitated the synthesis of viral DNA, since the activity we had observed in normal cells was not in excess of the activity required for cell multiplication (211). The isolation of thymine-requiring mutants of phage T4 (817, 666) appeared to permit a test of this hypothesis, because such mutants induce decreased amounts of the enzyme. These amounts range from less than 1% to about 15% of the wild type controls without affecting the induced levels of some other enzymes, such as the dCMP hydroxymethylase (653). Although the mutants, lacking this "td" function, multiplied very poorly on a thymineless bacterium in the absence of exogenous thymine, they appeared to multiply as rapidly as the wild type phage on a prototrophic bacterium (666). Thymine seemed to be in normal supply from the degradation of host-cell DNA and the activity of the host thymidylate synthetase. This seemed to mean that the host enzyme was adequate for the increased rate of DNA synthesis seen on infection. If this were true, why should there be a virus-induced synthetase?

When this subject was re-examined in greater detail by Mathews (492), it was found that the rate of DNA synthesis was twice as great after infection of *E. coli* strain B by the parent than by the mutant, as shown in Fig. 15. When phage multiplication was determined, it was observed that similar yields of wild type and mutant were obtained at high cell densities, where mutual feeding of infected cells was possible, but that markedly lower yields of mutant progeny were obtained with infected cultures incubated at low cell density (492). It appears then that the presence of the td function provides a selective advantage for the phage which induces a new thymidylate synthetase. This enzyme is useful but not essential in phage multiplication. The situation can be compared with that of strains of vaccinia virus resistant to iododeoxyuridine, which, having lost the ability to induce thymidine kinase, compete poorly with the wild type in infections in rabbit skin (203). This situation is

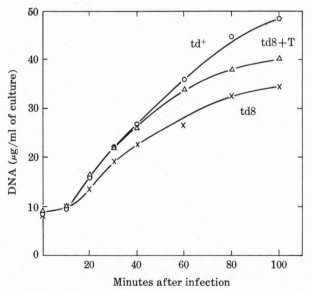

Figure 15. DNA synthesis in *E. coli* strain B infected by strains of T4 (492). Td+ = wild type T4r+; td8 = mutant strain unable to induce thymidylate synthetase; T = thymine.

unlike that for other enzymes, such as the dCMP hydroxymethylase, which in all but highly contrived situations must be considered essential for the multiplication of virus.

The Origin de novo of dCMP Hydroxymethylase   Although the evidence strongly suggested that the appearance of this enzyme was probably a product of protein synthesis after infection and that its primary structure was determined by the phage genome, the data at hand did not prove that the enzyme was made completely *de novo* after infection. We can imagine at least two other possibilities:

1. The enzyme is associated with a nondissociable moiety that inactivates the catalytic function. Protein synthesis after infection might produce a totally different type of enzyme which removes the inhibitory fragment, as in the conversion of pepsinogen into pepsin.
2. The enzyme is incomplete before infection. It comprises an inactive polypeptide precursor to which is added, by protein synthesis, a completing and activating fragment.

The existence of phage mutants which control the production of an altered hydroxymethylase is not entirely inconsistent with both of these possibilities nor with that of *de novo* biosynthesis. An altering enzyme controlled by mutant virus might eliminate the inhibited enzyme in a slightly different way or might add a polypeptide to a pre-existing precursor in a slightly different way. The experiments to demonstrate an altered hydroxymethylase induced by the mutants can be interpreted unequivocally only if we show a complete biosynthesis *de novo*. Actually, the notion of a phage-induced proteinase as an altering enzyme has become attractive in its own right, as we shall see in a subsequent discussion of the synthesis of polypeptides found in the phage head.

To test whether dCMP hydroxymethylase has a polypeptide precursor present in the host before infection, we decided to do an experiment in which host proteins were heavily labeled with a specific radioactive precursor. The formation of the enzyme was in-

duced by infection in an unlabeled medium, the enzyme was isolated, and its content of radioactivity was measured. This experiment actually took five years to perform properly. The initial
steps on enzyme purification and experimental design were carried
out with Dr. L. Pizer, and the final purification and modification required the efforts of Dr. C. Mathews and Dr. F. Brown. The detailed purification, which resulted in a very low degree of contamination of the hydroxymethylase by host protein, required three different types of chromatographic separations (497). This purification
was controlled by mixing normal bacteria grown in radioactive [35]S-
sulfate and infected bacteria grown in nonradioactive [32]S-sulfate.
Enzyme was isolated and shown to contain about 1% of the specific
radioactivity of the host protein. An experiment was then carried
out in the form presented in Fig. 16; cells were grown in limiting ^{35}S-sulfate and, after infection and incubation in [32]S-sulfate for
20 minutes, enzyme was isolated. The experiment revealed the
presence of ^{35}S in the enzyme with a specific radioactivity of 4% of
the host protein. Accordingly, the experiment had to be redesigned

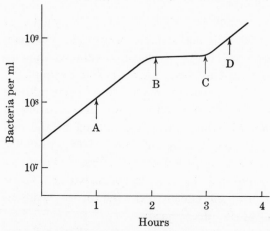

Figure 16. The design of an experiment to test the synthesis *de novo* of
dCMP hydroxymethylase. A. Grow in limiting ^{14}C-methionine. B. Starve
for methionine. C. Add excess ^{12}C-methionine. D. Infect; after 20
minutes isolate dCMP hydroxymethylase.

to eliminate three likely sources of error: the presence of a slowly utilizable ^{35}S-metabolite in the medium, which probably was mainly oxidized glutathione; a possible failure of the internal pools of precursors of labeled proteins to be depleted completely during sulfur "starvation"; and the possible breakdown of host cell protein to form ^{35}S-amino acids reutilizable in phage-directed protein synthesis.

We then repeated the experiment with ^{14}C-labeled methionine and a methionineless strain of *E. coli* unable to make enzyme in the absence of the amino acid. The methionine content of the purified enzyme was about 5%, equivalent to about 22 residues of methionine per molecule. Enzyme isolated from infected bacteria, prelabeled during growth in ^{14}C-labeled methionine, was found to be virtually devoid of radioactivity. The specific activity of the methionine isolated from the enzyme was less than 0.7% of the specific activity of the methionine of the cellular protein (497).

This value may be interpreted as follows. If the control value for contamination of enzyme by host protein is subtracted from the experimental value, the enzyme is totally devoid of radioactivity and hence of any pre-existing host precursor. If the control value, the contamination by host protein, is not subtracted and it is assumed that the label in methionine is representative of all the amino acids in general, numerous possible distributions of label in the enzyme can be imagined. At one extreme, it may be calculated that no more than 4 or 5 of about 680 amino acids can represent a polypeptide precursor of the enzyme; hence it seems highly unlikely that there is any specific polypeptide precursor for the enzyme.

If the label is concentrated, there would appear to be very few labeled polypeptide molecules in our enzyme preparation—the equivalent of perhaps 42 molecules of 6000 enzyme molecules made. However, we will recall that not even a single active molecule is found in the uninfected cell. The isolation procedure, in fact, revealed no peak of radioactivity at the position of the enzyme. Indeed, the control derived from the mixture of labeled uninfected cells and unlabeled infected cells suggested strongly that radioactivity present in the enzyme preparation had resulted from the carry-over of contaminant labeled protein eluted in a trailing fashion from the chromatographic column, rather than from the presence of a protein in normal cells chromatographically identical with the enzyme protein produced after infection. It is conceivable that the experiment could be done in such a way as to eliminate the possibility of a precursor relation for even the 42 molecules; for example, by a 10- to 100-fold scale-up of our actual 40-liter batch of infected cells or by development of an even better purification. However, we have taken the position that the totality of the data is currently convincing and does not now warrant the effort attendant on increasing the sensitivity of the experiment 100-fold.

This experiment rests as the sole effort and demonstration to show that, in the acquisition of a totally new physiological activity, there has been the acquisition of a totally new protein in response to the presence of new genetic material. No doubt the phenomenon proved to the limits described above was only to be expected, but we felt that the experimental demonstration of the validity of the supposition was warranted. It is by no means evident that this result can be automatically extrapolated to other systems.

There is much still to be done with the dCMP hydroxymethylase. The isolation is slow and tedious and warrants efforts toward improvement. The molecular weight is sufficiently high to suggest the existence of aggregable subunits. Virtually nothing is known about the structure of the enzyme. A good inhibitor has not yet been found for the enzyme, a detailed immunologic study has not yet been done, many physical constants have not been obtained, and so on. In short, we do not presume to have exhausted the reaction or the enzyme, but our interests have moved to other problems.

Virus Genes and the dCMP Hydroxymethylase   Conditional lethal phage mutants, permitting the isolation of the T-even phages which had lost the ability to perform essential functions, became available late in 1961 as a result of the work of Epstein, Edgar, and their colleagues (196). Two groups of them were isolated, the amber (*am*) mutants which can multiply in a permissive bacterium or the temperature-sensitive (*ts*) mutants which can multiply at a permissive temperature. The nature of these mutations is discussed in greater detail in Chapters 4 and 5. Groups of such mutants were recognized which lacked the ability to effect synthesis of phage DNA (811), and infection of a cell with some of these mutants permitted an exaggerated synthesis of early enzymes other than that controlled by the altered viral gene. Some of these mutants are unable to produce the dCMP hydroxymethylase under restrictive conditions. By using such mutants, a gene controlling the appearance of dCMP hydroxymethylase has been located in the viral chromosome and designated gene 42. Amber mutants bearing a mutation in gene 42 cannot produce the enzyme in *E. coli* strain B, but do so in other permissive strains. The interpretation of some of the early work with *am* mutants is not absolutely precise; for example, *am* N122 which was used extensively (811, 171) in the early studies is blocked in the synthesis of a viral-induced DNA polymerase as well as in synthesis of the dCMP hydroxymethylase (811). Differences in temperature sensitivity of the enzyme were obtained when one mutant was used to infect three different permissive hosts. The enzymes induced by different mutants in a single host also showed differences in stability. These results are consistent with the view that in an *am* mutation the replacement of one base by another in the viral DNA leads to the formation of a messenger RNA which cannot be translated past the altered codon; that is, incomplete polypeptides are formed. A permissive host may translate such nonsense as one type or another of acceptable missense, in which the polypeptide chain is extended with a single amino acid alteration in the normal primary structure of the polypeptide, that is, amino acid sequence. Such alterations in primary structure presumably result in instabilities in the folded conformation of the enzyme, revealed most frequently in increased sensitivities to temperature.

Similar results were also obtained with the hydroxymethylases produced by *ts* mutants, in which the site of mutation also maps in cistron 42 (810). The enzymes produced by two of these mutants at the permissive temperatures in *E. coli* strain B were also more temperature-sensitive than the wild type enzyme and, in addition, differed between themselves. These analyses revealed both the stabilization of wild type enzyme by dCMP and dHMP and the ability of the enzyme to be extensively reactivated after inactivation at 40°. These results were consistent with the view that a base replacement in a viral gene resulted in the production of an altered messenger RNA which could be translated completely to give missense, that is, a slightly altered polypeptide whose abnormal primary structure unfolds more easily with thermal stress. Thus a *ts* mutant induces a temperature-sensitive protein that can be conserved and is functional at a permissive temperature.

These results strongly suggest that a site, gene 42, in the viral genome is the structural gene for the virus-induced enzyme, dCMP hydroxymethylase. The completion of the evidence for this theory will require the demonstration that the different enzymes elaborated by wild type and mutant phages show single amino acid differences in the polypeptides.

It is clear, then, that two types of evidence, metabolic and genetic, contribute to the demonstration of the role of virus DNA in determining the structure of a virus-induced enzyme, the dCMP hydroxymethylase. This evidence, although limited, still is more complete in establishing the relation of this DNA-containing genetic site to its determined protein than that for any other virus-induced enzyme and indeed for almost any protein, as the data have some unique features not yet elaborated in the analysis of other phenotypic expressions. I close by noting that, in the ten years that have followed the discovery of the virus-induced dCMP hydroxymethylase and dTMP synthetase, dozens of other virus-induced enzymes have been detected in this and other systems. I shall evoke your dismay by suggesting that each one warrants these types of detailed analysis.

I don't believe it. / It's not interesting. / I did it several years ago. REMARKS HEARD AFTER A SEMINAR

Chapter 4

OTHER EARLY PROTEINS
IN T-EVEN PHAGE INFECTION

The decade in which we explored the nature and origin of the dCMP hydroxymethylase and the dTMP synthetase was one in which many biochemists became intrigued by the problems posed by the cellular division of labor: the separation of genetic elements, identified as nucleic acids, and the enzymatic machinery for protein synthesis. Having become aware of the existence of some chemical data in this area, first in the Watson-Crick model of DNA and then in the large body of accumulated and growing chemical knowledge in the field of the nucleic acids, biochemists and chemists began to recognize the challenges and opportunities for discovery in cellular biology. In the decade after World War II microbes were recognized by biochemists as manageable sources of problems and enzymes; after 1958 significant numbers recognized the advantages of the viruses in studying the role and metabolism of the nucleic acids, as well as the relations of these components to protein synthesis. In 1959 numerous groups began to explore the T-even phage systems and quite naturally made many discoveries, of which those of new phage-induced enzymes concern us here. Although initially the T-even phage systems received most of the interest, the biochemical and biophysical work soon spread to other systems which appeared to have some special advantages, to be discussed to some extent in Chapter 5.

Even classical animal virology became unable to withstand the successes of the phage methodology, and the development of tissue culture technology opened the way for the younger men to begin biochemical studies in this difficult field. In 1962, working with the RNA-containing Mengo virus in tissue culture, Franklin and his collaborators discovered the existence of an apparently virus-induced RNA polymerase (219, 30). At about the same time, increases in certain other enzymes, thymidine kinase and DNA polymerase, for example, were detected after infection by the DNA-containing vaccinia virus (263, 475, 505). With these initial discoveries the search for virus-induced enzymes in many virus infections grew; this has become a very active field indeed. As I indicated earlier, time and space compel me to limit my discussion of these events. In this chapter I wish to discuss the nature of the numerous early enzymes which appear in T-even phage infection, other than the dCMP hydroxymethylase and dTMP synthetase, and the problems presented by them.

In Chapter 3 I described in considerable detail the pursuit since 1957 of the two phage-induced enzymes with which this period of chemical virology began. I described the reactions catalysed by these enzymes, their isolation and characterization, and the efforts involved in discovering their genetic and physiological determination. There seems little doubt in these instances that these enzymes are new polypeptides made entirely after infection. Their primary structures are determined by virus genes operating in the structured enzymatic milieu presented by the parasitized host.

Such a conclusion cannot be extrapolated automatically to the virus-induced enzymes of plant and animal cells, however; for them, the data are far less complete and convincing. Indeed, in some systems we even have increases of certain enzymes in sufficient profusion to permit the conclusion that not all of these enzymes can be determined by the virus genome. For example, in mouse kidney cells in tissue culture, which have stopped DNA synthesis as a result of contact inhibition, infection by polyoma virus leads to an increase in the activities of not less than nine enzymes involved in DNA synthesis (354). Because the virus DNA is probably too small to code this number of enzymes, and no qualitative differences can be detected as yet between the enzymes of infected and noninfected cultures, Kára and Weil (354) concluded that viral infection leads to a derepression of this enzymatic apparatus, which is normally coded by the host genome and is involved normally in preparation for mitosis. Nevertheless, polyoma virus infection does lead also to the production of apparently new early proteins, that is, a new intranuclear antigen preceding the later appearance of virus capsids. It is clear that the problem presented for each new or increased activity by the existence of two potentially operable genomes requires the kind of rigor which has been developed for the dCMP hydroxymethylase in the T-even phage systems. Nevertheless, even in the latter systems in which a functional elimination of the *E. coli* genome occurs, sources of possible confusion can exist. For example, the increase of some activities, as for the nucleases, were not immediately interpretable as clearly as for the hydroxymethylase, because of the presence of numerous host nucleases and their inhibitors. For these reasons as well, the analysis of the status of the new activities induced in T-even phage infection warrants our interest from many points of view.

How Many New Proteins Are There?   It will be recalled that, in 1954, ^{35}S-sulfate was used to show the production of nonviral proteins immediately after T-even phage infection (308). This technique was utilized further by Watanabe who showed that proteins which incorporated ^{35}S before 10 minutes were not reactive with antisera to intact phage (789). In 1960 Thomas and Suskind described the use of antisera prepared against extracts of infected bacteria. Their report of strong reactivities of these antisera to intact phage, and even stronger reactions with disrupted phage, suggested the presence of internal phage antigens in the extracts. Even after absorption with intact and disrupted phage and extracts of uninfected cells, these antisera were still reactive with extracts of infected cells in precipitin and agar diffusion tests, indicating the presence of nonphage early proteins (752).

In our early experiments (574) on the isolation of the dCMP hydroxymethylase the initial chromatographic fractionation of extracts of infected cells which had incorporated ^{35}S after infection had revealed at least nine different separable peaks of radioactivity, which presumably represented separable proteins. The development of disc electrophoresis on polyacrylamide gels, with its high resolution of individual proteins, has been exploited by Levinthal and his collaborators (434). Combining this method of separating proteins with a pulse-labeling technique involving radioactive leucine, they have described three groups of early proteins, the last two of which are represented by the dCMP hydroxymethylase and the dTMP synthetase, respectively. Levinthal believes that he has discovered a group of very early proteins whose synthesis stops at about 3 minutes after infection; I have not yet seen enough data to be certain that these syntheses represent phage-induced proteins determined by viral genes.

The publication from Levinthal's laboratory in this field (434) presents evidence for the presence of about fifteen early proteins synthesized before the inception of DNA synthesis and about sixteen late proteins. The experiments in our laboratory by Dr. C. Freda using the Levinthal technique have yielded comparable results (220). In this technique, gels containing electrophoretically separated proteins which contain radioactive amino acids are placed in contact with a film. The developed autoradiographic banded film reveals the migration of the various proteins and is then analyzed in a densitometer. Typical tracings revealing the patterns of proteins which had incorporated ^{14}C-leucine in pulses between 7 and 9 and 19 and 21 minutes after infection are presented in Fig. 17. The two patterns differ quite markedly, and each reveals a minimum of 17 separable protein peaks. Thus at least 34 polypeptides are produced in these two intervals.

A T-even phage contains 2×10^5 nucleotide pairs, and a polypeptide of molecular weight about 20,000 may be expected to contain about 200 amino acids requiring codons of 600 nucleotides in RNA and 1200 nucleotides in DNA. It can be estimated that the information content of the phage DNA can permit the formation of about 300 polypeptides, a value greatly in excess of the number of proteins actually found. Of course, this calculation turns on the average size of the proteins, and in this connection it will be re-

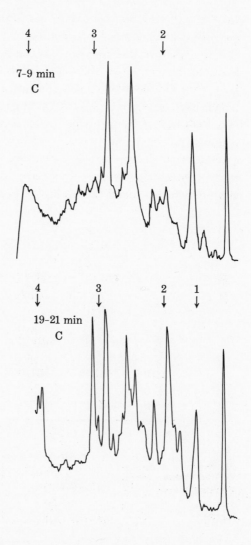

Figure 17. Densitometric tracings of autoradiographic films placed on gels containing electrophoretically separated radioactive proteins. They were derived from extracts of T6-infected *E. coli* strain THU which had incorporated ^{14}C-leucine in 2-minute pulses. Upper portion = pulses between 7 and 9 minutes. Lower portion = pulses between 19 and 21 minutes.

called that the hydroxymethylase has a molecular weight of 68,000 and may contain several polypeptides.

At this moment the functions attributable to the various proteins detected by combined disc electrophoresis and autoradiography have not been identified. I have, however, compiled a list of thirty-two virus-induced proteins possessing metabolic and structural functions detected so far in extracts. This list is presented in Fig. 18; it grows each year, but it is useful in orienting us to the types of activities and the approximate sequence of their emergence in extracts of infected cells. Among the early proteins are included seven enzymes which expand the ability to made H-DNA, a DNA con-

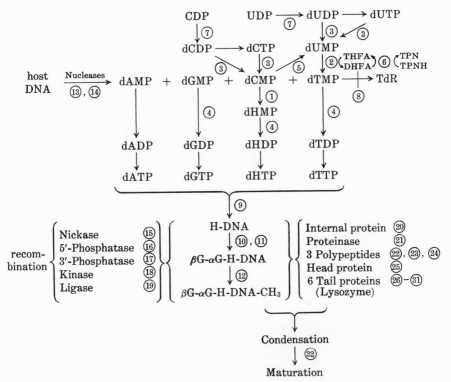

Figure 18. Enzymes and other proteins synthesized in T4 infection (1967).

taining hydroxymethylcytosine. Some slight evidence suggests the existence of an eighth which inhibits dTMP phosphatase. Three proteins are known which modify H-DNA by glucosylation and methylation. There appear to be at least two nucleases which degrade host DNA, and evidence has been adduced for at least five additional enzymes involved in recombination. There is also the internal protein of the phage, designated ⑳ in Fig. 18; this is the only phage protein known to be made early in infection. It is also the sole early protein whose synthesis is not cut off after DNA synthesis. There is thus evidence for twenty functional entities, elaborated relatively early after infection, which are conceivably all represented by different virus-induced proteins. In addition, there is evidence for some twelve more late proteins, including three polypeptides. Ten of these units are present within the virus; internal protein, two polypeptides, and seven external structural proteins of the virus. I have not included here reactions related to coding; they are discussed later. In this chapter I propose to consider only the early enzymes.

In 1959 the laboratories of Kornberg (390), Greenberg (684), and Buchanan (381) confirmed our report on the existence of the dCMP hydroxymethylase. They, in turn, described the presence of new or increased activities of deoxycytidine triphosphate (dCTP) pyrophosphatase, a deoxynucleotide kinase, DNA polymerase, and enzymes for the glucosylation of H-DNA in T-even phage-infected cells. Kornberg's laboratory also studied extracts of cells infected with a cytosine-containing virus, T5. During the ensuing eight years, these laboratories as well as ours not only continued studies in this area but also spurred the establishment of new laboratories led by younger workers who have both extended the earlier discoveries and made important new contributions of their own. Because this burgeoning area has now established so many parallel paths, it has become difficult to maintain historical continuity in this treatment, and I have decided to treat each new enzyme separately.

Deoxycytidine Triphosphatase (dCTPase)   After infection with a T-even phage, the DNA synthesized contains HMC exclusively.

How does an infected cell prevent the synthesis of DNA containing cytosine? The answer to this question began to be clarified by the discovery of an enzyme which destroyed dCTP. The existence of this enzyme in extracts of infected cells was detected in two types of assay. In the search for kinases for dHMP and dCMP, Kornberg and his co-workers (390), found that extracts of infected cells appeared to have lost the normal capability of phosphorylating dCMP. This apparent inhibition was actually due to the presence of an enzyme which degraded the products of phosphorylation, dCDP and dCTP. The normal level of dCMP kinase could be demonstrated in extracts by the use of fluoride (8×10^{-3} M) which is far more inhibitory to the dCTPase than to the kinase. Also, in the search for DNA polymerase in T2-infected bacteria, activity was not obtained initially with dCTP but was observed with dHTP (381). A DNA polymerase active with dCTP was then separated by chromatography from an enzyme which degrades dCTP.

This mechanism for destroying dCTP is found at a very low level in systems with a cytosine-containing DNA, as in the normal cell or in T5 infection. However, the dCTPase is increased 100-fold in T-even phage infection (Fig. 19), where it appears early and reaches

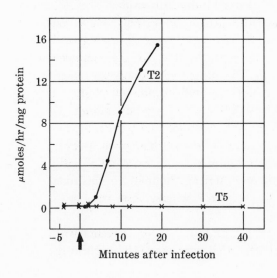

Figure 19. dCTPase levels before and after infection with phage T2 or T5 (390).

a maximal level at 20 minutes. The reactions have been shown to
be

$$dCTP + H_2O \rightarrow dCMP + \text{inorganic pyrophosphate} \quad (390, 381)$$

$$dCDP + H_2O \rightarrow dCMP + \text{orthophosphate} \quad (826)$$

The enzyme does act on dCDP (826) despite an initial report that
it is inactive on this substrate (381). The purified enzyme has little or no activity on ten deoxy- and ribonucleoside triphosphates
including dHTP and CTP. The activities on both dCTP and dCDP
are believed to be activities of a single enzyme, because the relative activities with the two substrates remained constant during
purification and the activities were similar with respect to Mg^{++}
activation, kinetic constants, and sensitivity to fluoride inhibition.
These two substrates are competitive inhibitors, and presumably
they act at the same reaction site on the enzyme.

The activity present in the uninfected cell is more active on
dCDP than on dCTP, whereas the reverse is found in infection. The
pre-existing activity is also essentially uninhibited by fluoride, in contrast to that present after infection. The degradative activity after
infection appears to be about sixty times greater than that of the
synthetic activity of the kinase which converts dCMP into dCTP.
The dCTPase thus appears to play two roles in T-even phage infection: the enzyme eliminates the substrate, dCTP, which is essential to the formation of a cytosine-containing DNA; and it converts dCDP and dCTP into dCMP, which serves as the substrate for
the dCMP hydroxymethylase. Indeed it appears that the enzyme is
essential for the synthesis of dCMP and hence of dHMP (581a).

It has been shown by Bessman and his colleagues (57) that the
DNA polymerase is capable of inserting dUTP in place of dTTP
into DNA, although natural DNA does not contain uracil. The exclusion of uracil from DNA in *E. coli* was then found to be controlled by a dUTPase which catalyses the hydrolysis of dUTP to
dUMP and PP_i (270, 54) and does not act on dUDP. Greenberg
subsequently showed that an enzyme possessing both dUTP and
dUDPase activities was also formed in extracts of infected cells

(269). After observation of its pH optimum, its inhibition by fluoride and dCTP, as well as its properties during purification, he suggested that these activities also may be due to the dCTPase. This hypothesis is strongly supported by the work of Warner and Barnes (787) who tested *am* phage mutants containing an altered gene 56, which were previously described as deficient in production of either dCTPase or dUTPase. The loss of the ability to produce one of the enzymes was always accompanied by the loss of ability to produce the other activity. Thus dCTPase appears to be a new enzyme, a polyfunctional pyrimidine deoxyribonucleoside pyrophosphate pyrophosphatase. Despite its activity on dUTP, the enzyme does not cleave dTTP.

It is of interest that, on infection with *am* gene 56 mutants, DNA does not accumulate; furthermore, the existence of host dCTPase and host dUTPase does not "rescue" the infection. However, phage mutants deficient in dCTPase are able to synthesize DNA (809) when the development of a nuclease facilitating destruction of host DNA is also blocked by the presence of a mutation in gene 46 or 47. The inference was drawn that such nucleases are probably fairly specific for cytosine-containing DNA and that dCTPase-less mutants might permit synthesis of cytosine-containing phage DNA, which is degraded by the new nuclease (809). Kutter (405) has shown that a *ts* dCTPase mutant of T4 makes normal amounts of DNA at 39° but only a quarter of the normal phage is produced; in such phage, cytosine was substituted for almost 21% of the HMC. Furthermore, such phage was normal in activity.

Not only do these data support the postulated role of dCTPase in excluding cytosine from phage DNA, but also they appear to suggest that HMC does not play a role distinct from that of cytosine in determining inheritance in T-even phage. We can imagine that the existence of HMC in phage was selected for protection against the nonspecific virus-induced nuclease which degraded both host DNA and cytosine-containing virus DNA. We suppose then that in phage evolution a cytosine-containing virulent phage preceded the HMC-containing phages, perhaps having evolved in bacteria lacking the nucleases found in *E. coli*. The acquisition of glucosylation suggested in Chapter 2 was a much later step; it followed the replacement of cytosine by HMC in the phage DNA.

Deoxynucleotide Kinase   The existence of dHMP, as well as of dCMP, had raised the question of the synthesis of dHTP for formation of virus DNA. Several laboratories undertook to test whether the phosphorylation of dHMP required a new enzyme. An enzyme capable of phosphorylating dHMP did develop in cells infected by T2, but not by T5 (390, 684). No trace of dHMP kinase could be detected before infection. This activity increases shortly after infection by T2; its concentration is essentially maximal at 20 minutes. In T-even phage infection, kinase activities also increase for dTMP and dGMP, but not for dCMP or dAMP, as shown in Fig. 20. As will be seen below, the increases of kinase activity for the three substrates, dTMP, dGMP and dHMP are three manifestations of a single newly formed phage-induced enzyme.

In T5 infection, on the other hand, no increase is observed for a dHMP kinase, but the kinase activity increases sharply for dTMP, dGMP, dCMP, and less so for dAMP (55, 390). With the exception of a lack of dAMP kinase in T-even phage infection the patterns of increase of kinase activities in T-even and T5 infections generally parallel their respective nucleotide compositions. The kinases do not appear to increase in T3 and T7 infection (55).

The study of deoxynucleotide kinases has been developed most extensively by Bessman and his collaborators. The reactions catalysed by crude extracts did not stop at the deoxynucleoside diphosphates; triphosphates were also formed. However, no increase was detected in the kinase for dHDP, which could be phosphorylated to the triphosphate by extracts of uninfected *E. coli* (46). This final step is considered to be the function of a pre-existing host enzyme, although this nucleoside diphosphate kinase has not yet been characterized. On the other hand, the appearance of a virus-induced deoxyribonucleotide kinase probably does represent new protein synthesis, since the presence of chloramphenicol at the beginning of T2 infection inhibits the appearance of this activity (55). Most of the dGMP kinase activity increased before any DNA replication

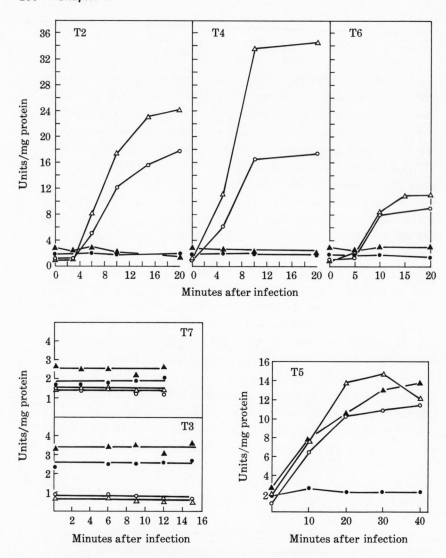

Figure 20. Deoxynucleotide kinases before and after infection with phages T2 to T7 (55). ○ dTMP kinase; △ dGMP kinase; ● dAMP kinase; ▲ dCMP kinase.

was detectable, and ensued even after infection with irradiated phage (393).

That the kinase formed in T2 infection probably represents a new type of protein also became clear with the fractionation studies. The dGMP kinase of normal cells was stimulated by potassium ions, that of infected cells was inhibited with increasing potassium concentration (58, 48). Furthermore, whereas chromatography of the extract of normal cells revealed only a single peak of dGMP kinase, two peaks appeared in chromatography of extracts of T2-infected cells, each possessing the appropriate response to K^+ noted above. Thymidylate kinase was also present in uninfected bacteria but was separable from the enzyme appearing in infection (49).

Inhibition of the new dTMP kinase by dGMP suggested the possibility of competition of both nucleotides for the same site. Purification and kinetic studies soon provided elegant evidence that the T2-induced deoxyribonucleotide kinase activities for the three substrates dGMP, dTMP, and dHMP reside on the same enzyme molecule, sharing the same catalytic site, and therefore act as competitive inhibitors of each other. Furthermore, the three activities show identical curves of inactivation by heat, acid, and trypsin (56, 47). Unlike reactions performed by crude extracts, the reactions catalysed by the purified enzymes stopped at the deoxyribonucleoside diphosphates (47). The existence of an amber mutant of T4 defective in gene 1 which appears to control the HMP kinase has been recorded (809). Amber mutants of T4 defective in gene 1 do not induce any of the kinase activities in nonpermissive *E. coli* strain B (179). In a permissive strain all activities come up simultaneously, although the enzyme has an increased lability to heat. Revertant phage derived from these mutants has regained all three kinase activities. It appears to be unequivocally proved that a single structural gene in the phage controls production of a protein that catalyses three activities.

The deoxynucleotide kinase of T5-infected bacteria was also purified and was shown to be separable from the activities present in the host. Chromatography of the host kinases yielded four separable peaks, whereas chromatography of the virus-induced kinase activities yielded one peak separable from the others. This single component was further purified extensively (570-fold purification) and was shown to be active on the four deoxyribonucleoside monophosphates characteristic of T5 DNA, that is, dCMP rather than dHMP. The enzyme uses either ATP or dATP as a phosphoryl donor. The product of the readily reversible reaction was the deoxyribonucleoside diphosphate. Competitive inhibition of each substrate by each of the remaining three natural deoxyribonucleotides suggested a common active site on the enzyme. However, this common site, which can react with dCMP, dAMP, dGMP, and dTMP, is evidently tailored in a most exquisitely different way from the site in the T2 enzyme which responds only to dHMP, dGMP, and dTMP and not to dCMP and dAMP.

The nucleotide kinases in normal cells for nucleotides other than AMP have not been extensively characterized. Separate enzymes appear to be required to phosphorylate the individual nucleoside monophosphates in uninfected bacteria (321a). Work on this subject has undoubtedly received a new incentive as a result of the studies on the phage-induced nucleotide kinases. The recent careful study of the *E. coli* enzyme, guanylate kinase, which catalyses the phosphorylation of GMP and dGMP to the diphosphates, is a case in point (545).

On Deoxycytidylate Deaminase   The initial discovery of this enzyme in infected cells turned on an observation whose validity has recently been challenged. The historical aspect is perhaps of more interest than the actual fact, as there is no controversy concerning its quantitative import. In 1959 we detected small amounts of 5-hydroxymethyldeoxyuridylate as a minor product (1.8%) of the dCMP hydroxymethylase reaction on dCMP carried out with crude extracts of infected cells (210, 211). Since we showed that this compound is not an intermediate in synthesis of thymidylate, which was also generated in that early experiment (211), we reasoned that the HMU nucleotide arose from the deamination of dHMP, and that dTMP was generated via dUMP, the product of deamination of dCMP, as follows:

$$dCMP + H_2O \rightarrow NH_3 + dUMP \xrightarrow[\text{THFA}]{\text{CH}_2\text{O}} dTMP$$

$$dHMP + H_2O \rightarrow NH_3 + 5\text{-CH}_2\text{OH}\cdot dUMP$$

We then sought and detected a dCMP deaminase (211). Recently it has been claimed that the dCMP deaminase isolated from T2- or T6-infected cells is inactive on dHMP (481, 214). The routine tests employed recently, however, were not designed to observe a rate of deamination less than 5% that obtained with dCMP. Indeed, although it is stated in the summary of one paper that dHMP is not deaminated, the text nevertheless states that the rate of deamination of dHMP determined spectrophotometrically was 1.6% that of dCMP (214). Of course, it would not be the first time that discoveries, such as our detection of the deaminase, evolved from incorrect observations; it would merely be nice to know whether our observation was really incorrect. The fact remains that there is a dCMP deaminase in cells infected by T-even phage. This enzyme discriminates quite well between dCMP and dHMP, carefully avoiding (for the most part) a reaction which would prevent the synthesis of T-even phage DNA.

The first serious study of the dCMP deaminase of infected cells was reported in 1960 by Keck and his co-workers (357a). The enzyme was reported to be absent in an extract of uninfected cells on the basis of a rather insensitive spectrophotometric assay. Nevertheless, more recent studies using labeled dCMP have yielded the same result (214). The enzyme appeared shortly after T2 infection, reached a maximum at 12 minutes, and declined thereafter. The enzyme appeared even after infection by an irradiated virus; the appearance was blocked by chloramphenicol (357a). These workers also noted the release of a soluble enzyme only after incubation of a lysate at 37°, a phenomenon exploited much later by Fleming and Bessman (214). It can be asked whether the adsorption of the enzyme to cell structure is not the reason for the apparent decrease in deaminase activity observed after 12 minutes.

In 1958 Scarano had begun a study of the dCMP deaminase of sea urchin eggs and embryos (631) and soon extended this to a series of other animal tissues. The sea urchin enzyme was purified and characterized as a 6-aminopyrimidine deoxyribonucleoside 5-phosphate deaminase, since it was almost equally active on dCMP and 5-CH$_3$-dCMP (632, 633). This enzyme was also active, although less so, on dHMP. It appears from this and other studies that the animal enzyme is far more active on dHMP than is the phage enzyme (481). Curiously, T6 enzyme is essentially inactive on 5-CH$_3$-dCMP (214), whereas the T2 enzyme is even more active on 5-CH$_3$-dCMP than on dCMP (481). The T2 enzyme is reported to be inhibited by dHMP (481), and the T6 enzyme is not so inhibited (214).

The study of the animal enzyme soon led to observations of the increase of this enzyme and others involved in pyrimidine and, particularly, thymidylate metabolism in cells before DNA synthesis. Coordinate increases have been observed in regenerating liver and in such systems as synchronized *Chlorella* (658) as well as in polyoma-infected cells (354). It has been postulated that the structural genes for all enzymes in the pathway of the synthesis of dTTP are located within the same operon in the chromosomes of higher cells. These would include the dCMP deaminase, which generates dUMP, thymidylate synthetase, thymidine kinase, and dihydrofolate reductase.

Mutants of T4 designated cd, which are unable to induce dCMP deaminase and are specifically altered in the structural gene for this enzyme, have been isolated (281). Such mutation does not prevent phage synthesis, probably because dUMP can be generated via the action of the dCTPase on dUDP. Nevertheless, cd$^+$ virus does appear to grow better than cd mutants (281).

The cd locus has been mapped as being closely linked to the td locus, which is the structural gene for thymidylate synthetase (282). Quite by chance a new mutant (wh) was also discovered whose gene is contiguous to the td locus, in the order cd, td, wh. The wh locus is also not essential for phage multiplication, and it presented a phenotype similar in one respect (white halo plaque) to that of the td mutants, thus suggesting the possible presence of a block in an enzyme of pyrimidine metabolism. It was supposed that the wh locus was the structural gene for dihydrofolate reductase (282), a hypothesis which has since been confirmed by Hall (280a) and by Mathews (494, 495). The following reactions are thus controlled by three contiguous nonessential genes:

$$\text{dCMP} \overset{cd}{\underset{1}{\rightarrow}} \text{dUMP} \overset{td}{\underset{2}{\rightarrow}} \text{dTMP}$$

$$\text{THFA} \overset{}{\underset{wh \atop 3}{\curvearrowright}} \text{DHFA}$$

As pointed out by Hall and his collaborators (282), this contiguity of genes for consecutive reactions appears to support the hypothesis that these genes may be organized into an operon and may be under a common control. It has been shown by Warner and Lewis (788), however, that in various amber mutants the control of the deaminase appears to differ from that of the dihydrofolate reductase; that is, the latter enzyme not only appears faster than the deaminase, but also, unlike the deaminase whose continued synthesis is like that of the dCMP hydroxymethylase, it is turned off in infection with amber mutants. It can be noted also that the loci for the dTMP (or dHMP) kinase and the dCTPase (or dUDPase) functionally related to thymine synthesis are far from the td locus and from each other. Nevertheless, the contiguity of the three functionally related nonessential genes is a striking phenomenon.

The existence of the virus-induced deaminase, which is capable of eliminating dCMP essential for the synthesis of dHMP, and of generating the substrate dUMP for synthesis of dTMP, raises the problem of how the levels of these crucial metabolites can be controlled. The activity of the enzyme in animal tissues is actually controlled by the concentrations of certain nucleoside triphosphates, of which dCTP markedly activates and dTTP sharply inhibits the enzyme. Thus an excess of dTTP derived from an excess of dUMP reduces the flow of dUMP; conversely, an excess of dCMP which permits the formation of excess dCTP activates the enzyme, reducing the dCMP concentration. These feedback controls operating on the animal enzyme were described by Scarano and his colleagues (634, 248, 635) and by the Maleys (480). Fleming and Bessman (213) were the first to show that the phage-induced enzyme has a similar pattern of feedback controls; see Fig. 21. Indeed, the dCMP deaminase induced by T-even phages is the first example of a phage-induced enzyme to be regulated by feedback inhibition. We shall see in Chapter 5 that the dCMP deaminase induced by the SP8 phage in *B. subtilis* is not similarly controlled.

The dCMP deaminases of eucaryotic cells and of T-even phage-infected bacteria are typical allosteric proteins containing distinct and separable sites for the substrate and for activators and inhibitors. In the case of the T2 enzyme, the size of the enzyme, presumably the association and dissociation of subunits, is affected by dCTP and dTTP. The activated aggregated enzyme has an $S_{20,w}$ of 7.2 in the presence of dCTP; in the presence of dTTP alone, a value of $S_{20,w} = 4.1$ was obtained (479).

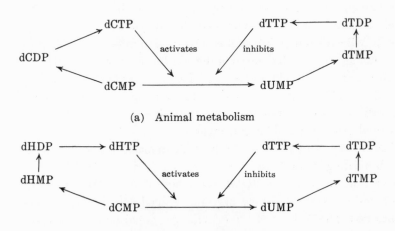

(a)   Animal metabolism

(b)   T-even phage metabolism

Figure 21. Schema of activation and inhibition of dCMP deaminase by nucleoside triphosphates.

The details of the kinetic behavior and allosterism of the T6 enzyme as compared to those of the animal cell enzyme have been presented by Fleming and Bessman (214). In the case of the T6 enzyme, it was shown that the activation can be effected by both dCTP and dHTP; it is maximal at about 0.15 and 0.20 mM, respectively. The Maleys believe that the virus-induced enzyme is totally inactive in the absence of either of these compounds (479). In still another instance, then, structural attributes of the enzyme have been selected for the specific facts of life within T-even phage-infected *E. coli*, which has a reasonable concentration of dHTP, but not of dCTP, because of the selective action of the dCTPase. Thus, as dHTP accumulates, activation of the virus-induced deaminase results in the elimination of the dHMP precursor, dCMP, to produce the dTMP precursor, dUMP.

Dihydrofolate Reductase   Mention has already been made of this enzyme, of its functional relation to thymidylate synthetase which converts tetrahydrofolate into dihydrofolate, and of the problem of its genetic control arising from the propinquity of the wh locus to the td and cd loci. The enzyme was sought first in infected cells when a study of the properties of thymidylate synthetase led Mathews and me to conjecture about the possible limitations in the cellular supply of tetrahydrofolate (499). We asked whether the level of dihydrofolate reductase in infected cells is sufficient to support the increased rate of thymidylate production in infection, or whether the former activity is induced as well. We quickly showed that on infection there is a 10- to 20-fold increase of the activity of the reductase, an increase which does not occur in the presence of chloramphenicol. A phage mutant deficient in the ability to produce the reductase does give reduced yields of virus and is restored to almost normal growth by addition of exogenous thymine in the medium (495).

The enzyme present in uninfected cells is readily separable from the new activity by $(NH_4)_2SO_4$ fractionation (499), and this initial step has been incorporated into a more extensive purification of the two enzymes (501). The host enzyme differs from the T6 phage enzyme with respect to pH optimum and is far more stable with respect to heat at 50° and treatment with 4 M urea. The host enzyme has a sedimentation rate of 2.7S corresponding to a molecular weight of 22,000, compared to 3.4S and a molecular weight of 31,000 for the phage enzyme (501).

The reaction carried out by dihydrofolate reductase is

$$\text{dihydrofolate} + \text{TPNH} + \text{H}^+ \rightarrow 1,\text{L-tetrahydrofolate} + \text{TPN}^+$$

Although the host enzyme is essentially unreactive with DPNH at pH 7.5, the phage enzyme is about one-fourth as active as the host enzyme with this coenzyme (499, 501). Initially this possible reactivity with DPNH was sought because it was known that the phosphogluconate pathway of glucose metabolism which generates TPNH was reduced in phage infection on glucose. The possibility of a limitation in TPNH supply was then postulated and, as noted above, the DPNH reactivity of the enzyme was in fact observed.

A test of the hypothesis that DPNH is the coenzyme operating in infection has been made by measuring levels of TPNH and DPNH in infected cells in a synthetic medium containing glucose as the sole carbon source. A significant increase in both DPNH and TPNH was observed until about 15 minutes after infection, when these increased levels slowly decreased (493). A similar result was obtained in a T6 system treated with fluorodeoxyuridylate to block THFA utilization. Although DPNH accumulation increased for about 15 minutes and then fell sharply, TPNH continued to accumulate. The results were interpreted to mean not only that different mechanisms are responsible for oxidation of DPNH and TPNH in normal infection, but also that TPNH is the physiological reductant for dihydrofolate *in vivo* (493). These experiments are interesting and do not support the initial hypothesis on which the DPNH reactivity was sought. However, it is relevant to note that in a glucose-NH_3 medium, in which the bacteria were grown, NH_3 is incorporated predominantly through the reversal of glutamate dehydrogenase. This is a TPN enzyme in *E. coli*, which catalyses the reaction

$$
\begin{array}{c}
\begin{array}{c} \text{COOH} \\ | \\ \text{CH}_2 \\ | \\ \text{CH}_2 \\ | \\ \text{CHNH}_2 \\ | \\ \text{COOH} \end{array}
\ + \text{TPN}^+ \rightleftharpoons
\left[\begin{array}{c} \text{COOH} \\ | \\ \text{CH}_2 \\ | \\ \text{CH}_2 \\ | \\ \text{C}\!=\!\text{NH} \\ | \\ \text{COOH} \end{array} \right]
+ \text{TPNH} + \text{H}^+
\end{array}
$$

$$
+\text{H}_2\text{O} \; \updownarrow \; +\text{NH}_3
$$

$$
\begin{array}{c} \text{COOH} \\ | \\ \text{CH}_2 \\ | \\ \text{CH}_2 \\ | \\ \text{C}\!=\!\text{O} \\ | \\ \text{COOH} \end{array}
$$

In other words, growth in such a medium has conditioned the organism to make large amounts of TPNH. It would be of interest to determine the reduced pyridine nucleotide content of organisms grown and infected in a medium rich in amino acids. Such a medium might conceivably mimic the ecological niche, the intestine, in which phage multiplication might have evolved, and it might reveal a different source of reductant for DHFA.

The requirement for protein synthesis and the appearance of a new type of dihydrofolate reductase in infected cells of course suggest that this virus-induced enzyme is a new polypeptide controlled by a virus gene. This suggestion is supported by two additional pieces of evidence. In a recent study (494) the reductase produced after infection by T2, T4, T5, and T6 showed considerable similarities with respect to pH optimum, pyridine nucleotide specificity, sensitivity to trimethoprim, and sedimentation coefficient, which was a bit higher than reported earlier (501). Mathews (494), however, has detected significant differences among these enzymes in catalytic efficiency, stability to heat and to urea, and inhibition by aminopterin. In addition, as noted earlier, he has shown that a wh mutant of T4 cannot induce the reductase.

Stoichiometric inhibition, observed in the reaction of the thymidylate synthetase with fluorodeoxyuridylate, is also seen in the inhibition of the reductase by aminopterin. In the inhibition studies by Mathews (494) the phage-induced enzymes resembled each other more than they did the bacterial enzyme. Baker has also observed that the phage enzyme is significantly different from the bacterial enzyme in inhibition studies (28). Curiously enough, the phage enzyme resembled a vertebrate enzyme more than a bacterial enzyme. A comparison of the sensitivities of *E. coli* and T6-induced enzymes, the reductase and the dTMP synthetases, with those of aminopterin and derivatives is presented in Table 8. The phage-induced enzyme can be 3- to 5-fold more sensitive to a given inhibitor; 70- to 90-fold differences in sensitivities between the two enzymes have been recorded by Baker in screening a series of 1-substituted-*s*-triazines (28). It is possible that the increased sensitivity of a virus-induced enzyme, as compared to the host activity, may have some interest in the development of chemotherapeutic agents against virus disease.

Table 8. Inhibition of Dihydrofolate Reductase and Thymidylate Synthetase by Aminopterin and Its Reduced Derivatives (501) †

	Concentration Required for 50% Inhibition	
Enzyme and Inhibitor	Host Cell Enzyme (μM)	Phage-Induced Enzyme (μM)
Dihydrofolate reductase		
Aminopterin	0.008	0.004
Dihydroaminopterin	0.03	0.009
Tetrahydroaminopterin	0.09	0.06
Thymidylate synthetase		
Aminopterin	320	80
Dihydroaminopterin	1.5	0.8
Tetrahydroaminopterin	11	2

† A 5-minute incubation was conducted before the reactions were started by adding TPNH in the reductase reaction and dUMP in the synthetase reaction.

From the stoichiometric inhibition of the various enzymes it has been possible to calculate (494) that the T4 reductase, for example, has a turnover number of 2060 molecules of dihydrofolate reduced per minute per aminopterin binding site, or per molecule, one inhibition site per molecule being assumed. In contrast, the T2 enzyme has a turnover number of only 830. On the other hand, the thymidylate synthetase has the low turnover number of 50. It has been observed that the level attained by the induced dihydrofolate reductase is about 10 times the activity of the synthetase. This difference in these activities is now seen to be related to differences in the catalytic efficiencies of these enzymes rather than to differences in the total number of enzyme molecules synthesized.

Ribonucleotide Reductase   In 1960 and 1961 Reichard and his collaborators began to describe the conversion of ribonucleotides into deoxyribonucleotides by extracts of animal cells (599) and of *E. coli* (600, 598). The activity found in extracts of *E. coli* was rather feeble, accounting for only a very small fraction of the activity necessary to produce the deoxyribose present in the dCMP of this bacterial DNA. Nevertheless the elegant analysis of the reaction by these workers revealed that the substrates are a ribonucleoside diphosphate and a low-molecular-weight sulfhydryl-containing protein, thioredoxin, which in the presence of Mg^{++}, an activator such as ATP, and catalytic enzyme fractions comprising ribonucleotide reductase, are converted into the deoxyribonucleoside diphospate and the oxidized thioredoxin. One atom of hydrogen is inserted stereospecifically into the substrate, replacing a hydroxyl group in the course of the reaction without loss of other hydrogens (181). The ATP or another activator is not required in stoichiometric amounts. The reaction for conversion of cytidine diphosphate may be written as

$$CDP + \text{thioredoxin-(SH)}_2 \xrightarrow[\text{ATP, Mg}^{++}]{\substack{\text{ribonucleotide} \\ \text{reductase}}} dCDP + \text{thioredoxin-(S)}_2$$

The reduction of the oxidized form, thioredoxin-$(S)_2$, and regeneration of the $(SH)_2$ may be effected by dihydrolipoate or by TPNH via an absolutely specific flavoprotein, thioredoxin reductase (181) as in the reaction

$$\text{TPNH} + \text{H}^+ + \text{thioredoxin-(S)}_2 \xrightarrow{\substack{\text{thioredoxin} \\ \text{reductase}}} \text{TPN} + \text{thioredoxin-(SH)}_2$$

A conformational change in thioredoxin accompanies its reduction to the sulfhydryl form (748).

The same ribonucleotide reductase appears to act on all four ribonucleoside diphophates (417, 416, 517). ATP or dTTP is an activator only for the reactions with CDP and UDP. Activators other than ATP are optimal for the other reactions. The enzyme system in *E. coli* is comprised of two nonidentical protein fractions which associate in the presence of Mg^{++} (416, 83). The system is also subject to numerous feedback inhibitions, and dATP and dTTP are quite active as inhibitors in this regard. In short, the enzyme appears to possess its own set of allosteric complexities which are even more complicated than those present in dCMP deaminase.

At about the time that these important findings of Reichard were first appearing, we began to explore the fate of RNA made after T-even phage infection in extracts of infected cells. This was done both as an approach to the role of RNA in the general problem of the synthesis of phage enzymes and as an approach to the mechanism of deoxyribose synthesis. We had several implausible hypotheses concerning the latter which we were able to disprove in our initial experiments on this subject (128). Incubation of the extract of phage-infected bacteria containing uracil-labeled RNA permitted rapid disappearance of the RNA and very rapid appearance of deoxyribonucleotides (128). The disappearance of RNA has been shown to be due to the action of two preexisting host enzymes, to be discussed in Chapter 6. The products were 5'-ribonucleotides which were rapidly converted into deoxyribonucleotides (see Fig. 22) at a rate greatly in excess of that observed previously. The reductive reaction in crude extracts had a TPNH requirement. We had in some measure reproduced in a cell-free extract the observation reported by Volkin on the *in vivo* turnover of phage-induced RNA, in which label contained in RNA then appeared in DNA.

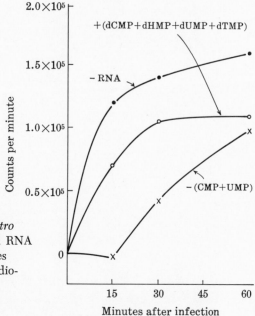

Figure 22. The conversion *in vitro* of uracil-labeled phage-induced RNA into soluble deoxyribonucleotides (128). −RNA = decrease in radio-activity in acid-insoluble RNA.

Our attempts to fractionate the system and to clarify the reductive reaction present in phage-infected cells were far from satisfying. In addition to the apparent lability of the enzyme, an extract from phage-infected cells contains numerous potential sources of enzymatic confusion, providing nucleases to generate inhibitory deoxynucleotides from DNA. In addition, polynucleotide phosphorylase generates competing ribonucleoside diphosphates from RNA. We were able to minimize these degradative processes by extracting cells with spermidine in the absence of Mg^{++} (127). A marked increase of ribonucleotide reductase was observed in the course of infection, as shown in Fig. 23. However, the increase began after 10 minutes and, although at 20 minutes the activity was 20-fold greater than the initial detectable activity, the maximal level detected was not greater than 25% of that needed. We therefore asked if the apparent low activity observed at zero time is not masked by inhibitors, a possibility which would cast serious doubts on our curve of appearance of enzyme. The interesting work of Beck and his

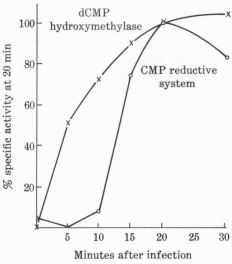

Figure 23. The increase in ribonucleotide reductase in spermidine extracts of infected cells (127).

collaborators has revealed that in fact the level of ribonucleotide reductase in extracts of *E. coli* is determined by both repression and the presence of inhibitors in the cell (59). Starvation of a thymine-less auxotroph for thymine or treatment of a prototroph with fluorodeoxyuridine permits a rapid and marked, perhaps 10-fold, increase of detectable reductase in the cells. Furthermore, mere dialysis also produced a significant increase of activity in the extracts. These workers have also reported about a 5- to 6-fold increase in ribonucleotide reductase after infection with T2 but state that this increase began immediately (59). It is evidently important to resolve and clarify these differences. We had observed the sedimentation of reductase activity with particles of the order of ribosomes (127). The recent experience of Fleming and Bessman with "nascent" dCMP deaminase and the need to autolyse preparations to solubilize this enzyme raise the question whether the reductase might not also be "nascent" in a comparable sense. It is not yet certain that ribonucleotide reductase is a phage-induced enzyme, although it has been included in Fig. 18. It will also be of great interest to see if a phage-induced ribonucleotide reductase, assuming that it does exist, will be subject to the complexity of controls observed with the host enzyme.

Synthesis of Viral DNA-Phage-Induced DNA Polymerase   It does not appear that any new mechanisms of RNA and protein synthesis are developed after T-even phage infection, although some modifications of the existing mechanisms have been detected; they are discussed below. On the other hand, a careful comparison of lipid or polysaccharide synthesis in normal and infected cells has not even been made. Actually, only the enzymes involved in DNA synthesis in uninfected and infected bacteria have been studied very extensively.

Despite the important work of Kornberg and his collaborators in isolating and characterizing DNA polymerase from these systems (389), it has not been possible until recently (see 513, 260, 260a) to synthesize *in vitro* a native DNA polynucleotide sequence possessing specific genetic activity. It has long been apparent, therefore, that there is much to be learned about the *in vitro* and *in vivo* mechanisms of DNA synthesis. It is not clear that the enzyme isolated from *E. coli*, previously described as DNA polymerase, is solely responsible for the replication of both DNA strands *in vivo*, although its potentiality for complementary synthesis of at least one strand is considered unequivocally demonstrated. Undoubtedly the problem of the functional relationship of a DNA polymerase of normal and infected cells to its bacterial sites, DNA template and substrates will be with us for a long time. It may be noted that several different forms of a DNA polymerase have been reported in *E. coli* (438) and a purified enzyme preparation combining activities of DNA and RNA synthesis has even been described (422), although these reports have not yet been confirmed. Nevertheless, for the most part, the basic enzymology of the bacterial and phage-induced DNA polymerases rests on most rigorous, elegant, and sophisticated experimentation and provides a foundation for the future exploration of these difficult and complex problems.

The increased rates of DNA synthesis observed in T-even and T5 phage infections are paralleled by a greater than 10-fold increase of the DNA-dependent DNA polymerase in extracts of infected cells (390, 557). Unlike the bacterial enzyme which can use native DNA as a primer, both the T2 and T5 enzymes have a strict requirement for single-stranded DNA (390, 557, 13). It is possible to assay both the bacterial and the virus-induced enzymes in the same extract by estimation of polymerase activity in the presence of heated (single-stranded) and native (double-stranded) DNA. The two activities are additive in the presence of a partially degraded DNA; that is, the host enzyme does not further denature the primer to increase the apparent activity of the virus-induced enzyme (13).

This property of the virus-induced enzyme can be used to test the strandedness of the intracellular pool of phage DNA as a function of time. The intracellular T2 phage DNA isolated at different stages of the growth cycle is inert to the T2 DNA polymerase, and hence shows no evidence of single-strandedness (491). The mechanism for presumed intracellular strand separation is therefore unknown and perhaps presages the existence of mechanisms of DNA synthesis as yet undiscovered.

The purified T2 enzyme or the *E. coli* enzyme works with either dCTP or dHTP (389); it does not function with the monoglucosyl derivative of dHTP (381, 382, 383). Indeed, this observation completes the evidence that glucosylation must proceed on the intact preformed H-DNA (390).

The DNA polymerase of T2-infected cells has been purified 600-fold by Aposhian and Kornberg (13). This virus-induced enzyme is readily separated from the host enzyme by chromatography on phosphocellulose. In addition, the virus-induced enzyme is inhibited readily by p-chloromercuribenzoate ($>98\%$) at concentrations which scarcely affect the host activity. Finally, antisera to the *E. coli* polymerase, which completely inhibit this enzyme, do not inhibit the T2 polymerase. Contrariwise, the antiserum to the T2 enzyme does not inhibit the *E. coli* enzyme but is highly inhibitory to the T2 polymerase. The results of these experiments are shown in Fig. 24. A similar approach has been used to suggest that the DNA polymerase appearing after infection with vaccinia virus (476) or herpes simplex virus (716) is immunologically distinct from the host cell enzyme.

At first the presence of a powerful nuclease in infected cells pre-

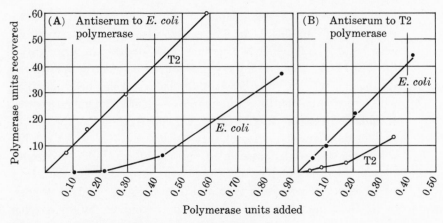

Figure 24. Selective inhibition of bacterial and
virus-induced DNA polymerases by specific antisera
to these polymerases (13).

vented the detection of the T5 polymerase, which was eventually
isolated. The DNA polymerase induced by this virus is readily
separated from the *E. coli* enzyme and has been purified about 400-
fold. Unlike the bacterial enzyme, it is activated several-fold by
0.2 *M* salt. In contrast to the host enzyme, which can effect a 10- to
20-fold net synthesis with a double-stranded DNA as primer, synthesis with both the purified T2 and T5 polymerases does not exceed
the equivalent of the amount of DNA present in the single-stranded
primer; between 0.7 and 0.8 replications have been observed (557,
13, 608). With both virus-induced enzymes, therefore, the system
comes to a halt because of a deficiency of primer. Unlike the host
enzyme, these DNA polymerases, as well as that induced by T4, are
unable to initiate new strands. A proposed mechanism for the action
of the T-even phage enzymes suggests that primer and product are
attached covalently and form a hairpin in which the primer and
product are aligned by complementary base pairing (259). In contrast to the product of the T4 enzyme, however, the product of the
T5 reaction does undergo normal thermal denaturation and appears
to be an unbranched linear duplex molecule (700).

Certain *am* mutants of T4 unable to stimulate DNA synthesis have been found to be unable to cause the synthesis of DNA polymerase (786, 169). Gene 43 has been identified as the structural gene for this enzyme. It is of interest that, despite the presence of the host DNA polymerase, the virus-induced polymerase is required for the synthesis of virus DNA. A similar result has been obtained with temperature-sensitive T5 mutants deficient in polymerase which are unable to make virus DNA (169). One hypothesis proposed to explain these results supposes that the host enzyme is not soluble within the cell and is associated entirely with cellular structures. This problem is heightened by a recent result showing that, in a mixed infection with wild type and polymeraseless mutant phages, the DNA of the latter can be replicated, presumably by the enzyme induced by the wild type (394). The essentiality of a phage-induced enzyme does not turn merely on the presence or absence of an apparently analogous cellular enzyme, but also on the availability of the host enzyme for virus functions during infection.

It will be recalled that the template mechanism of DNA replication postulates that the hydrogen-bonding mechanisms derived from the polynucleotide primer selects the complementary nucleotides. The discovery of *ts* phages, mutant in gene 43, has permitted Speyer to ask if an altered DNA polymerase selects nucleotides less accurately than does the wild type polymerase (687). After production of T4 double mutants combining an rII mutation and a *ts* DNA polymerase mutation, it has been shown that the reversion frequency of the rII mutation to r+ was increased 2000-fold. AT-GC transitions, but not deletions, have been detected; the transitions are also readily revertible by the mutant polymerase. This finding has been interpreted to suggest that the polymerase plays a more direct role than had been supposed in the selection of the DNA nucleotides. One possible consequence of this result is that known mutagens may act directly on this enzyme rather than on the template.

A comparison of the genetic effects on the rII locus by T4 phages inducing normal or mutant polymerases has suggested that the normal enzyme rejects noncomplementary base pairs more effectively than does the mutant polymerase (222). Therefore the increased mutation rate observed with the mutant polymerase is not presumed to result from the failure of the initial recognition mechanism, which is thought to be specific for the position and structure of the sugar phosphate groups of the entering deoxynucleoside triphosphate, but to result from the breakdown of rejection of incorrectly paired bases (222).

Viral DNA as a Substrate for Glucosyl Transferases   In the preceding section we have considered the role of the virus-induced DNA polymerase in the formation of a DNA containing HMC instead of cytosine. The *in vitro* formation of DNA containing HMC nucleotides permitted Kornberg and his co-workers to determine if extracts of T2-infected cell could transfer glucose from UDPG to H-DNA (390). This group showed that such a reaction can in fact occur. An extract of T5-infected cells is unable to effect this transfer (390).

T5 contains neither HMC nor glucose. Neither a T2 DNA nor a DNA containing cytosine could accept glucose with an enzyme from T2 infection (390). This group went on to describe the appearance of glucosylating systems in T4- and T6-infected system (391) and sought to understand the differences in distribution of glucose in these three types of viral DNA in terms of the possible differences among these enzymes (391, 827, 343). The glucosylating systems induced by the different viruses, that is, α or β monoglucosylation or β diglucosylation, are:

Phage	Reactions
T2, T4, T6	$\text{H-DNA} \xrightarrow{\text{UDPG}} \text{G} \xrightarrow{\alpha} \text{H-DNA} + \text{UDP}$
T4	$\text{H-DNA} \xrightarrow{\text{UDPG}} \text{G} \xrightarrow{\beta} \text{H-DNA} + \text{UDP}$
T6	$\text{G} \xrightarrow{\alpha} \text{H-DNA} \xrightarrow{\text{UDPG}} \text{G} \xrightarrow{\beta} \text{G} \xrightarrow{\alpha} \text{H-DNA} + \text{UDP}$

Thus the presence of 25% nonglucosylated HMC and the absence of β-glucosyl linkage in T2 stem from the inability of T2 to induce the HMC-β-glucosyl transferase. No enzyme has yet been detected in T2-infected cells to effect the β-glucosylation of a small percentage of the α-glucosyl residues observed in T2 DNA. The problem of why the T2 enzyme is unable to α-glucosylate all HMC residues is presumably in some measure the problem of polynucleotide sequence, as described in Chapter 2. However, the T4 and T6 α-glucosyl transferase can transfer small amounts of glucose to T2 DNA, although the T2 or T4 enzyme is unable to glucosylate T6 DNA. As Table 9 shows, these purified α-glucosyl transferases differ in a number of other properties, which include the K_m's for DNA and UDPG and pH-activity relations. They are all-SH enzymes and are inhibited by Mg^{++} (343).

T4-infected cells contain an HMC-β-glucosyl transferase in addition to the α-glucosylating enzyme. As summarized in Table 9, this enzyme differs in numerous properties from all of the other α-glucosyl transferases. In addition, it can glucosylate nonglucosylated residues of HMC in T2 and T6 DNA (391, 343).

T6 infection, like T2 infection, lacks the HMC-β-glucosyl transferase; the T6-infected cells, however, contain an α-enzyme and an α-glucosyl-HMC-β-glucosyl transferase, which adds a second glucose unit in β-linkage to a preexisting α-glucosyl-HMC nucleotide in DNA. This enzyme readily glucosylates T2 and T4 DNA but not T6 DNA (391).

Table 9. Comparison of Monoglucosyl Transferases (343)

| | Transferase | | | |
Property	T2α	T4α	T6α	T4β
Requirement for sulf-hydryl	+	+	+	0
Inhibition by Mg^{++}	+	+	+	0
Inhibition by tris	0	0	0	+
K_m: DNA	$3 \times 10^{-5}\,M$	$2.5 \times 10^{-5}\,M$	$3 \times 10^{-5}\,M$	$3.3 \times 10^{-5}\,M$
K_m: UDPG	$3.6 \times 10^{-5}\,M$	$0.7 \times 10^{-5}\,M$	$1.5 \times 10^{-5}\,M$	$2.1 \times 10^{-5}\,M$
Behavior in phosphate buffer: $\dfrac{\text{activity at pH } 6.5}{\text{activity at pH } 7.0}$	4.0	4.0	1.0	0.8
Glucosylation of T2 DNA	0	+	+	+
Glucosylation of T4 DNA	0	0	0	0
Glucosylation of T6 DNA	0	0	0	+

The three infections therefore produce five different enzymes of three different types. In general, the variations observed in glucosylation in the T-even phages or among hybrids (581) are explained by the successive actions of these new enzymes. Furthermore, some of the differences among these infections may be explained by differences among the α-glucosyl transferases on the basis of the specificities of the enzymes for specific polynucleotide sequences. An example of this type of specificity is the ability of the T4 and T6 α-transferases to glucosylate HMC next to purine; however, the T2 α-transferase is only 8% as active at such a site (167, 168). Nevertheless, as will be noted below, the actual fixed distributions which have been observed in wild type phages cannot be accounted for entirely by the observed specificities of the glucosyl transferases for base sequences in the DNA.

That heat-denatured H-DNA is glucosylated poorly by all the glucosyl transferases emphasizes the requirement for a double-stranded structure (827), as shown in Fig. 25a. The α-transferases are stimulated by salt, 0.01 M $(NH_4)_2SO_4$ for example, and a similar stimulation was obtained with spermine, which is known to increase the melting temperature of DNA (827).

The glucosylation reactions are reversible, and DNA with reduced levels of glucosylation can be prepared (827). Thus removal of β-glucosyl residues from T4 DNA has permitted addition of some α-glucosyl residues. The reverse is also true, and it appears that the apparently fixed 70:30 ratio of α:β glucosyl residues added by the two enzymes in T4 DNA is not determined entirely by the base sequence of the DNA. The β-enzyme can in fact β glucosylate all the available HMC, even in a synthetic H-DNA. Because the T4 α- and β-glucosyl transferases appear at the same time as early enzymes, as shown in Fig. 25b, and the enzymes have similar affinities for DNA (see Table 9), it has been suggested that the specificity of the glucosylations by the two T4 enzymes may be determined by the secondary and tertiary structures, as in the compacted folded DNA (343). It has been possible to distinguish various stages of glucosylation in T6 infection and it has been shown that this reaction begins after 9 minutes, when a condensation of DNA

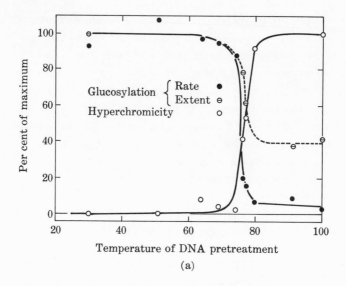

Temperature of DNA pretreatment

(a)

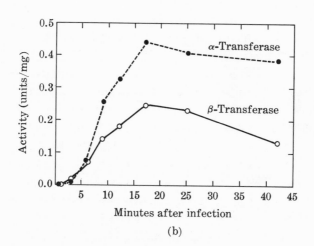

Minutes after infection

(b)

Figure 25. (a) The activity of T6 HMC-α
glucosyl transferase on T2 DNA preheated to
different temperatures (827). (b) The appearance
of α- and β-glucosyl transferases after T4 infection
(391).

is known to begin (197); however, a careful correlation of the configuration of the glucosyl residues in relation to the structure of the DNA has not yet been undertaken.

On the Restriction on Nonglucosylated T-Even Phages The phenomenon of host-induced restriction of T-even phages produced by growth in *E. coli* strains unable to make UDPG, discussed in Chapter 2, has made available nonglucosylated phage which can multiply in permissive hosts, such as *Shigella*. The nonglucosylated DNA of such phages, designated T*, does contain HMC in place of cytosine. Since chloramphenicol cannot prevent degradation of T* DNA in infected cells, it appears that the restricting enzymes are of bacterial origin. Indeed, *E. coli* extracts degraded the T2 DNA more slowly than T*2 DNA. After α glucosylation, the T*2 DNA is converted into a substrate which is hydrolysed slowly like the wild type phage DNA. The T*2 DNA has been shown to be degraded by *E. coli* exonuclease III, which requires double-stranded DNA, at a rate 20-fold greater than the wild type T2 phage, as shown in Fig. 26 (606). However, *E. coli* mutants permissive for nonglucosylated phages have been isolated (602) and have been

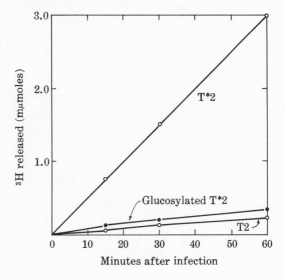

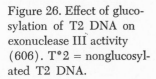

Figure 26. Effect of glucosylation of T2 DNA on exonuclease III activity (606). T*2 = nonglucosylated T2 DNA.

shown to contain normal levels of the bacterial endonuclease I and exonuclease III. These had been suspected to be responsible for degradation of poorly glucosylated DNA. The role of these enzymes in restriction, therefore, is not clear.

The DNA of a T* phage, unable to multiply in a restricting host, is degraded actively but nevertheless can perform some functions, such as complementing some *am* mutants (289). The *am* mutant 122 of T4, unable to make dCMP hydroxymethylase, does multiply in mixed multiple infection with T*2. Infection alone with T*2 permitted 40% of the hydroxymethylase production found with wild type T2; however, little production of α-glucosyl transferase was obtained. In these experiments little DNA was made, but the arrest of hydroxymethylase production occurred at the normal time.

Mutants of T2, T4, and T6 have been obtained which were defective in α-glucosyl transferase (604). Such mutants may be multiplied on permissive hosts; like the T* strains, they contain little or no glucose. In a restrictive host such a mutant, T2gt-1, behaves like T*2 and produces small amounts of all early enzymes with the exception of the transferase (291). The mutant T2gt-1 can complement hydroxymethylase-defective *am* mutants but not *am* mutants of gene 44; thus the latter may be the genetic site for the α-glucosyl transferase. In these experiments the apparently normal turnoff of early enzyme synthesis in restrictive bacteria was ascribed to the degradation of nonglucosylated viral DNA rather than to the normal regulatory process.

A mutant of T4 deficient in an α-glucosyl transferase, T4αgt, has been isolated which can form plaques on both *E. coli* B and on *Shigella dysenteriae* Sh (316). In this instance it is suspected that the β-glucosyl transferase, also induced by T4, may have glucosylated sites on the virus DNA which ordinarily would have been nuclease-sensitive and occupied by α-glucosyl moieties. However, the degree of glucosylation in this mutant is not known. Phage mutants deficient in both α- and β-glucosyl transferases have also been described recently (247).

DNA Methylases   This interesting subject began with the study by Borek and his collaborators (66) of an unusual methionine-deficient mutant of K12 which was able to make significant amounts of RNA in a methionine-deficient medium. The genetic trait (695) controlling this·"relaxed" phenotype, that is, the ability to make ribosomal RNA (rRNA) in the absence of protein synthesis, has been studied recently in our laboratory. Our data are consistent with the hypothesis that the synthesis of rRNA is under the control of the polyamines, as well as other factors. We have shown that in relaxed strains, such as that studied by Borek, the ratio of intracellular spermidine to putrescine is sufficiently high to initiate a synthesis of RNA in the absence of protein synthesis (134).

The RNA and DNA made in methionine deficiency in Borek's strain were low in their proportion of methylated bases and permitted a test of the presence of methylating enzymes in cell-free extracts; methyl-labeled S-adenosyl methionine was used as methyl donor and the methyl-deficient nucleic acids as acceptors. At least eight enzymes are now known to be involved in the methylation of amino acid transfer RNA (tRNA) and rRNA, as reviews by Stacey (689) and by Borek and Srinivasan (67) relate. The tRNA methylases of tumor tissues are reported to differ significantly from those of normal tissues (763). Two *E. coli* enzymes probably methylate DNA, giving rise to 5-methylcytosine and 6-methylaminopurine (256, 229). One animal cell DNA methylase found in nuclear particulates appears to be specific for cytosine (656). The pyrimidine, 5-methylcytosine, is known in the DNA of *E. coli* strain K12 and λ phage. 6-Methylaminopurine is known in the DNA of T2 and T4, as well as in the host DNA. The enzyme preparations isolated from different strains of *E. coli* appear to differ in their specificities and other properties. For example, the preparation of DNA methylase isolated from *E. coli* strain K12 is active on both cytosine and adenine in DNA, that from *E. coli* strain B is active on adenine alone, suggesting the absence in strain B of one of two different DNA methylases.

In T2 infection there is about a 50-fold increase in a DNA methylase, as Fig. 27 shows (255). Smaller but very significant increases are seen in T4 and T1 infection (294). The T2-induced methylase is clearly an early enzyme, and its appearance is blocked by chloramphenicol or amino acid deficiency (294, 646). It is active on adenine alone, whether generated in strain B or in strain K12 (294,

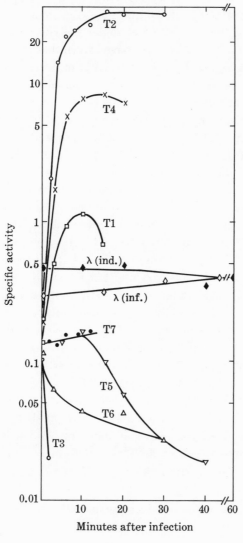

Figure 27. DNA methylase activity in cell-free extracts of phage-infected cells (294).

229). Nonglucosylated phage DNA is several times more active as a methyl acceptor than is normal phage DNA. The T2 DNA methylase is inhibited by the lipopolysaccharide of *E. coli* cell walls; this inhibitor is inactivated by *E. coli* extracts (200).

As Fig. 27 demonstrates, infection with T3, T5, or T6, which do not contain methylated bases, produces decreases in activity (255). In T3 infection, prelabeled host DNA, which donates 16% of its nucleotides to virus DNA, is nevertheless unable to transfer methyl-labeled bases to T3 DNA (239). The absence of 6-methylaminopurine from T6 DNA is one of the few known chemical differences among the T-even phages. Presumably, its absence is due to the absence of both a DNA methylase and host methylase. T7 and λ, which do have methylated bases, do not effect significant changes in the level of host enzyme. In these instances it can be imagined that host methylase is still functional.

The disappearance of DNA methylase activity is a striking phenomenon in T3, T5, and T6 infection, but it is most precipitous in T3 infection. In this instance an enzyme was found which destroys S-adenosyl methionine (239). Such an activity was not detected in normal or T2-infected *E. coli*. The reaction is

$$\text{S-adenosyl methionine} \rightarrow \text{thiomethyladenosine} + \text{homoserine}$$

This enzyme is not found with T7 infection, despite the similarities of T3 and T7. Nor was it found with any other T phage or λ, including T5 and T6 which cause a decrease in DNA methylase activity. The T3-induced enzyme appears early until 10 minutes, and then the activity decreases. The presence of this enzyme, which destroys S-adenosyl methionine, effectively prevents the methylation of RNA and DNA in T3-infected cells. Infection with ultraviolet-irradiated T3 permits an extended synthesis of this enzyme to three or four times its level in normal infection. Cells infected with ultraviolet-irradiated T3 virus are still able to support T2 and T4 multiplication, and such progeny are devoid of 6-methylaminopurine. Nevertheless, such methyl-deficient T-even phage is indistinguishable biologically (including burst size) from the wild type. The role played by DNA methylase and of 6-methylaminopurine in T2 and T4 multiplication remains obscure. No amber mutants have been found deficient in the DNA methylase. As this enzyme appears to be nonessential, this result is reasonable.

It may be asked, however, if the T3-induced S-adenosylmethioninase is not active in another crucial relative area, that of preventing spermidine biosynthesis. It is conceivable that the rapid lysis and relative lack of net synthesis of DNA in these systems arise from the deficiency in this polyamine, since S-adenosyl methionine is

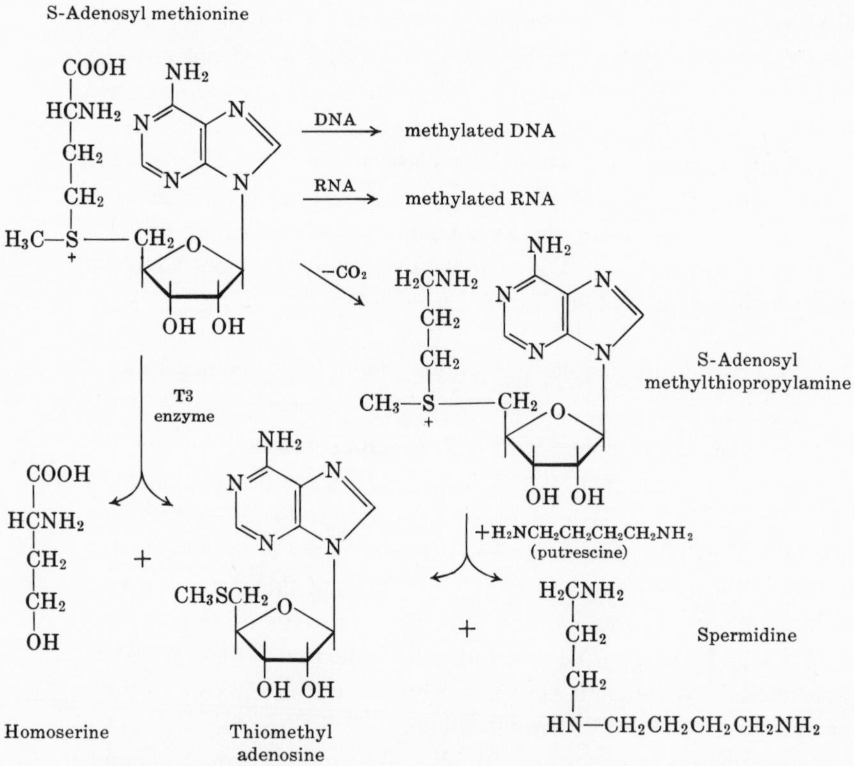

Figure 28. Reactions of S-adenosyl methionine in nucleate methylation, spermidine synthesis, and cleavage by a T3-induced enzyme.

an essential precursor in such reactions. This possibility could be tested easily with T3 mutants unable to induce the enzyme; such mutants have been described recently (293). These metabolic relations are presented in Fig. 28.

When the thymine-deficient strain 15_{T^-} is grown in a medium low in thymine or containing a thymine analogue such as 5-aminouracil, the 6-methylaminopurine content of the bacterial DNA increases greatly (180). Such growth conditions, as well as treatment with inducing agents such as mitomycin C, lead to the formation of a new DNA methylase (824), after induction of the defective lysogenic virus contained in these strains and with the addition of thymine essential for DNA synthesis.

Not all thymineless bacteria produce such an increase of methylaminopurine after exposure to thymine deficiency. We may infer that the new methylase is also absent and may suggest either that a presumably defective lysogen lacks such a methylase or that thymineless death in such organisms does not require the presence of an induced lysogen. The possible relation of methylation of DNA and lysogenic induction provoked by thymine deprivation has recently been studied in some detail (319).

Polynucleotide Kinase and Polynucleotide Ligase   In addition to reactions such as glucosylation and methylation which modify nucleic acids at the polynucleotide level, an enzyme has been described in T4-infected *E. coli* which catalyses the transfer of orthophosphate from ATP to 5′-hydroxyl termini of polynucleotides (605, 540, 541). The reaction may be written as

$$\text{APPP} + \underset{\substack{\text{HO} \diagdown \; P \; P \\ 5'}}{\overset{\substack{A \quad B \\ 3'}}{\diagup}} \xrightarrow[\text{Mg}^{++}]{\substack{\text{Polynucleotide} \\ \text{kinase}}} \text{APP} + \underset{\substack{\text{P} \diagdown \; P \; P \\ 5'}}{\overset{\substack{A \quad B \\ 3'}}{\diagup}}$$

This enzyme also operates with other ribonucleoside triphosphates. The enzyme is absent in growing *E. coli* or in bacteria infected by T5, T1, or λ (43). It is reported to be present in rat liver nuclei (43, 543). The enzyme appears in T2- or T4-infected cells, reaching a maximum at about 20 minutes; it is not formed in the presence of chloramphenicol. In the absence of either substrate, there is no hydrolysis of DNA or of ATP. The enzyme requires 5'-hydroxyl end groups, which may be generated by treatment of DNA with certain nucleases, micrococcal for example, or by elimination of 5'-phosphoryl end groups with a monophosphatase, such as the *E. coli* alkaline phosphatase or a recently described T4-induced 5'-polynucleotide phosphatase (44). After such treatment the enzyme phosphorylates the dephosphorylated RNA and DNA in the native or denatured state. The products may then be completely dephosphorylated by a monophosphatase; thus terminal addition is proved. The polynucleotide kinase is also active on dinucleotides and 3'-mononucleotides but not on nucleosides.

The enzyme is being actively studied as a tool in characterizing viral DNA. For example, T7 DNA cannot be phosphorylated before treatment with phosphatase. Addition of ^{32}P-phosphate from ATP after treatment with the kinase then defines the number of ends per DNA (607). In the case of T7 the nucleotide residues per single strand have been calculated to be 4×10^4, a value in agreement with the determined molecular weight. The terminal nucleotides, having been labeled in the treatment with the kinase, were identified after enzymatic digestion as deoxyadenylate and deoxythymidylate (Fig. 29a). Indeed, the terminally labeled separated strands, after degradation by *E. coli* exonuclease I, gave rise to the terminal dinucleotides d-^{32}pApG and d-^{32}pTpC (803). These procedures are presented in Fig. 29a and Fig. 29b.

This elegant series of methods has been extended to the analysis of the terminal nucleotides of λ DNA, which can form a circular molecule by the coherence of complementary overlapping ends, as shown in Fig. 29c. The molecule has been defined (816) as having the heavy strand, separated in CsCl gradients, terminating at the 5' end with deoxyguanylate, and the light strand terminating with deoxyadenylate. In this important study Wu and Kaiser have defined the DNA of other phages, 21, 80, and 186, which also yield only two terminal nucleotides. Therefore these phages also have nonpermuted nucleotide sequences, comparable to this type of order in λ and T7. Takanami has used the polynucleotide kinase to

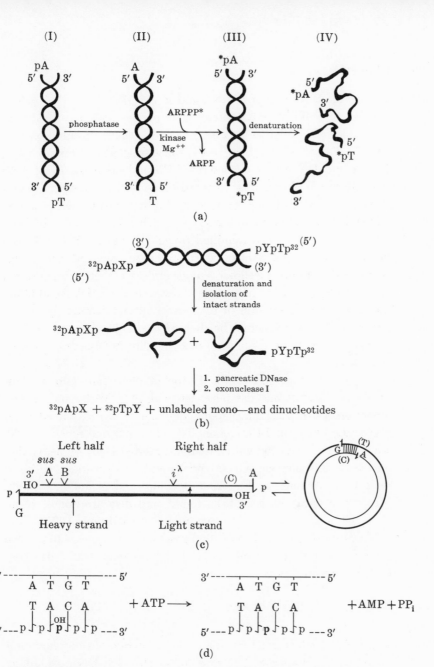

Figure 29. (a) Summary scheme for determination of 5'-termini of T7 DNA (607). (b) Summary scheme for determination of the 5'-terminal dinucleotides of T7 DNA (803). (c) Termini of λDNA as determined by polynucleotide kinase and the formation of circular molecules (816). (d) Reaction catalysed by polynucleotide ligase (802).

analyse the 5'-termini of f2 RNA and *E. coli* ribosomal RNA (732).

Extracts of T4-infected *E. coli* have been reported to have several additional activities relating to DNA termini. In addition to a specific 3'-deoxynucleotidase active on 3'-phosphate termini (43), Becker and Hurwitz have described the induction by T4 of a 5'-polynucleotide phosphatase. The existence of the latter perhaps relates to the need, as yet undefined, for the polynucleotide kinase which is elaborated in infection (44). The development of both phosphatase activities is inhibited by chloramphenicol. The T-even virus-induced 5'-polynucleotide phosphatase may be partly distinguished from other cellular 5'-nucleotidase activities because the latter are inhibited by mononucleotides such as dTMP. In addition, the continued elaboration of the former after infection by an appropriate T4 amber mutant has helped in the development of high levels of virus-induced enzyme, more readily isolable from the extracts (44).

An activity that converts a 5'-labeled phosphate into a phosphodiester linkage has also been detected (43). Weiss and his collaborators (801, 802) have found the same enzyme, named polynucleotide ligase, in T4 infection. The latter enzyme repairs single-strand breaks produced within double-stranded DNA by deoxyribonuclease. This enzyme effects end to end condensations within a molecule, as shown in Fig. 29d. Both *am* and *ts* mutants of T4, mapping in gene 30, have been found, and they are unable to induce the active ligase under nonpermissive conditions (201).

The reaction mechanism of the ligase reaction appears to involve the formation of an enzyme-adenylate intermediate (802, 804) generated in the reaction

$$\text{ligase}_V + \text{ATP} \rightleftharpoons \text{ligase}_V \sim \text{AMP} + \text{PP}_i$$

This isolated intermediate mediates the formation of phosphodiester bonds in the absence of ATP in a double-stranded DNA containing a 5'-terminal phosphoryl group at a single-strand break (804).

Becker and his colleagues (42) report that a similar enzyme produced in T4 infection converts hydrogen-bonded circular λ DNA into a covalently closed circular DNA. The ligase, termed "sealase" by this group, is also found after infection by T3 and T7 but not by T5 or λ (44a). Such an enzyme is also present in uninfected bacteria, although in far less amount and varying considerably in concentration from strain to strain (245, 238, 553). Unlike the virus-induced enzyme, however, the bacterial enzyme utilizes diphospho-pyridine nucleotide (828, 554) instead of ATP, apparently generating a similar active enzyme-adenylate in the reaction

$$\text{ligase}_B + \text{DPN} \rightleftharpoons \text{ligase}_B \sim \text{AMP} + \text{nicotinamide mononucleotide}$$

It has been suggested that the polynucleotide ligase is active, not only in recombination, but also in normal synthesis *in vivo* of one or both DNA strands. This might occur in the event of multiple initiation of DNA chains on one or both strands of the template. The ligase might then be employed to join small pieces of DNA to form a long continuous strand. Normal DNA synthesis *in vivo* might involve therefore the joint action of both DNA polymerase and polynucleotide ligase.

The numerous stages in the conversion *in vivo* of linear λ DNA into circular covalently linked double-stranded molecules have recently been summarized and discussed by Ogawa and Tomizawa (547). It has been reported that the synthesis of circular λ DNA *in vivo* does not involve the incorporation of thymine or inorganic phosphate (627).

Enzymes and Recombination   The recent studies on polynucleotide kinase and polynucleotide ligase discussed above are obviously of the utmost interest in the analysis of the mechanism of genetic recombination. Parental phage DNA is extensively fragmented and dispersed among parental and progeny molecules. It has been suggested that, after strand alignment in recombinant molecules, single-strand interruptions are repaired by the mechanisms noted above to form covalently linked molecules. Whether these are indeed the mechanisms is obscure; in any case, current hypotheses on recombination invoke steps of nucleate cleavage, phosphorylation, and pyrophosphate eliminations, for each step of which virus-induced enzymes have now been detected. However, the gaps existing between the assignment of specific roles to these enzymes and the observed physiological phenomena can be seen in the following summary.

In 1963 Kozinski and his collaborators (396) presented evidence implicating the formation of new enzymes in recombination. Tomizawa and his colleagues have studied initial stages in the recombination of T4 amber mutants containing DNA labeled with radioactive ^{32}P or the highly dense bromouracil to form joint molecules, combined by hydrogen bonds rather than phosphodiester bonds (754a). Joint molecules then contained ^{32}P and had a high density. DNA synthesis did not appear to be necessary because joint molecules could be produced after infection with mutants blocked in DNA synthesis or in the presence of fluorodeoxyuridine (10). Mutants recombined in different ways, some effecting hydrogen-bond linkages only, and others were also linked covalently. It was observed in one case that recombination involved the formation first of hydrogen-bond linkages and subsequently of covalent linkages (11). The formation of the second step has appeared to require the capacity for DNA synthesis, possibly to fill a gap between polynucleotides of the same polarity in a joint molecule (10).

The blocking of formation of joint molecules by chloramphenicol suggests a requirement for protein synthesis (11), perhaps in the formation of one or more early enzymes necessary to form such molecules. It was found that an *am* mutant defective in gene 32 and in DNA synthesis could not form joint molecules (755). It appears, then, that not only is this function, presumed to be effected by an unknown early protein, under the control of a defined gene, but also that the formation of joint molecules is thought to be necessary for DNA synthesis.

The nature of the substrates for all of these reactions is also unclear. Frankel has presented evidence, based on sedimentation in sucrose density gradients, that the vegetative pool of DNA does not contain normal phage DNA but contains molecules sedimenting at an unusually high rate (217, 218, 218a). It has been suggested that this pool is comprised of uninterrupted continuously growing super molecules. The latter suggestion has been challenged by Kozinski and his associates (395) who, on the basis of work with hybrids isolated in a CsCl gradient, believe that there is no covalent association of DNA synthesized early with parental DNA. They have reported that the strand size of DNA molecules made early in the presence of chloramphenicol is that of mature phage DNA. These workers consider that sucrose gradients cannot be used to demonstrate the molecular size of replicating DNA. They suggest that large molecules of DNA found by Frankel at late stages after infection are products of recombination.

At 5 to 7 minutes after infection, chloramphenicol inhibits the formation of an enzyme that introduces nicks into the parental DNA; such breaks in recombinant molecules generated in normal infection are readily revealed by denaturing the DNA. Nicking and exposure of single-stranded regions are believed to be a prerequisite for recombination (393a). In striking parallelism to these findings, J. Hurwitz and his collaborators have recently detected a T4-induced nickase, a new endonuclease which introduces single-strand breaks into double-stranded DNA (321b). At 7 to 9 minutes after infection the breaks in parental DNA are partially repaired; thus this material is linked to newly synthesized DNA (395).

Despite the apparent dependence of these systems for nicking and repair on relatively late protein synthesis after infection, evidence has recently been presented to suggest that the nicking and repair of nicks of ultraviolet-irradiated T4 DNA involves at least two preexisting host enzymes (397). Such nicking and repair proceed in the presence of chloramphenicol. A rec⁻ bacterial mutant does not nick such DNA readily, and an ultraviolet-sensitive mutant does not repair nicked DNA readily.

An additional phenomenon of dark repair of ultraviolet irradiation damage appears to be controlled by the V⁺ gene which is present in T4 (277) but is lacking in T2. The presence in T4 of this function, whose nature is unknown at present, is considered to determine the greater resistance of T4 to ultraviolet radiation. Surprisingly, the radiation-sensitive T4v mutant phage DNA is apparently unaffected by the host repair enzymes; this result has been attributed to its inaccessibility to host enzymes (397).

It is evident that the detailed relationships among the biological phenomena, the states of the numerous host- and phage-induced enzymes involved in these reactions, are just on the verge of significant clarification. Such clarification will evidently require collaborative investigations of the effects of particular phage mutants which control the elaboration of defined virus-induced enzymes, and of the state of labeled parental and recombinant DNA molecules. Such studies may reveal the existence of new and unsuspected enzymatic steps in DNA cleavage, strand transfer and reassembly, or may affirm that the enzymes so far detected are sufficient to the apparently very complicated physiological quadrille in which the strands participate.

On the Coding Problem   With the rediscovery of the finding that bacterial DNA is degraded fairly slowly during T-even phage infection, new types of ideas began to be formulated about the mechanism of turning off synthesis of host proteins. Such hypotheses extended also to the mechanism of the controls for sequential syntheses of viral proteins, despite the unique character of the former and the generality of the latter problem. Among these hypotheses has been the notion that a virus may operate according to a code that may differ from that used by the host. This may mean that entirely new codons, contained in new types of tRNA, are used for the amino acids at some stage of the multiplication cycle as a result of the expression of viral genes.[11] Alternatively, we can imagine the existence of a degenerate code for a given amino acid,

[11] It has also been proposed that in some instances the composition of viral DNA may be sufficiently dissimilar from that of the DNA of the host to require the production of new types of tRNA to facilitate the translation of viral codons (713). It has been reported, for example, that the DNA in herpes simplex virus codes for some of the tRNA, i.e., arginyl-tRNA, found in infected cells (714, 717). It is suggested that this type of change in tRNA composition relates mainly to the quantities of amino acids called for by the unusual base composition presented by herpes simplex virus. The DNA of this virus is quite rich in guanine and cytosine, as contrasted to the DNA of a mammalian cell which is rich in adenine and thymine.

embodied in several codons in several types of tRNA, each of which may fulfill the requirements of different groups of host and viral genes. Infection may destroy or modify particular groups of RNA, leading to the nontranslatability of certain genes and the preferential translation of others. Such effects might be sought in almost any developmental system, embryonic differentiation or sporogenesis for example. They might also require the modification or synthesis of new amino acid-activating enzymes.

In 1964 Sueoka and Kano-Sueoka (719) reported that T2 infection resulted in an early change in the structure of one or two components of the multicomponent group of tRNA molecules reactive as leucyl tRNA, as revealed in the chromatographic profile of these molecules. The tRNA obtained from infected cells could be charged with ^{14}C-leucine by extracts of either infected or uninfected cells. The change was therefore in the tRNA itself and not in a leucine-activating enzyme. No changes in tRNA for other amino acids were detected. The changes did not occur in infection with phage ghosts, nor in the presence of chloramphenicol. The changes were specific for T-even phage; no changes were detected in T1, T3, T5, T7, or λ multiplication (353). A recent study employing a more elaborate chromatographic technique has confirmed and extended these results; this study suggests the virus-induced specificity of these effects (790, 791). It is of interest that a sharp difference was similarly revealed between the patterns of valyl-tRNA's of vegetative and sporulating cells of *Bacillus subtilis* (351).

The change in leucyl-tRNA, amounting to a marked decrease in one easily eluted component with increases in at least two more slowly eluted components (353, 791), is one of the earliest events detected in T2 infection. It is accompanied by a distinct change in the codon response pattern (720). The alteration begins within a minute after infection under conditions of protein synthesis (353, 720). The rapidity of this result has suggested that this change may have some role in the arrest of host protein synthesis. However, as the effect on host synthesis is best defined as an arrest of host RNA synthesis which can occur in the absence of protein synthesis, as described in more detail in Chapter 6, I believe this is unlikely. Nevertheless, it will be of interest to see if a bacterial protein can be made with bacterial mRNA and the protein-synthesizing system from T2-infected cells. Since the protein of f2 virus can be synthesized from f2 RNA in extracts of uninfected cells, a simple test is to see if extracts of T2-infected cells may similarly be used, or simply to see if f2 virus can multiply in T2-infected cells. Superinfection by T6 of a bacterium infected with an RNA phage markedly inhibits RNA virus production, depending on the time of superinfection, but the nature of this effect is obscure at present (321).

The change in leucyl-RNA is completed very early, within 8 minutes, and it had been suggested that the end of this change might be responsible for the turning off of genes controlling early functions. The time course of this tRNA change is essentially unchanged in infection with ultraviolet-irradiated phage, under conditions in which synthesis of numerous early proteins is continued. The alteration of leucyl-tRNA, then, does not eliminate the continuing expression of these early genes, nor does it in itself permit the expression of late genes. The role of this interesting change is therefore unknown, but it is possible that the change does relate to the expression of some special viral genes. Codon-specific changes for tRNA have also been reported in infection of *E. coli* with Qβ RNA phage (320).

It was imagined that methylation might produce the alterations observed, and indeed T2 infection is reported to affect the activities of RNA methylases in such manner that more thymine and 6-methylaminopurine can be produced (784). Although *in vitro* methylation of tRNA by extracts of T2-infected cells has not been observed (353), the *in vivo* incorporation of methyl groups into the ribosylthymine of RNA in T4 infection has been detected (62a).[12]

---

[12] Data on the level of tRNA methylase on induction of λ-infected *E. coli* are contradictory (784, 785, 294). However, it has been reported that extracts of SV 40-induced tumors are capable of hypermethylating homologous tRNA extracted from normal hamster liver, while extracts of normal tissues cannot (513a).

Numerous other chemical alterations are possible with tRNA. For example, such nucleic acids have been found to contain thionucleotides (446), which contain 4-thiouridine, 2-thiouridine, and possibly a third purine derivative. It has been shown that, in the presense of a suitable enzyme, cysteine can donate its sulfur to a uracil moiety in *E. coli* tRNA to form 4-thionucleotides (448, 298). The reaction requires cysteine, ATP, Mg^{++}, and pyridoxal phosphate to form β-mercaptopyruvate (447). The formation of an addition compound containing β-mercaptopyruvate and cysteine, shown to be the immediate sulfur donor, has been postulated as an intermediate step in thionucleotide synthesis. After T4 infection the pattern of incorporation of ^{35}S into the tRNA of *E. coli* has been found to be different from that in uninfected cells; such change in infection requires early protein synthesis (318). These results are specific for T-even phage and are not obtained in infections with T7, ϕX174, and MS2 viruses. One question posed by these interesting results is whether infection merely affects thiolation or leads to the formation *de novo* of completely new types of tRNA (318). Preliminary results have indicated that purified T4-induced ^{35}S-labeled tRNA hybridizes preferentially with T4 DNA rather than with *E. coli* DNA (214a).

In addition to possible direct effects on tRNA through methylation, thiolation, and so on, for which incomplete evidence has so far been obtained, an effort has been made to see if new aminoacyl tRNA synthetases also appear. *E. coli* mutants containing thermolabile activating enzymes have been used. Protein synthesis in T4 infection appears to make use of the host activating enzymes for phenylalanine, glycine, and histidine. However, infection by T4 but not by T5 or λ of a bacterium with a temperature-sensitive valine-activating enzyme permits valine incorporation at the restrictive temperature (183, 528). This effect requires protein synthesis, but it has been shown that the activity of the enzyme appears through modification and stabilization of the pre-existing structure in a new, possibly dimeric, form (528, 529, 102a). This startling result reaffirms the necessity for our effort on the *de novo* synthesis of the dCMP hydroxymethylase.

Phage-Induced Nucleases   This area of investigation has been very difficult, and it holds numerous pitfalls. I present the history of this subject in some detail because of the misleading aspects of Stent's description (693). In 1949 I reported that lysates resulting from abortive infection by T-even phage were highly active in deoxyribonuclease (112). Pardee and Williams observed increases of DNase in extracts of T-even phage-infected cells (562) and, in collaboration with Kunkee, began to analyse the metabolic control of such increases (403). In 1953 Kozloff had shown that nucleases present in uninfected *E. coli* were strongly inhibited by existing RNA species (398); the increase of DNase after infection was then thought for some years to represent an "activation" of existing DNase (403), presumably by destruction of the inhibitory RNA. Kunkee and Pardee (403) described the curve of "activation" of DNase after T2 infection and inferred a requirement for various specific metabolic events related to infection, that is, energy production, a requirement for amino acids, and the like, as a result of inhibition of "activation" of DNase by cyanide, β-2-thienylalanine, proflavine, chloramphenicol, and so on.

The systematic studies by Lehman revealed that normal *E. coli* contains numerous exonucleases and an endonuclease. One nuclease is associated with the DNA polymerase of *E. coli*. He also described a DNA-specific endonuclease which is inhibited strongly by several kinds of RNA, of which tRNA is the most potent (425, 426). Having thus detected in 1962 the apparent basis of the Kozloff phenomenon in the preexisting host, Lehman and his colleagues nevertheless went on to suggest that the relations between this enzyme and its inhibitor were probably not adequate to account for the increase in DNase, in short, that a new nuclease might be generated in infection, although this was not yet proved. The work of Stone and Burton (704) extended the previous studies of Pardee and showed that the DNase increase was magnified after infection by treatment of extracts with ribonuclease; T5 infection also increased DNase activity. Inhibition by chloramphenicol at different times after infection was consistent with an inhibition of continuing synthesis of an early DNase. Also, the DNase produced in T2 infection was more sensitive to *p*-chloromercuribenzoate than were the preexisting host activities.

In retrospect, it appears to me that the atmosphere of the fifties suggested the activation of preexisting DNase, while that of the sixties has presented the clear possibility of new phage-induced enzymes. In 1964 several groups initiated efforts to characterize the isolated nucleases of infected cells. Weissbach and Korn detected an increase in exonucleases in both T4 and λ infections (806). The latter is indeed a very real phenomenon, and the exonuclease elaborated in λ multiplication is the one early enzyme known to be produced in this infection.[13] In the case of the T4 infection, however, Weissbach and Korn were unable at that time to separate the new exonuclease from the newly formed DNA polymerase, and it was not clear if this was not merely an additional activity built into the DNA polymerase. At this time Oleson and Koerner (552) also detected and partially purified a new exonuclease; this enzyme could not be detected in normal cells, and it acted on heat-denatured DNA, which it degraded to 5′ mononucleotides. In this respect it is quite different from exonuclease II, which is associated with the

---

[13] Although more than 25 genes are believed to exist in λ DNA, of which perhaps a dozen are thought to represent early functions, only three early proteins have been detected. One of them is the recently isolated λ repressor, another the λ exonuclease, and a third a phage-related protein named β whose function is unknown. The nature of the exonuclease and the physiology and genetics of its production have been studied in some detail by three groups. The appearance of the exonuclease is the first known physiological event detected after induction, but its exact relation to the release of the prophage from the bacterial chromosome is not understood (387, 388). The production of this enzyme occurs on induction by thymine deficiency and continues until thymine is supplied (388). Various phage mutants altered in regulatory genes made different amounts of the enzyme (591, 586), but the structural gene for the enzyme has probably been located just recently (592). The enzyme itself has been crystallized (451) and has been compared to other nucleases in some detail (450). It is distinguished from other *E. coli* (451) nucleases in that it begins its attack on the 5′-phosphate terminus of DNA molecules and is far more active on native DNA than on denatured DNA (450). Numerous temperate coliphages, hybridizable with λ, direct synthesis of new DNA exonucleases after lysogenic induction. These nucleases have distinctive group properties but are catalytically quite similar (582). Some induced temperate coliphages do not direct the synthesis of this type of nuclease, however (661).

host DNA polymerase. These workers have also recorded (552) a discovery, as yet unpublished, by Greenberg of a new T2-induced RNA-inhibited endonuclease, which is maximally active on heat-denatured DNA.

In a subsequent study Short and Koerner (660) were able to separate the new exonuclease from the phage-induced DNA polymerase, and they observed, as have other workers, that the polymerase is associated with an exonuclease having similar activities. Nevertheless, the nuclease associated with the polymerase appears to be a different, highly active enzyme. We are thus concerned with at least three new virus-induced deoxyribonucleases in a host containing at least six of its own DNases.

The roles of these enzymes are far from clear. It has been suggested that, in addition to their possibilities of nicking in preparation for recombination and excision for repair, the nucleases act to exclude too many infecting phage DNA molecules, as in superinfection breakdown (429, 261), and to degrade host DNA. Both of the latter reactions are also observed in T5 infection where, however, it is believed, host DNA is mainly degraded before the appearance of a new very active nuclease (704, 149). This has been taken to mean that, in this system, host enzymes can serve to destroy host DNA. A comparable situation may exist in T3 infection, where no new nucleases have been detected but host DNA is degraded and used for synthesis of virus DNA. However, this use of host enzymes does not appear to be very active in the degradation of host DNA in T-even phage infection.

To see if T-even phage controls a function for degradation of host DNA, Wiberg (809) has used a double mutant phage containing a mutation of gene 42, blocked in dCMP hydroxymethylase, and a mutation of another gene. With such double mutants the degradation of host DNA is not obscured by synthesis of virus DNA. In such infections, phage carrying mutations for genes 46 and 47 were unable to cause degradation of the bacterial DNA. These two genes are apparently contiguous, and mutations in either locus produce phenotypically similar phages, whose rates of DNA synthesis diminish shortly after infection and which have very low yields of progeny in all cells. As discussed earlier (405), it is suspected that these genes control nucleases specific for DNA containing cytosine and inactive on DNA containing HMC. Thus it is thought that these virus-induced nucleases degrade not only host DNA but also virus DNA containing cytosine. It will be recalled that some host DNases, exoIII for example, are capable of distinguishing between glucosylated and nonglucosylated DNA (606), although their role in restriction of nonglucosylated phage is not clear (602).

It is not as yet clear which of the many nucleases of phage-infected *E. coli* are responsible for superinfection breakdown of phage DNA (429, 261). The rapidity of the reaction suggests that host nucleases effect this breakdown, but only some of the six enzymes so far described (342), endonuclease I (606) and exonuclease IV-A or IV-B (342), can be expected to have a significant rate of hydrolysis of fully glucosylated T4 DNA. Which of them, if any, is in fact responsible may perhaps be clarified by experiments with appropriate bacterial mutants or with infected protoplasts which may have lost some of these degradative components.

Internal Protein(s)   Our discussion thus far has related to virus-induced enzymes whose synthesis is expressed early and which are believed to be controlled by the parental viral genome. A possible exception among the T-even systems, which we have discussed, is the enzymes apparently involved in recombination. It will be recalled that one of these enzymes may appear fairly late in infection, and the data are simply inadequate to tell if this is truly an early or late function. The expression of the other defined early functions is normally stopped shortly after DNA synthesis; possibly this will be a useful criterion for grouping numerous early genes. The pattern of expression of the recombination systems defined by Kozinski is not known as yet.

Another important exception which has been known for some time is the internal protein present in T-even phage. This protein has been described by Levine and his colleagues (431); it is antigenic and serologically active only if phage is disrupted. The material is also released from the phage by osmotic shock; it is found in the supernatant fluid, after digestion by DNase and extended centrifugation, in a fraction containing about 7% of the total phage protein, that is, 7% of the acid-soluble sulfur (511). This fraction, then, not only contains all the internal antigen, but a small amount of other protein as well. Labeled internal protein in parental phage does not appear in progeny (511). The internal protein is basic and associates at low ionic strength with DNA; it is dissociated from DNA at high pH or at neutrality at concentrations of 0.1 M NaCl and of 0.01 M MgCl$_2$ (511). The protein is reported to be rich in lysine and arginine and lacking in cysteine (147). The viscosity of phage or thymus DNA is reduced by association with the internal protein; other basic proteins also produce this effect (101), and it is not known if this effect has physiological significance.

At least three different functions of the internal protein in phage multiplication can be suggested: internal protein is made before DNA synthesis begins (511), and the substance may provide a core for the organization of phage DNA; the protein is an enzyme of function as yet undefined; and the protein may act in regulating or modifying DNA transcription by analogy to the postulated function of a histone. In connection with the first hypothesis, it should be noted that after release of DNA a high percentage of particles of λ bacteriophage has been found to contain cores (346). The cores have the density of protein and not of DNA, and indeed similar objects have been observed in other DNA viruses. Similar cores have not yet been observed in the T-even phages. (However, see p. 160.)

Recently Bachrach and Friedmann (22) have purified the internal proteins and presented evidence that these materials do reduce RNA transcription on phage DNA. Their results are confusing, however, because addition of internal proteins to DNA reduced the hypochromicity developed on increasing the temperature, rather than shifting the melting temperature. Although this can possibly be interpreted as suggesting that various fractions of the phage DNA structures are prevented from denaturation by binding internal protein, other data are needed before such conclusions can be made.

Murakami and his collaborators (523) had studied the synthesis of internal protein in T2-infected cells by means of serological methods and had observed that this substance is detectable 2 to 3 minutes after infection. Synthesis of this protein was blocked by chloramphenicol but not by proflavine. No mutant has yet been described which lacks the ability to produce the protein. Although a correlation was initially reported between the amount of DNA synthesized and preformed internal protein (523), this result was not obtained by Minagawa (511), who does not believe that the presence of stoichiometric amounts of this protein is a condition for at least the continuing synthesis of DNA. Since both internal protein and DNA enter phage with different kinetics, it is thought that these substances are not associated in the precursor pools. The rate of synthesis of the protein is maximal at 10 minutes and falls somewhat thereafter, but the important point is that the synthesis of this early protein, apparently unlike that of the nonstructural virus-induced enzymes, is continued throughout infection.

SUMMARY AND COMMENTS

In the decade since the discovery of the virus-induced dCMP hydroxymethylase and the dTMP synthetase, at least eighteen additional proteins have been discovered which are synthesized early in infection. Figure 18 does not include the rII protein, to be discussed in Chapter 5, the several "proteins" implicated in altering tRNA, and others. Ten of these early proteins presented in the figure have been shown to be determined by defined viral genes and to be involved in the redirection of nucleic acid metabolism in infection. Evidence has also been obtained to suggest the possible existence of other not well-characterized enzymes, such as those engaged in modifying tRNA. Each of the new activities presents interesting problems, and the existence of the internal protein, synthesized continually throughout infection, presents one of the more challenging problems because its function is quite mysterious.

Three groups of such early proteins have been reported in T-even phage infection. A group of "early" early proteins detected in pulse-labeling experiments (434) have not been defined functionally, nor have they been demonstrated to be unique products of virus infection. Although I still have reservations about the existence of T4 virus-induced "early" early proteins, the existence of a somewhat similar phenomenon and its analysis in T5 infection lead me to think that it may be real enough. In 1965 Y. Lanni (411) showed that injection of T5 DNA occurs in two steps, of which the first involved 8% of the DNA and did not require protein synthesis. However, the injection of the remainder of the T5 DNA did require protein synthesis, for which the first piece of DNA injected carried the information. This is consistent with the findings that, unlike T-even phage, the T5 genetic map is linear (202) and that the DNA molecules in a population have the same nucleotide sequence (751, 750). The existence of at least one phage gene in the first piece of DNA inserted was shown by genetic tests (412). The study by McCorquodale (507) has shown that three major classes of proteins are produced in T5 infection, of which a very "early" group related to the 8% piece of T5 DNA is synthesized between 2 and 8 minutes. The remainder of the DNA controls synthesis of a second group of early proteins at 8 to 20 minutes and a late group at 15 minutes to lysis. Thus T5 infection does involve two sets of switches to stop synthesis of the two main classes of early proteins. This is not exactly analogous to the T-even phage infection, but it certainly presents a precedent to be considered.

Table 10. Virus-Induced Synthesis of Proteins

	Early	Late
Enzymes of Nucleic Acid Synthesis	+	−
"early" early proteins, 1–3 min.		
dCMP hydroxymethylase 2–15 min.		
dTMP synthetase 5–15 min.		
Internal antigen	+	+
Internal polypeptides	−	+
External proteins	−	+
Lysozyme	−	+

The dCMP hydroxymethylase and many other proteins unequivocally induced by T-even viruses appear next, to be followed by thymidylate synthetase and possibly some other systems involved in recombination. The synthesis or at least the accumulation of most, if not all, of the early proteins stops shortly after DNA synthesis begins, with the single known exception of the phage internal protein. We can therefore distinguish four groups of proteins, as shown in Table 10, and at least three additional groups of proteins and their derivatives constituting late functions. The latter are discussed in Chapter 5, although in far less detail. Although at first we appeared to be concerned in T-even phage multiplication with a simple sequence comprised of three main steps, synthesis of early proteins, of DNA, and of late proteins, our data now suggest a greater degree of complexity. The detailed dissection of the early stages of the cycle of multiplication in T-even phage infection is not really greatly advanced as yet.

Biochemical studies have clarified several questions and answered at least one. We now know that the second half of the latent period is not devoted solely to the conversion of immature to mature phage. It is a period of rapid synthesis of viral material, and very probably a period of continued viral multiplication of vegetative phage.   HERSHEY, 1952 (303)

Chapter 5

THE LIFE CYCLE OF SOME VIRULENT DNA PHAGES. LATE FUNCTIONS; SOME OTHER PHAGE SYSTEMS

It is not my intention to treat the late steps in the development of phage as comprehensively as I discussed the early proteins. Recent developments suggest, however, that a detailed chemical exploration of these late events fully comparable to that discussed in earlier chapters is beginning. In the first half of this chapter, therefore, I consider some recent methodological and experimental trends which relate particularly to late events in the multiplication cycle. Current results in this area are frequently incomplete and confusing, but they are sketching in the major phenomena and problems requiring clarification and will prepare us more adequately for our discussion of the control of the sequential events in a T-even phage cycle in Chapter 6. In addition, I wish to compare some of the phenomena observed in the overall cycle with those which have been found in other DNA phage systems.

The Genetic Approach to Virus Physiology   In earlier chapters I have described the use of mutant phage to answer several problems. Is the genetic information for the synthesis of a virus-induced enzyme in the host or in the virus? Is the function of such an enzyme essential to virus multiplication, as are dCMP hydroxymethylase, the dHMP kinase, and DNA polymerase, or inessential to multiplication, as are dTMP synthetase, dCMP deaminase, and dihydrofolate reductase? The availability of certain mutant phages has facilitated the development of solutions for many of these problems. In addition, a mutant phage, such as that lacking dCTPase, permits exploration of the role of other genes, such as those controlling nucleases. In one instance the phage permits a finer dissection of the virus cycle of multiplication, in another the rII systems point to the existence of unsuspected functions yet to be discovered. This recently expanded genetic armamentarium is obviously a major tool currently in the hands of the phage biochemist.

The development of this armamentarium originated from a determined effort to define the viral genome in far greater detail than was possible before 1960. In response to the biochemical discovery of virus-induced enzymes, the search for the viral genes controlling such functions was accelerated, but in order to discover such genes the geneticist had to solve the general problem of how to find genes for essential functions. Actually, this general problem had been solved several times before, as a recent essay of R. S. Edgar makes clear [14] (187). Our genetic armamentarium has multiplied by virtue of two methods of obtaining "conditional lethal" mutations, mutations in which the genes cannot be expressed at normal conditions of temperature or in normal bacterial

[14] "Why was there a thirteen-year lag between the papers of Horowitz and Leupold and of Edgar and Lielausis? Unlike the rediscovery of Mendel's work, we cannot blame ignorance. One might argue that during the 1950's the "time was not ripe" for physiological genetic studies of systems other than those concerned with intermediary metabolism. . . .

"Fifteen years ago, phage workers and other geneticists, such as those working with non-prototrophic bacteria like Pneumococcus and Hemophilus, were desperately in need of good markers for formal genetic analysis. Why did the relevance of Horowitz's work not occur to them?

"Scientific publications are, in a sense, 'fabrications' pieced together to create pleasing stories, which, although they are sometimes reflections of nature, are rarely mirrors of the scientist at work. . . ." R. S. Edgar, 1966 (187)

hosts, although they can be expressed in certain permissive conditions. A temperature-sensitive function, a *ts* mutant, can usually be expressed at 25°C instead of at 35° to 40°C; an *amber* or *am* mutant can be expressed in a permissive host carrying a suppressor gene which permits the suppression (*sus*) of the viral mutation.

These methods of obtaining and preserving mutations for essential functions have proved so powerful in virology that they now constitute an independent approach in this discipline. This approach has been adapted in the last few years to such diverse systems as other DNA phages, for example, ϕX174, S13, and M13, or to RNA phages, for example, f2, as well as to DNA and RNA viruses of animals, such as the pox viruses and arboviruses (Sindbis for example), respectively. With these systems the isolation of such mutants is undertaken as an initial preparatory step and frequently precedes a detailed analysis of chemical events during the life cycle. The mutants, when isolated, are used to reveal additional critical events during multiplication, events which may now presumably be explored by biochemical techniques.

Although, as noted above, the mutants for the T-even phages have been explored more than any group in biochemical terms, this application of the methodology developed mainly from the commitment of the phage community to these particular phages. Actually, the initial approaches to the isolation of phage, mutant in essential functions, had been developed with lysogenic rather than virulent phages, but were soon applied to T-even phages. It is obvious from the standpoint of this methodology that smaller phages having fewer genes might permit an easier comprehensive solution to the dissection of a viral multiplication cycle. Indeed, smaller viruses, such as ϕX174 and S13, and numerous others are being approached in this way for this very reason, but, as we shall see, the use of smaller phages may introduce new qualitative problems, such as that of the increased contributions of host elements to the multiplication process.

The success of these methods in detecting new viral genes has matched the growth of biochemical knowledge to the extent that biochemistry and genetics are generally recognized as opposite

sides of the same study; a virologist is sorely deficient if he ne-
glects either. The aims of virology have concomitantly become en-
larged to encompass nothing less than the complete description of
the viral cycle of multiplication and the sequential contributions
of virus and host cell to this development.[15] Such an analysis evidently requires the definition of each viral gene in terms of its
position within the viral chromosome, of the nature and control of
its expression, as well as of the nature and role of each gene product.
Although ambitious and arduous and likely to be long in its completion, such a perspective no longer appears to affront the philo-
sophic sensibilities of contemporary biologists as being beyond the
capacities of modern experimental science, particularly the complementary disciplines of genetics and biochemistry.

On Conditional Lethal Mutants   The steps in the rediscovery of
conditional lethal mutants, and their particular application to the
T-even phage systems, have been described in the interesting and

[15] Although my statement of the aims of biochemical virology does note the
problem of the contributions of the host cell, few studies in virology, with the
possible exception of studies of host-induced modification, approach this question with the vigor usually addressed to the viruses themselves and their
activities. Nevertheless, it will be obvious that the definition of host genes in
a manner comparable to the definition of the viral genes will also be essential to provide full insight concerning the dialogue between host and virus.
The problem has been obscured in the T-even phages by the apparent elimination of bacterial control over polymer syntheses during infection. Nevertheless, we have mentioned in Chapter 4 the apparent role of host nucleases in
degrading phage DNA under certain conditions, and can expect many more
of these host effects to become apparent. The analysis of the apparent evolution of glucosylated HMC-containing phages suggests that nonglucosylated
HMC- and cytosine-containing antecedents of modern T2, T4, and T6 may
have begun in permissive nuclease-deficient organisms comparable to Shigella.
It implies that the evolution of *E. coli* with its defensive equipment against
such primitive phages may have occurred precisely in selection for such survival mechanisms against viruses. We must assume that present-day hosts, no
less than present-day viruses, contain, exquisitely tooled within their structures, evidence for the requirements for virus multiplication, requirements
which have been selected by the evolving viruses. On the other hand, these
hosts also contain a series of structural defenses of the cell selected during
its evolution against invading viruses. I regret that there is too little time
(and information) to permit a more detailed discussion of this important area.

thoughtful essay of Edgar (187). He recalls that Hadorn (278) had worked with such mutants in *Drosophila* and indeed had named them. The work of Horowitz and Leupold (315) on *ts* mutants of *Neurospora* had been no less important,[16] and indeed had been pursued and discussed in the very halls containing a center of phage genetics without really impinging on the collective consciousness. As Edgar relates (187), the recognition that his studies on *ts* phage mutants coincided with these earlier studies emerged quite slowly, and particularly after discussion in 1960 with Campbell (91). Campbell had also rediscovered such mutants, particularly one class of mutants similar to the *am* type in the λ system. Campbell went on to isolate *ts* and pH-sensitive mutants of λ in 1961 (92). The first clear and comprehensive discussion of the *am* and *ts* conditional lethal mutants in the T-even phages appeared in 1963 (196), and additional detailed papers followed in 1964 (188, 189). In one of them, for instance, it was shown that the temperature sensitivities of the mutants do not result from inactivation of the phages themselves but from a temperature-sensitive stage during growth (189). I give these dates to show how very rapidly the shock of recognition can become translated into discovery in this field. The speed with which this approach was seized by major virology laboratories almost matches the speed with which the galvanizing effect of the Watson-Crick model made itself felt in experimental work a decade earlier.

[16] I had heard the presentation of Horowitz and Leupold (315) at Cold Spring Harbor in 1951 on the use of temperature-sensitive mutants of *Neurospora* in the study of indispensable functions, and have even frequently discussed this paper in class in terms of the problem of the limitations of nutritional techniques. In that paper Horowitz and Leupold (315) estimate that indispensable functions, which cannot be replaced by exogenously supplied metabolites, make up only about one-quarter of the total genetic functions. This important point was challenged by Atwood and Mukai (18) who in studies with *Neurospora* were able to preserve nuclei carrying "lethal" mutations in heterokaryons. These authors concluded that indispensable functions made up a very high proportion (>95%) of genetic functions in *Neurospora*. These discrepant views have never been resolved in the literature, but clearly they will soon become a subject of active discussion again, because the isolation of such bacterial mutants is now being actively pursued as an approach to the study of the role of bacterial membranes, division, polymer syntheses, and so on.

Epstein had described *am* mutants of T4 which could multiply in *E. coli* K12 (strain CR 63) but were unable to complete a cycle in strain B. In contemporary terms it appears that *am* mutations are "nonsense" mutations in which an altered code letter (codon) in mRNA cannot be translated in strain B. Incomplete polypeptides, formed in strain B, terminate at the carboxyl end just before the nonsense codon. In strain CR the altered nonsense codon can in fact be translated as one of several amino acids, depending on the particular suppressor gene carried by the bacterium. This inserted amino acid may well be something other than the amino acid normally present in the polypeptide and is thus termed "missense." The resulting protein may then have some altered properties, such as an increased sensitivity to temperature, relating to an instability in secondary structure. The *am* group of mutants (called N1 in bacteria) carry the nonsense codon, UAG. Such a codon prematurely terminates translation but may be suppressed by at least three different genes in *E. coli* which can permit the continuation of the polypeptide by insertion of serine, glutamine, or tyrosine (237, 798, 799). Another group of nonsense mutations known as *ochre* mutants in phage, similar in many respects to N2 mutants in bacteria, is probably represented by the codon UAA (77, 800). It has been suggested that UAA and UGA are used normally to terminate polypeptides in *E. coli* (628).

Bacteria containing suppressor genes for amber mutants have acquired new transfer RNA molecules for the translation of amber codons. It has recently been shown most elegantly that the suppressor gene is the structural gene for the new tRNA. The su$^+$III gene, which is responsible for the insertion of tyrosine at the UAG (*am*) codon, has been placed in a transducing phage which, on infection of *E. coli*, causes the production of a new tRNA that can hybridize specifically to the transduced DNA (679, 407). The new tRNA contains the anticodon CUA, instead of the anticodon GUA, which is present in the tRNA of the su$^-$ bacterium. The two types of RNA appear to differ only in this single nucleotide contained in their anticodon regions, as determined in a study involving the elucidation of the complete nucleotide sequences of these tRNA molecules (678).

On the other hand, *ts* mutants give rise to a codon which can be translated as missense in strain B, leading immediately to the production of unstable and easily denaturable proteins. Both *am* and *ts* groups of mutants are known for gene 42 controlling dCMP hydroxymethylase. In fact, suppression of an amber mutation for gene 42 in T4 was the first demonstration of altered temperature sensitivity in the resulting protein derived from such missense (171). The production of *ts* dCMP hydroxymethylases (810) under the influence of appropriate *ts* mutants has similarly assisted in defining the molecular nature and consequences of these mutations.

In 1956 and 1957 Jacob and Wollman (331, 328) had detected the existence of defective lysogenic strains which lysed after induction but produced incomplete phage. Arber and Kellenberger (16) examined such products in the electron microscope and were able to characterize the formed elements rather easily. This study became a prototype for a screening operation with the electron microscope on the nature of the developmental blocks imposed by conditionally lethal phage in restrictive conditions (196). It is clear that this instrument will yield most information in the study of late functions and morphopoiesis, since it is only at this stage that discernible particulates are formed (196, 360). Of course, we might also observe the absence of formed elements and the presence or absence of a DNA pool which might permit us to say that the mutation did or did not prevent DNA synthesis. However, this conclusion clearly covers a multitude of early functions and can be attained more easily by direct DNA analysis, which is also one of the screening tests. DNA analysis will also be more informative because we can see a delayed inception or a decreased rate of DNA synthesis, as with mutants deficient in glucosylation or in nucleases. The determination of incorporation of ^{14}C-uracil into DNA and RNA is a more sophisticated screening method recently used to classify the mutants (787a). With this technique some mutants previously categorized as unable to induce synthesis of phage DNA have been found to make significant amounts of DNA. Phase microscopy was also used to determine if the bacterial nucleoid and DNA were degraded during infection (196). Additional screening operations used to classify the mutants have included observation of lysis and the development of antigenic activities, both of which measure late functions (196). In analysing a series of *ts* mutants Alikhanian and his colleagues (5) have performed one-step growth curves at different temperatures and have detected four physiological groups of such mutants. Thus the initial identification of the mutants characterized phages blocked in early functions, DNA synthesis, and numerous morphogenetic steps. As we have described, the biochemists, concerned mainly with problems of biosynthesis, enzymatic activities, and soluble proteins, have studied particularly the mutants blocked in early functions and have succeeded in assigning those functions to 10 of the defined genes.

On the Genetic Map   The discrimination of genes among the mutants is effected by complementation tests. Single or multiple infection of a bacterium by an *am* or *ts* mutant under restrictive conditions does not result in the production of active progeny. Multiple infection under restrictive conditions with several mutants defective in different genes produces progeny. If two independently selected mutants are unable to produce progeny in such a test, they are considered to be defective in the same function, in the same gene. These results are unequivocal among *am*, but less so among *ts*, mutants (188). Also, *am* and *ts* mutants in the same gene do not complement each other. At the time of the last published report (191), almost 70 distinct genes had been detected by such tests; their relative locations and sizes on a genetic map have been assigned after an analysis of intragenic recombination frequencies, as shown in Fig. 30. Two independent analyses have tended to confirm these estimates of distances between genetic markers (519, 257). Although the positions and lengths of 66 genes are recorded on this map, at least half of the DNA remains to be accounted for as genetic material. However, the blank spaces appear to be increasingly difficult to fill in. We note at this time that similar tech-

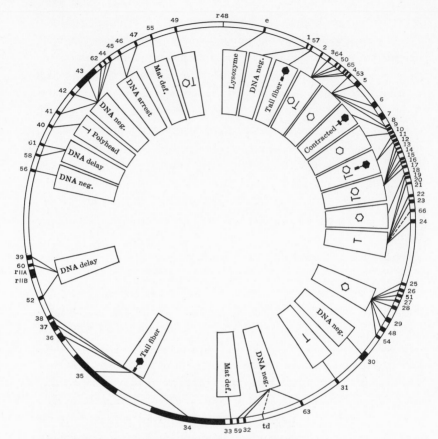

Figure 30. Defective phenotypes of conditional
lethal mutants of T4D under restrictive conditions
(191). Characterized genes are represented by
shaded areas illustrating relative locations and, if
known, approximate map lengths.

niques have assigned no fewer than 25 genes to λ DNA and 6 or 7
genes to the tiny φX174, S13, and M13 phages.

In Fig. 30 the T4 map is presented as a circle (706), although no
circular form of T-even phage DNA has ever been found in isolated
phage or during multiplication. The map is drawn in this way because the linear array of genes established by genetic cross closes

on itself. It is believed that this mapping result stems from a circular permutation of linear molecules; that is, different T-even phage DNA molecules start at different genes in the same basic linear sequence. Such a circularly permuted genetic map has not yet been found in other viruses. T3, T5, and T7 all map as linear molecules and appear to begin infection with the same gene and nucleotide sequence (751, 750). Actually, λ DNA, which is linear in phage, is physically circularized as an essential step in attaching to or releasing from the host chromosome. Circular DNA molecules do exist in numerous phages, φX174 S13, and M13 for example, and indeed appear to maintain this form during multiplication. Although this reaction appears to be an unnatural one, T-even phage DNA can be made to circularize (750) because it frequently ends with a small extra piece of DNA, a terminal redundancy, which repeats the polynucleotide sequence found at the other end. Denaturation and reannealing permit complementary strands to be linked, and either one re-forms the original linear molecule or circular molecules. In addition, a brief exposure of the ends of a nonglucosylated T2 DNA to *E. coli* exonuclease III that removes nucleotides from the 3′ ends of both strands has also predisposed the linear molecules to circularize (471).

Although T3 and T7 DNA are not circularly permuted, they do appear to be terminally repetitious, as demonstrated by the re-annealing techniques described for T-even phage DNA. Annealing in such systems, unlike that with T2 DNA, can produce dimers, trimers, and higher concatemers as the concentration of the strands is increased (609). At present all of the linear viral DNA's examined appear to be terminally repetitious, they end with their beginning sequences. It may be asked if this is not a necessary consequence of the mechanism of DNA multiplication.

It has been recently shown that T-even phage chromosomes containing long deletions seem to carry proportionally longer terminal redundancies; that is, the average lengths of phage chromosomes are approximately equivalent (707). Several workers have suggested that the length of phage DNA is determined by the capacity of the phage head, which plays a role during synthesis in the measurement of DNA length. This hypothesis is discussed in a later section in the context of what is known about DNA synthesis. Since ends of the DNA strands do not reanneal to other DNA molecules, it appears that the ends of essentially all T2 DNA molecules do differ in polynucleotide sequence. Because they do circularize, that is, one strand reanneals to an opposite end, the existence of the terminal redundancies has been considered proved by this and by the numerous genetic studies.

The Co-linearity of Gene and Polypeptide   The genetic data and their representation in linear array have relatively direct chemical consequences, and some phage geneticists confronted with such problems have undertaken to test the rigor of their chemical extrapolations. The mutants of defined function which were studied earliest were those relating to the virus proteins themselves. The virus proteins could be isolated in relatively large amounts by fairly simple procedures. It is quite reasonable, then, that the geneticists have turned to chemistry with this group of proteins.

One such chemical problem involved the proof of the concept that the nucleotide sequence of a virus gene specifies the amino acid sequence of the polypeptide chain. This hypothesis was verified by the elegant experiments of Sarabhai and his collaborators (629) on the head proteins and polypeptides produced by T4 and a series of specially prepared *am* mutants. This head protein constitutes about 80% of the protein of normal phage (769, 76); the subunit is quite large, having a molecular weight of about 80,000 (95). At least seven genes appear to be involved in the synthesis of head protein, as presented in Table 11 (361), and gene 23 appears to control the synthesis of the major subunit of the head capsid. Since about 60% to 70% of the protein made late in infection is the head protein, it has been possible to detect fragments of the polypeptide fairly easily after infection with appropriate mutants (629). Ten different (noncomplementing) *am* mutants of gene 23 were isolated, and the position of the mutation in gene 23 was mapped from the recombination frequencies determined in a series of intragenic crosses. The polypeptides were produced after infection of the nonpermissive hosts in isotopic media, and they were degraded by trypsin to permit detection of the smaller peptide sequences. Fingerprinting techniques showed that certain peptides were missing from these head protein fragments; that is, *am* mutations led to the synthesis of only a fragment of the normal chain and did not permit reinitiation later in the chain. The segments of the gene, from its point of initiation to the site of the mutation, were in each case approximately proportional in length to the size of the polypeptide fragment synthesized; that is, the gene is apparently co-linear with the polypeptide whose sequence it determines (629).

On the Synthesis of Late Proteins   The pulse experiments of Hershey and his associates (308) in 1954 appeared to show that no phage antigen is synthesized in infected cells before about 10 minutes after infection. We have also seen that this is true only if we are referring to external phage antigen, since an internal antigen is made from the beginning of infection. Maalöe and Symonds (469) had detected noninfectious phage-like particles in cells late in infection. Such particles were mainly DNA-free (468). The studies by Levinthal and his colleagues (433, 162) showed that cells infected with a T-even phage or T5 in the presence of proflavine lysed and liberated particles approaching the size and morphology of phage heads. These particles, familiarly called "doughnuts," lack nucleic acid and react with antiphage sera, although not with neutralizing antibody which is directed at tail components. Similar particles which go on to become mature virus are synthesized at about the same time, after 10 minutes in a culture lacking proflavine, and it was suggested that the proflavine particles were actually precursors of virus blocked in a maturation step. Thus heads were formed and tails were subsequently added (162). The absence of DNA from the "doughnuts" was thought to result from an artifact of preparation, that is, that the DNA had leaked from the incompletely packaged head. Apparently, immature phage which does possess a nucleic acid core would lose this DNA on opening the cell (362). Nevertheless, the view that the proflavine "doughnuts" are actually the normal immature head coats of incomplete phage is not unequivocally proved. This point relates to the important questions: Is a phage coat made normally around a shaped DNA support? Is such a support necessary for the formation of a phage head?

In studies of sections of infected cells with the electron microscope, the DNA pool has been shown to develop areas of condensation in the apparent form of polyhedral DNA cores (362), and it has been commonly assumed that the head proteins deposit on that core. Although the DNA condensates have not been isolated, several studies have been made of the packing of DNA in T2 heads. A recent paper reports that the phage head was disrupted lengthwise by treatment with phosphotungstic acid, and the released DNA was found to emerge in a condensed form containing ring structures (374). These rings revealed a small central cavity, previously detected by other workers with intact phage (153). However, such rings have not been seen in sections of phage, and are assumed to form in the transformation of some other symmetrical structure after rupture of the phage coat. In any case, within the phage the DNA fiber is thought to be tied together into multistranded bundles (374), possibly by internal protein, polyamines, and divalent cations, though this role for these substances is entirely conjectural.

A block in "protein" synthesis by addition of chloramphenicol between 8 to 10 minutes after infection prevents the formation of DNA condensates (362). The nature of the steps involved in condensation is quite obscure, as suggested in Chapter 4 in the section on the internal antigen. Since the latter is accumulated before DNA synthesis, it would be expected that a late application of chloramphenicol should not block DNA condensation if the internal antigen were the immediate cause of condensation. The electron microscopists have been unwilling to record that an outer protein film is ever seen on such condensates. No visible intermediate has been described, therefore, between condensate and immature phage head.*

---

* NOTE ADDED IN PROOF: Improvements in the fixation of samples for electron microscopy reported in 1968 have now permitted the description of a visible membrane on DNA "condensates" (361a). The inability of dense DNA condensates to form in cells infected by phage mutants defective in genes con-

The study of phage-precursor protein by Koch and Hershey (380) is relevant to the mystery of the relationship during assembly of DNA and head protein, although their study provides problems of its own. Phage-precursor proteins, labeled with ^{35}S- or ^{14}C-arginine, appear in three approximately equal fractions in artificially lysed cells. They include large particles precipitable with antisera (presumably empty phage heads), smaller antigenically similar particles, and small nonprecipitable particles. The uptake of isotope in the fractions suggested that none was a precursor of the others, a result which puzzled these workers. In a more recent study based on the characterization of proteins by polyacrylamide gel electrophoresis, Levinthal and his collaborators (434) detected three head proteins solubilized by urea which were controlled by genes 22, 23, and 24. These proteins subsequently entered a head structure and thereby became insoluble in urea. Whether the kinetics of formation and of entry of these proteins into completed heads are identical in the three cases is not clear, nor have any data been presented to indicate whether these urea-soluble proteins were originally soluble or present in large insoluble structures which became solubilized.

In any case, Koch and Hershey suggest that a head membrane consisting of most of the amino acids in a phage particle is assembled around DNA; this process takes only 1 minute and generates an unstable structure. On premature lysis, this structure is degraded to produce free DNA, empty head membranes, and other protein fragments. In normal development the unstable head structure is maintained for about 5 minutes and then within a minute is transformed to phage without major additions of protein. Although phage

trolling various head proteins implies a role for head proteins in the organization of virus DNA within the phage head. No evidence exists at the present time for a naked DNA core as a precursor particle. The introduction of this evidence can be seen to reverse the formulation of the meaning of DNA condensation from "how is the protein shell deposited on DNA" to "how is the protein shell stuffed by DNA?"

In addition, head-related structures such as T4 phage itself and the aberrant "polyheads" and membrane-associated tau particles have been shown to contain a labile low density (protein?) core. This material may also be imagined to play a morphopoietic role in the development of a fully packed phage head (361a).

DNA is made about 10 minutes before it appears in intact phage particles, some DNA is present in the free state (about 17 phage equivalents per cell in the conditions tested) and a larger amount (about 28 phage equivalents) seems to be condensed inside unfinished phage membranes. From this analysis, unfinished protein particles containing DNA are made and appear to be waiting for something to happen. Whatever this something is, when it does happen, the completion of the particles is effected rapidly. Since the completing steps were not found to involve gross synthesis, we may ask if the terminal steps merely involve an assembly of subunits or even a crystallization of degraded head subunits. In line with the latter guess, it would be important to know if a protein exactly comparable to the major head protein is made as such before aggregation or is fashioned to this form after assembly.[17]

It is generally believed that the proflavine "doughnuts" are normal intermediates, because, if the proflavine is removed shortly before the end of the normal latent period, numerous complete active particles are formed and released (215). This theory suggests that proflavine blocks a very late step in maturation. Indeed, cells infected in the presence of proflavine develop all the normal components, including tail parts of phage, without forming intact phage. Electron microscopy shows that the cells contain the polyhedral bodies characteristic of condensed DNA and, occasionally, poorly filled "doughnuts" (362). If the acridine dye is removed by dilution into a solution containing an inhibitor of protein synthesis, such as puromycin or 5-methyltryptophan, maturation nevertheless continues until the exhaustion of a preformed phage component, such as tail fiber protein (722, 568, 569). Furthermore, these experiments by Piechowski and Susman showed that condensation of phage DNA, as well as maturation, can occur in the presence of puromycin (569).

---

[17] ADDED IN PROOF: It has now been shown that normal T4 head capsids contain three electrophoretically distinct proteins. A major component, identified as the product of gene 23, appears to be present as such in lysates prior to assembly (361b). It is also found in an apparently normal form in the capsids isolated from the abnormal assembly "polyheads," produced by mutants in genes 20 or 22. Although these mutants do produce the two minor capsid proteins, the polyhead capsids nevertheless lack these components.

The last experiment seems to contradict the chloramphenicol experiment, which suggests a role for protein synthesis in condensation. If the rapidity of maturation depends on a pre-existing pool of soluble head protein precursor being deposited on condensed DNA, it would then appear that "poorly filled pre-existing doughnuts" in the cells are probably not a normal intermediate in phage multiplication. Thus these "poorly filled pre-existing doughnuts" may represent an artifact of preparation or a physiological abnormality imposed by the presence of proflavine. These experiments on maturation and assembly without protein synthesis are a startling confirmation of the conclusion of Koch and Hershey (380) concerning the lack of gross synthesis in terminal stages in the maturation of phage. However, Piechowski and Susman (568) estimate a larger pool of protein precursor than do the earlier workers, and they think that it may even be larger than the pool of vegetative DNA.

The development of abnormal head condensates has been seen to occur under several sets of conditions. As seen in Table 11, mutations in gene 20 produce polyheads comprised of unusually well-ordered and readily visible subunits. Of particular relevance to this discussion is the fact that the polyheads lack DNA and have not required this substance for aggregation (361). Nevertheless, the

Table 11. Known Genes Implicated in Formation of the Phage Head (361)

Gene	Result of Mutation in Gene	Function of the Gene
20	Polyheads	Morphopoietic factor?
21	Abnormal heads, adhering to the envelopes	?
22	No heads	Minority subunit of the capsid? (See footnote 17)
23	No head	Majority subunit of the capsid
66	Increase of short-headed variants	Morphopoietic factor?
24	No heads	?
31	Aggregation of subunits (protein 23)	Morphopoietic factor Solubilizer of protein 23?

capsids present in both normal heads and polyheads are reported alike in at least one antigenic determinant, and it may be asked if normal capsids can aggregate in the absence of DNA. Such subunits have been isolated after alkaline dissociation of the phage and they do aggregate readily (577), although only into a two-dimensional crystal form and not into a polyhead. Phage components of both head and tail sheath (576) show some capacity for the self-assembly seen earlier for protein subunits of tobacco mosaic virus.

The aggregation and deposition of head precursor protein into amorphous structures near the bacterial membrane is seen in mutations of gene 31. It is stated that this gene constitutes one of the early functions (361) and in some way appears to control the solubility of head protein. Other genes such as 66 seem to control the production of short-headed variants (241), a form which has been seen in "normal" stocks (516) and found to contain about 70% of the normal DNA; such particles are possibly comparable to the particles of Mosig (519). Polyheads, produced by defects of gene 20, have also been observed in normal lysates; such lysates also may occasionally contain two-tailed phages and very large heads, and particles with abnormalities of sheath structure, as reviewed by Kellenberger (361). These observations lend support to the notion that the numerous protein precursors of phage evidently have a preferred mechanism of self-assembly but one which permits certain departures under abnormal physiological conditions. These observations then are perhaps comparable to the work of Markham, who showed assembly of subunits of tobacco mosaic virus protein into spiral tubes in the presence of RNA, but observed formation of discs in the absence of the nucleic acid (483).

These results are heightened by the recent results of Cummings and his colleagues (151) who have observed that several amino acid analogues, p-fluorophenylalanine, 5-methyltryptophan, and 7-azatryptophan, produce many such anomalies nonspecifically in phage populations. Even more striking were the specific effects produced by several analogues. The arginine analogue, L-canavanine, produces polyheads; the proline analogue, L-azetidine-2-carboxylic acid, gives rise to polytail tubes; and a histidine analogue, 1,2,4-

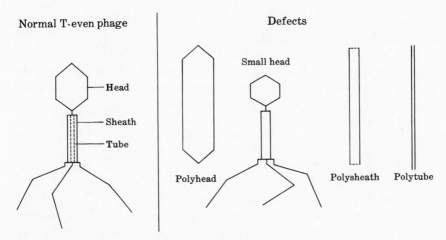

Figure 31. Schematic diagram of the morphology
of T-even bacteriophage and some aberrant
structures (151).

triazole-3-alanine, proflavine, and actinomycin D, cause the formation of small-headed phage, diagramed in Fig. 31. A tail tube has
an unusually high proline content (630), and the specificity of the
effect of a proline analogue in producing polytail tubes suggests
that the analogue takes advantage of the unusual composition of
the structure. These findings clearly make available a number of
chemical agents that will be useful in studying the production of
the protein units of these phage structures.

Additional Remarks about the Packaging of Viral DNA   Despite
the elaborate genetic, physical, and chemical picture we now have
of viral DNA, discussed earlier, the structure of vegetative phage
DNA is far from clear. As described in Chapter 4, the study of the
state of intracellular DNA by sucrose density gradients appeared to
reveal unusual rapidly sedimenting particles of viral DNA (217,
218). They were postulated to represent very long covalently linked
growing chromosomes. This presumed concatenated structure appeared to provide a molecular basis for the generation of circularly
permuted terminally redundant chromosomes if a simple measuring

and cutting device was imagined to exist during assembly (749). If the measuring device were grossly inaccurate, it might generate the types of DNA found in short-headed phage (519) or in over-large phage. It has even been suggested that the assembly of the head units themselves produces the necessary measuring and cutting device. Unfortunately, the characterization of early vegetative DNA by centrifugation in CsCl density gradients (395) has not supported the initial postulate of the model. The replicative molecules were found to be of the same size as phage DNA (within a factor of 2) and, for this reason, a model of continuous growth of the DNA molecule has not been generally accepted. A recent report (386) indicates that very low concentrations of actinomycin D inadequate for blocking synthesis of DNA, RNA, and protein prevent the condensation of newly synthesized phage DNA, that is, the maturation of the late-replicating pool DNA. In such a system single strands studied in alkaline gradients were stated to have the apparent size of the strands of phage DNA (386). Nevertheless Frankel has detected the existence in alkaline media of unusually rapidly sedimenting single strands derived from the relatively late-replicating DNA (218a). Thus the existence of unusually long DNA is affirmed by Frankel, regardless of its mechanism of formation.

Kozinski and his collaborators (395) have suggested that recombinational events might well produce long intermediates which provide the circularly permuted DNA molecules which are found in phage. If this can be proved, the resolution of the experimental results alluded to above will not require an unusual mechanism for DNA replication and the possibility of a measuring and cutting device will still have to be considered. In addition, the problem of the condensation of DNA, prevented by chloramphenicol and actinomycin D but not by puromycin, and the problem of the formation of the head proteins around DNA condensates as yet nonisolable, provide a series of difficult and important questions. Perhaps the various initial results cited above suggest the existence of some as yet unexplored mechanisms. Recent data on the origin of the phage polypeptides, to be discussed below, tend to support this view.

Phage Polypeptides   In 1957 Hershey described the presence in T-even phage of a group of polypeptides accounting for about 1% of phage carbon and comprised mainly of aspartic acid, glutamic acid, and lysine (305). He also showed that these substances are not made, as is DNA, in the presence of chloramphenicol. The polypeptides assumed less interest at that point of scientific history when it was demonstrated that they were not transmitted from parent to progeny and could not be considered an essential constituent of the viral genetic apparatus. In a recent paper Eddleman and Champe (186) showed that the formation of these substances in infected cells requires the operation of the 6 or 7 genes controlling

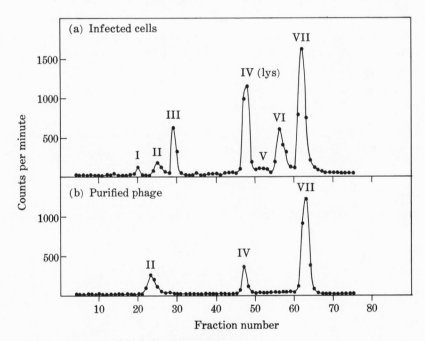

Figure 32. Lysine-labeled cationic substances present in acid extracts of phage and of T4-infected cells (186). The presence of two polypeptides, II and VII, is seen in purified phage, whereas infected cells contain three, II, VI, and VII. I, III, and V are found in extracts of uninfected cells; IV is free lysine.

production of the head proteins. The polypeptides are formed, for example, on infection with tail mutants.

The acid-soluble polypeptides may be labeled by giving ^{14}C-lysine to infected cells; they can be separated readily on cation-exchange columns. Two of the polypeptides isolated from T4 have the approximate composition (185)

$$\mathrm{asp_{22}\ glu_{12}\ lys_4\ gly_1\ pro_1\ ser_2}\quad (\mathrm{MW} = 4900),\ \mathrm{and}$$

$$\mathrm{asp_1\ glu_9\ lys_6\ ala_4\ ileu_1\ val_1}\quad (\mathrm{MW} = 2600)$$

Extracts of infected cells contain three polypeptides (II, VI, and VII) not observed in extracts of uninfected cells (see Fig. 32). Purified phage, however, contains only two of these polypeptides. A study of the origin and fate of the third polypeptide has revealed that all of these substances begin to appear at about the time when intact phage appears, at about 13 minutes.

As Fig. 33 shows, both phage and nonphage polypeptides are formed from an acid-insoluble prelabeled precursors. Whereas a

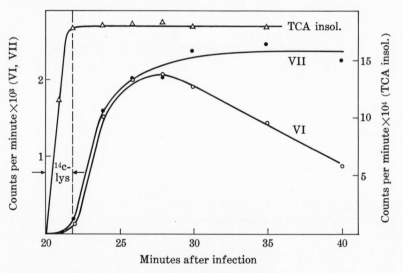

Figure 33. The precursor-polypeptide relationship in T4-infected cells as revealed by pulse labeling with ^{14}C-lysine (186).

phage polypeptide, VII for example, continues to be made, the rate of accumulation of the nonphage polypeptide, VI, falls off by 20 minutes and this substance is then actually degraded (Fig. 33). These remarkable results suggest that one virus-induced function is a proteinase which operates in phage infection to liberate the polypeptides.

It can be imagined that the polypeptide precursor is a structural component of the virus which must be modified before assembly can occur. Another interesting suggestion is that the polypeptide precursor is a core component which must be eliminated to permit injection of phage DNA. To my mind, the idea of a proteinase at work can do much to explain not only the presence of the polypeptides but also the apparently abrupt transition without net protein synthesis from phage DNA condensates to mature phage head.

Assembly in Cell-Free Systems   The biology of phage assembly revealed in the studies described up to this point establishes the preconditions for another paradise for biochemists. The system of phage assembly requires merely a trigger (proteolytic degradation of soluble proteins?) for a complicated sequence of events not involving protein synthesis to take place to form the evidently complicated active phages. Such reactions ought to be able to proceed in late extracts of infected cells, and they do.

The published work of two laboratories has so far been directed to assembling heads and tails *in vitro*. It has not yet been extended back to the level of the soluble polypeptide precursor and the DNA condensates, presumably because of the fragility of the latter materials in extracts.[18] Nevertheless, the results already obtained are quite remarkable in revealing the extent to which self-assembly has apparently evolved.

[18] The awe-inspiring results of Mackal and his collaborators (472) and Zgaga (825) on the formation of infectious λ bacteriophage in systems containing DNA and disrupted cells (472) or crude extracts of sensitive bacteria (825) are presumed to require at the very least all the intermediate stages of synthesis of phage protein, in addition to assembly. Perhaps the analysis of the steps in this system will eventually provide a very important system for the study of all the terminal steps in morphogenesis of this phage.

Conditional lethal mutants of T4 have been isolated which have difficulties in the construction of tail elements (196, 190). For example, genes 34, 35, 36, 37, and 38 control the construction of tail fibers, which appear to contain at least three different antigens. An unlinked gene, 57, specifically affects the production of these antigens (190). Lysates of cells infected with appropriate tail fiber mutants contain defective phages, lacking tail fibers although they do contain particular antigens, particular tail fiber components (190). Lysates of cells infected with head mutants contain all of the essential tail fiber components. In the studies of Edgar and Wood (191) such an extract was added to purified tail fiberless phage and produced a thousandfold increase in phage activity; such phages had the genotype of the tail fiberless phage. With this technique, T2 tail fibers were added to defective T4 particles, which now had the adsorption properties of T2. Electron microscopy confirmed these results; that is, phage acquires tail fibers during incubation. The studies have also been pursued with extracts made with phage deficient in specific tail fiber genes, and observation of complementation of extracts has permitted dissection of early steps of tail fiber assembly.

In *in vitro* tests with 35 morphogenetic genes other than tail fiber genes, numerous assembly steps have been examined. Heads can be attached to tails, but some genes (genes 13, 14, 15, and 18) apparently produce components required for their attachment. Eight others are involved in completing or altering the head to prepare it for attachment (191). Some steps in assembly do not proceed easily, and the requirements for these steps have not yet been determined. It is obvious that the chemical and physical problems presented in this system are almost innumerable. Nevertheless, the quantitation possible with the phage assay, as well as the unusual biological material afforded by the use of the phage mutants, will clearly permit major progress in the analysis of phage structure and assembly.

In a similar study by Israel, Anderson, and Levine (325) of *in vitro* morphogenesis of phage P22, heads and tails were isolated from lysates produced with appropriate mutants and then mixed. A million-fold increase in infectious titer was obtained; electron microscopy and genetic analysis confirmed the postulated assembly. Since the reaction occurred with purified components in the absence of an extract, there is no need to postulate an enzymatic role in the system. The chemical aspects of this reaction have been studied in greater detail than those of the T-even phage system, which seems to be considerably more complex.

From the point of view of the biochemist, there appear to be significant advantages in studying a less complex system such as P22 or even simpler systems. The existence of a very simple system capable of self-assembly, the polymerization of tobacco mosaic virus protein, has been known since 1943 (418), but it has not evoked a great deal of excitement among molecular biologists or biochemists, nor has it enticed many of them into work with that readily accessible experimental system. Nevertheless a very few chemists have remained faithful to the plant viruses precisely because of the numerous advantages of using these molecules (see 418). It should be noted that some viruses are known that are even less complex than viruses such as tobacco mosaic virus.[19]

Lysis and Lysozyme   The clearing of a bacterial culture as a result of bacterial virus multiplication is one of the more startling phenomena in virology. Lysis as a result of virus infection has been known for about fifty years, and of course lysis, the development of a plaque on a bacterial lawn, is the basis of the misnomer bacteriophage. In the last few years bacterial viruses have been de-

---

[19] Although the packaging of virus nucleic acid into a protein coat almost always facilitates infection and survival of the viral genome, the nucleate alone can often multiply in many cells. Indeed, some infectious "viruses" are known which appear to consist entirely of the nucleate; that is, they are devoid of protein. Occasionally they are found and are considered interesting laboratory freaks. For example, a defective mutant of tobacco mosaic virus, PM2, is sensitive to ribonuclease. The coat protein whose synthesis is induced remains free in the plant cytoplasm and is unable to bind with the infectious RNA which can multiply and maintain an infectious cycle (664). Among viruses reported to exist in nature as free nucleic acid, we note the recent description of potato spindle tuber virus as a particle of 10S, comprised entirely of double-stranded RNA (170). Obviously, the definition of a virus as an organism comprised of nucleate and protein breaks down in such an instance.

scribed that multiply and leave their host cells without producing cell lysis. Nothing is really known of the mechanism of this trick; I shall discuss it in greater detail later, as a clarification of the nature of this phenomenon promises to involve a real understanding of the organization of the bacterial cell.

As described earlier, the T-even viruses produce plaques, although only those derived from r plaques are large and clear. The r strains also clear cultures dramatically, and it is possible to detect an endolysin in such cultures. Such an endolysin is present both on the tail of isolated phage and in a soluble state in the lysate; the enzyme therefore appears unique in this system in its role both as a virus structural protein and as a late virus-induced soluble enzyme.

"Endolysin" is also produced in r+ cultures, but a recent study has demonstrated a markedly lower rate of endolysin production in superinfected cultures (618), although the beginning of lysin synthesis occurs at about the same time. This unusual effect has been attributed to the presence of the soluble substances injected by superinfecting phages, which in some way alter the course of the infection for a limited time (618). A role for DNA in this effect may have been excluded (618). On the other hand, there is nothing as yet to suggest that polyamines, polypeptides, or internal antigen can indeed produce such an effect.

Many mechanisms of enzymatic bacteriolysis, from specific peptidases (176) to specific carbohydrases (711), are known. In the case of *E. coli*-T-even phage systems, the "endolysin" has been shown to be a lysozyme, defined as an enzyme that cleaves the N-acetyl-muramyl-N-acetylglucosamine linkage in bacterial cell walls, as presented in Fig. 34. The T2 lysozyme is like numerous plant and animal lysozymes and some bacterial enzymes in this respect (711). According to Weidel and his collaborators and others (379, 796, 583, 470), the nature of the product of activity of egg white lysozyme is very similar to that produced by T2 phage lysozyme.

The enzyme was isolated and characterized initially by Weidel's group (356, 797) and then in greater detail in the laboratory of Anfinsen (9). It may be easily obtained from lysates by adsorption and elution from a cation-exchange resin. Although originally

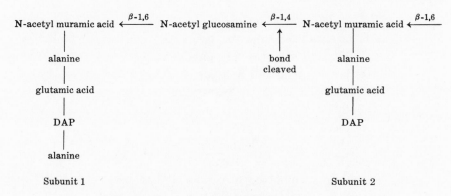

Figure 34. The linkage in the *E. coli*
cell wall cleaved by phage lysozyme,
an endo-β(1,4)-N-acetylglucosaminidase.

thought to differ slightly from the tail-bound lysozyme (356), the
enzyme is no longer thought to be different from the latter. The T2
and T4 lysozymes, isolated from lysates, were shown to differ in the
composition of their fragments produced by trypsin (9). Most work
has been done on the soluble lysozyme, which is present in lysates
in amounts of 1 to 2 mg per liter. A variety of molecular weights has
been reported on the basis of physical methods: 13,900 (782), 14,500
(9), 15,200 (797). However, a recent analysis of T4 lysozyme by
Tsugita and his colleagues (761) records the presence of 163 to 165
amino acids with a calculated molecular weight of 19,000. The
reason for the discrepancies among all these values is not clear from
the literature. Nevertheless, the knowledge of amino acid sequences
for normal and mutant lysozymes has permitted the analysis of the
nature of proflavine-induced frameshift mutations by Streisinger and
his collaborators (709).

Many carbohydrases have been described in phage lysates but
not all of them are lysozymes. Sertic discovered the presence of a
lysin in lysates of a mucoid strain of *E. coli* (648), but it must be
asked if this "enzyme" was actually a lysozyme. Numerous phages
for *E. coli* K12 have been isolated which produce exopolysac-
charidases capable of depolymerizing bacterial polysaccharides essentially devoid of muramic acid (724). Adams and Park (564, 4)

studied a *Klebsiella pneumoniae* phage which carried an enzyme capable of depolymerizing the polysaccharide capsule of the organism. The enzyme was also produced in soluble form. Such enzymes are evidently not lysozymes, although they are controlled by the phage genome. Actually, a similar polysaccharide hydrolase has recently been defined as a fucosidase (723). The possible significance of these systems in permitting the virus to approach the host has been discussed by Sutherland and Wilkinson (724).

Although the *Klebsiella* phage enzyme may prove useful to the phage in approaching the bacterium, it had been suggested that T-even phage lysozyme helps the phages in injection of viral DNA. Nevertheless, many phages that infect *E. coli*, T5 for example, and λ, do not contain virus-bound lysozyme. Thus penetration of the cell wall in these instances does not require lysozyme to cleave the cellular mucopeptide. Since, as we shall see below, infection can be effected by lysozyme-deficient T-even phage, it appears that the enzyme is not involved in penetration at all. In point of fact, it probably should be asked if phage lysozyme is not an adsorbed contaminant on the T-even virus particles.*

---

* NOTE ADDED IN PROOF: It seems quite appropriate at this point to mention the numerous enzymes found associated with the phage particle. Kozloff has done an extraordinary amount of work on structures isolable from phage and activities associated with these structures. His laboratory has localized a masked enzyme on the proximal portion of T2 and T4 tails; the enzyme releases up to 15% of the total nitrogen from host cell walls. The activity is conceivably that of lysozyme, as stated by Kozloff (398a), but this has not been proved rigorously. Numerous properties of the enzyme and its unmasking have led to the suggestion that the activity is important in penetration and is involved in the release of a cell wall component, possibly Zn^{++}, which triggers contraction of the tail sheath (398a). If this enzyme is indeed lysozyme, the infectivity of lysozyme-deficient mutants is an evident difficulty for this hypothesis.

The contraction of the sheath is superficially similar in numerous respects to muscular contraction. The contractile sheath is comprised of numerous protein subunits, each of which appears to contain an atom of bound Ca^{++} and a nucleoside triphosphate such as ATP or dATP. This sheath protein has been clearly shown to be a nucleoside triphosphatase, whose exact role in the contractile process has not been defined as yet. The sheath contraction is believed to force a tail core through the cell wall, permitting the phage DNA to pass through the hollow tail into the bacterium. It would be of interest to know

If the enzyme is not involved in injection, perhaps it is involved in lysis itself. However, it will be recalled that numerous systems, φX174 (482) for example, lyse without the production or participation of lysozyme.

The hypothesis that lysozyme operates mainly in lysis is supported by the work of Streisinger and his collaborators, who have been studying many aspects of the genetics of lysozyme synthesis. This group has isolated mutants which lack this function or produce altered enzyme (708). The detection of such mutants, altered in the e gene, involves the exposure of plaques to chloroform vapor at 37°C. This treatment produces large halos around the plaques as a result of the lytic action of diffused lysozyme in the presence of chloroform. A mutant phage with a deficient lytic mechanism, including a deficiency or alteration of lysozyme, does not develop these halos. Such strains, which are unable to synthesize lysozyme, nevertheless infect bacteria. However, phages unable to make an active lysozyme are unable to lyse cells (98), although such infected cells can be lysed by exogenous addition of egg white lysozyme (705, 520a). Cells infected with lysozyme-deficient phage do not lyse at the usual time but do stop oxygen consumption at about that time (520a). The arrest of oxidation and linked metabolic reactions appears to occur concomitantly with damage to the bacterial membrane, which may trigger the lytic action of the enzyme. It appears also that there are T-even phage genes controlling lysis which do not control lysozyme; they have been detected by the inability of chloro-

if a soluble dATPase, other than that in the sheath, increases in the cell during infection.

The T4 tail has also been shown to contain six molecules of dihydropteroyl hexaglutamic acid, a dihydrofolic acid conjugate which does not occur in the uninfected bacterium (399a). Destruction of this folic acid derivative prevents phage attachment to the host. Most recently binding sites for the folic acid on the phage tail have been reported to be phage-induced dihydrofolate reductase. The phage-associated enzyme is found entirely in purified tail base plates, to which the six tail fibers attach (769a). Thus dihydrofolate reductase is thought to be a structural component of the phage tail plate. Since (reductase-deficient) mutants adsorb and multiply, the evidence for a functional role of this enzyme in adsorption appears incomplete as of this writing.

form vapors to produce lytic zones with such mutants (708). Such genes may therefore relate to the integrity of the bacterial membrane. It should be evident at this point that the chemical steps involved in lysis and phage liberation are quite obscure.

Lysozyme is a late enzyme whose production depends on a sequence of early enzyme production, phage DNA synthesis, and synthesis of RNA essential for late proteins (645). The relation of the late appearance of lysozyme to the dCMP hydroxymethylase and dTMP synthetase in T6r$^+$-infected *E. coli* strain THU is presented in Fig. 35. The figure also shows the effect of a uracil deficiency on such syntheses; these results are discussed in Chapter 6.

We note that the lysozyme levels were obtained by an adaptation of a turbidimetric method in which chloroform-treated cells lyse in the presence of the enzyme (645). Although the detailed studies of the lysozyme reaction and its specificity have revealed chitotetraose to be an apparently minimal substrate for cleavage without a lag by the enzyme (559, 654, 401), chemically defined substrates have not generally been available to phage biologists. Nevertheless, with the turbidimetric method we can easily detect enzyme of the order of 1% of the maximal level of the enzyme in infected cells. The enzyme is certainly at a level lower than this at all early stages of infection, that is, before the inception of DNA synthesis; and it does not appear in infected cells if DNA synthesis is completely prevented, as in infection with ultraviolet-irradiated virus (645). We have recently observed that, in infections of strain THU, streptomycin stops synthesis of lysozyme fairly late (after 30 minutes) after considerable lysozyme synthesis has already occurred (221). Lysis of such cells takes place earlier rather than later than normally (221).

The Problem of the rII Product   Although the rII gene is believed to be an early function, its exact role is quite unclear. I am treating it among late functions because the r$^+$ and r character do relate to lysis.

The dissection of the rII gene by Benzer is one of the most important contributions to the definition of the structure of a gene; this work has been reviewed many times (51, 119). The rII region

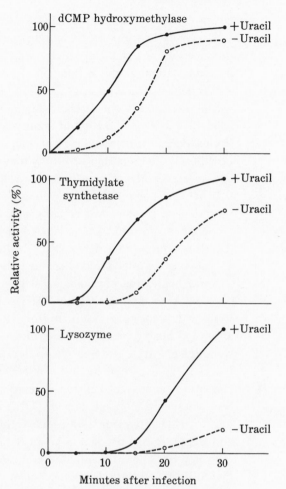

Figure 35. The formation of some early and late enzymes in *E. coli* strain THU in the presence and absence of exogenous uracil (645). Bacteria were incubated in a medium lacking uracil for 15 minutes and then infected with T6r+ at a multiplicity of 4. Suspensions were incubated with and without uracil for deoxycytidylate hydroxymethylase, for thymidylate synthetase, and for lysozyme.

is known to comprise two cistrons and to contain less than 1% of the T4 DNA. Many hundreds of different rII mutants have been isolated. Mutants in the rII region cannot develop in *E. coli* lysogenic for phage λ, although they can develop in nonlysogenic bacteria which permit the ready propagation of these phages. It has been observed that r strains do produce lysis inhibition, as do the wild type r+ strains, in bacteria devoid of a defective prophage related to temperate phage P2 (620). The biological relations of the rII cistrons and of lysis inhibition thus appear to be rather complicated.

A phenotypic suppression of amber mutants of rII mutants can be produced by fluorouracil, which on insertion into mRNA permits a new translation of the codon (52). Another suppressive agent is streptomycin, which appears to affect the ribosome in a manner to permit the translation of the nonsense codon as viable missense (555). The ready detection of suppressed rII mutants on indicator strains normally incapable of developing plaques has led to the broad use of these mutants in studying many aspects of mutagenesis and, most recently, of transformation (38).

It has been reported recently that a polypeptide characteristic of the rII gene product has actually been demonstrated (506). This polypeptide, detected via a labeled peptide produced by trypsin digestion of an appropriate extract, begins to be synthesized within 3 minutes after infection and ceases to be made at 10 minutes.

Nevertheless, the physiological nature of the rII mutation is still obscure. After infection with a T4rII strain of *E. coli* K12 (λ), development continues normally for 10 minutes and then stops abruptly. Mg^{++} (236) or one of the polyamines, spermine or spermidine (204), restores phage development at high concentration, but the nature of the lesion affected by these substances is not known. In the arrest of phage development by an rII mutant, protein synthesis is stopped, as is the DNA synthesis which had barely begun (643). Other functions, such as the synthesis of phospholipids and RNA, are also blocked at about the same time. Respiration also falls off a bit later, at about 15 minutes (236, 643). The cells do not lyse; in fact, very little lysozyme is made, even though the cells have made virtually a full complement of dCMP hydroxymethylase (643) and other early enzymes (619).

In the work of Ferroluzzi-Ames and Ames (204), it had been observed that the spermidine is most effective in permitting continued development of the rII mutant when added at the eighth minute after infection. After infection there had been a loss of putrescine from the cells into the medium for 7 minutes; in r^+-infected cells this leak is repaired at about 7 minutes, but it continues with the rII mutant. Thus it has been suggested that the rII effect relates to membrane repair. Indeed, addition of exogenous cations generally appears to facilitate continued development, as if the cations were sealing leaks or replacing lost cations or both. Sekiguchi (643) and Colowick (143a) have observed a sharp and rapid drop in the ability of rII-infected cells to generate ATP, which then shows a continuing fall. It has been suggested that the very low ATP level reached is the cause of the later decreases in synthetic activities. However, the cause of the phosphorylation effects are themselves obscure, although these effects are consistent with the hypothesis of a lesion of an unknown nature in the bacterial membrane.

It may be mentioned that two other T2 phage genes, pr and q, controlling resistance to proflavine and quinacrine, respectively, affect the leakage of the bacterial membrane to these compounds (665a). The function of the pr gene therefore may be connected to the development of the early and transient leaky state detected in T2-infected bacteria (589a). The repair of this leakiness appears to be disturbed in certain infections by rII mutants (204, 236). It should be asked also if the function of the pr gene relates to normal lysis, which, however, seems to require late damage to the bacterial membrane. In any case it is evident that the integrity of the bacterial membrane is affected by the expression of several specialized viral functions throughout the course of a cycle of multiplication.

Sequential Syntheses in Phage Multiplication   In Fig. 36 I have tried to present a composite picture of the timing of the various virus-induced syntheses I have been discussing thus far. Several guesses are made in the diagram aside from those deliberately labeled as such, because few of the analyses have been made under comparable conditions. For example, it is suggested that lysozyme, polypeptide precursor, and virus structural components begin at the same time, but this is not known to be true. It is suggested that the polypeptides are formed before infectious virus appears; this has in fact been shown (186), although it would be more to the point to know if the appearance of the polypeptide coincided with the

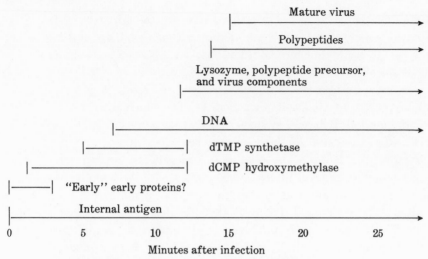

Figure 36. The sequence of early proteins, DNA,
and late proteins in T-even r⁺ phage infection of
E. coli strain B in a glucose-mineral medium at 37°.

formation of intact phage heads. Primitive as it is, the figure does
reflect our body of existing knowledge and perhaps pinpoints some
of our outstanding problems.

ENZYMES INDUCED BY SOME OTHER DNA-CONTAINING BACTERIAL VIRUSES

Biochemical Phenomena among Some Phages Infecting B. subtilis
Since *B. subtilis* is readily transformed by exogenous DNA, work
with phages for this organism offered the potentiality of inserting
into the bacteria the DNA both of mature phage and of the replicative pool. This possibility has been realized with relatively great
difficulty in T-even phage-*E. coli* systems, as shown in the work of
Van de Pol and his collaborators (768), of Goldberg (257), and of
Bautz (38). These workers have used a urea-damaged phage (109)
to help the penetration of various bits of phage DNA, serving as
transforming DNA. Kaiser and Hogness (345) had initiated this

ingenious approach with normal λ phage as helper and had carefully separated bits of DNA of various λ mutants to insert particular markers. This technique has been most elegantly refined by the latter group in studies of λ virus multiplication and gene expression.

Transducing phages have also been found in *B. subtilis* systems. Genetic studies relating phage markers to physical properties of transforming phage DNA in *B. subtilis* phage systems are beginning to be reported (261a, 262). Nevertheless, although there is every reason to believe that *B. subtilis* infections will be most interesting to explore with these genetic tools, much of the work with these phages since 1962 has been diverted as a result of the surprising initial biochemical findings on phage composition, findings which have revealed additional new and exciting biochemical problems.

Marmur (483a) has prepared a survey of five major groups of phages; they include transducing phages, virulent phages, temperate phages, defective phages (PBSX), and some others. Among these viruses, many of which have normal base compositions, may be found such phages as PBS1 and PBS2, which contain uracil instead of thymine (729, 730), and SP5, SP8, SPO-1, and φe, which contain 5-hydroxymethyluracil instead of thymine (347, 550, 12, 613). Many other *B. subtilis* phages have aberrancies in melting temperatures of DNA or an excess of adenine over thymine, which suggest the presence of unusual bases, but such bases or other specific DNA anomalies have not yet been demonstrated. It is also stated that the DNA found in the defective phage PBSX is entirely host DNA (641, 718). Thus *B. subtilis* phages contain unusual DNA and DNA components, which, though differing chemically from HMC in the T-even phages, nevertheless pose some similar problems. Among them are: How are these distinctive nucleotides made? How are the normal bases, in this instance thymine, excluded? Glucose, initially reported to be present in some of these phages, eventually proved to be a contaminant in the phage preparation, and to be derived from the polymer, teichoic acid, present in these host bacteria.

Before leaving the DNA phages containing uracil, it may be

noted that the insertion of uracil into DNA requires the loss of a very effective method of exclusion of dUTP from the bacterial metabolites. As described earlier, an enzyme normally present in the bacteria degrades dUTP to dUMP + PP$_i$, and also appears to be responsible for the degradation of fluorodeoxyuridine triphosphate, which is generated when this nucleoside analogue is fed to cells. *B. subtilis* infected with PBS2, which contains uracil instead of thymine, readily incorporates fluorodeoxyuridine into phage DNA (457).

Some Virus-Induced Enzymes for HMU Phages   I shall focus on several phages which contain HMU (for structure see Fig. 2A in Chapter 2) instead of thymine. The synthesis of the new base and the exclusion of thymine are effected by the virus-induced reactions presented in Table 12. An enzyme similar to the dCMP hydroxymethylase in T-even phage infection operates at the deoxyribonucleoside monophosphate level to add formaldehyde to dUMP with the aid of THFA. No less than three virus-induced proteins assist in the exclusion of thymine: an enzyme destroys dTTP to yield dTMP + pyrophosphate; an enzyme destroys dTMP; and a protein inactivates dTMP synthetase irreversibly.

Table 12. Some Enzymes of B. subtilis Infected by HMU Phage

Enzyme	Reaction	References
dCMP deaminase	dCMP → dUMP	(344, 533, 612)
dUTPase	dUTP → dUMP + PP$_i$	(344)
dTTPase	dTTP → dTMP + PP$_i$	(344)
dUMP hydroxymethylase	dUMP + CH$_2$O $\xrightarrow{\text{THFA}}$ CH$_2$OH-dUMP	(344, 612)
dTMP-5′-nucleotidase	dTMP → thymidine	(12, 14)
Inhibitor of dTMP synthetase	dUMP $\nrightarrow$ dTMP	(612, 613, 288)

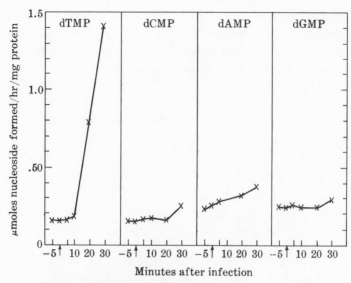

Figure 37. Nucleotidase activity of *B. subtilis*
before and after infection by phage SP5C (12).

The existence of an enzyme capable of degrading dTTP had not previously been detected; its presence in SP8 infections must also serve to turn off bacterial multiplication. Although a very active specific dTMP nucleotidase is known in *E. coli* and seems to be inactivated during infection (12a), nonspecific nucleotidases exist at a very low level in uninfected *B. subtilis* and only the dTMPase is increased after infection by SP5C. These results are presented in Fig. 37. Unless the inhibition of dTMPase in T-even infection represents the production of a specific inhibitory protein, the appearance of the protein inhibitor for dTMP synthetase represents a completely new type of virus-induced protein. The solutions to the two questions we have asked when confronted with the existence of HMU phages are seen to be new and ingenious, and admirably selected for the needs of these viruses.

The supply of dUMP for CH_2OH-dUMP is produced with the aid of an increase of a dCMP deaminase which is insensitive to dTTP or 5-hydroxymethyldeoxyuridine triphosphate as inhibitor and to dCTP as activator (533). Unlike the deaminase induced in T-even phage infection or the animal enzyme which shows these allosteric controls, the SP8-induced enzyme is the first example of a dCMP deaminase which lacks these feedback controls. This phenomenon seems suited to this system in at least one respect: dTTP is absent in these infections. The supply of dUMP may also be controlled by a dUTPase, which may merely be another aspect of the dTTPase activity.

The overall sequence of the known mechanisms induced to assist in the production of an HMU-containing DNA is

$$
\begin{array}{c}
\qquad\qquad\qquad \overset{\text{dUTP}}{\underset{\text{dUDP}}{\big\uparrow}} \\
-PP_i \Bigg(\\
\text{dCMP} \xrightarrow{\text{deaminase}} \text{dUMP} \xrightarrow{\text{hydroxymethylase}} CH_2OH\text{-dUMP} \\
\Big| \text{blocked} \\
\xrightarrow{\quad\quad} \text{dTMP} \underset{-PP_i}{\rightleftarrows} \text{dTTP} \\
-P_i \Big\downarrow \\
\text{thymidine}
\end{array}
$$

It should be evident that, although the form of the problems presented and the solutions generated by the HMU phages is quite similar to those generated by HMC phages, the chemical differences in the HMU systems give new and unique chemical content to the specific solutions. These solutions are also independent, in an evolutionary sense, from those adopted by the T-even phages.

In addition to these strikingly new enzymatic phenomena, we can also point to numerous specific differences in the physiology of infection with an HMU phage, as compared to T-even phage, although some interesting similarities are also to be found. Infection with the nonlysogenic SP8 resembles infection with a temperate phage in the sense that the synthesis of RNA, including bacterial mRNA, continues at a normal rate (484, 485). Furthermore, bacterial DNA is not extensively degraded (484, 485); thus, presumably, the generation of dTMP is avoided. In contrast, I note that one of the enzymes induced by the thymine-containing phage SP3 in *B. subtilis* is a very active deoxyribonuclease (760).

In examining the kinetics of synthesis of some of the early enzymes and proteins, it appears that the complete disappearance of the dTMP synthetase takes about 10 minutes (288), whereas the dUMP hydroxymethylase begins at 5 minutes, falls off at 15 minutes, and essentially stops at 25 minutes (288). It should be noted that the disappearance of dTMP synthetase is more pronounced in φe phage infections than in SP8 infections, and it has been suggested that in the SP8 infections this inhibitor is not the major preventive in freeing phage DNA of thymine (288).

Pene and Marmur have studied (565) the development of early and late proteins in phage 2C infections and have compared the production of dCMP deaminase and lysozyme. The synthesis of the former enzyme is said (565) to continue until the end of the latent period, although a break in rate can be seen in its rate of increase at 20 minutes, a result quite dissimilar from the result with dUMP hydroxymethylase (288). Lysozyme, the typically late protein, does not appear before 15 minutes; thus it follows the inception of DNA synthesis at 10 minutes. Actinomycin D, which can penetrate *B. subtilis* readily, has also been used in this study. Addition of the antibiotic at 13 minutes, which was thought to block mRNA synthesis uniquely, causes a prompt arrest of dCMP deaminase. This result is interpreted to mean that there is a continuous requirement by the deaminase for synthesis of the mRNA. Lysozyme did not appear either, and this enzyme was therefore thought to require production of a new message (565). Lysozyme does not appear unless DNA synthesis occurs, as we showed with T-even phage systems (644). In these respects, then, the sole qualitatively new result on the program of enzyme production is that there is a continued synthesis of one early enzyme, dCMP deaminase, a point warranting considerable elaboration. The general pattern of early enzymes, DNA synthesis and virus proteins plus lysozyme, is otherwise similar to that in T-even phage infection.

ON THE BIOCHEMISTRY OF SMALL PHAGES
CONTAINING SINGLE-STRANDED
CIRCULAR DNA

Biochemical work on the very small phages of this group, such as
ϕX174, was initiated by Sinsheimer (670) and others precisely because these viruses were so small. Since these viruses could not contain much DNA, and hence contained little genetic information,
either the requirements for virus multiplication were less in this
instance than for a T-even phage or the host cell participated in
these activities to a greater extent than in T4 multiplication. It is
now evident that the problems cannot be posed in this simple form;
the small phages are organized in a way that requires qualitatively
distinctive solutions for various stages of their life cycle. The participation of the host cell structure in these steps is similarly unexpected and challenging and points to a role for mechanisms unsuspected from the study of the T-even phages or T5 or the *B.
subtilis* phages studied so far.

Virus Form and Protein Synthesis   The small phages ϕX174,
ϕR, and S13 lack a tail and contain DNA within an icosahedral
protein coat (70). Two clearly defined morphological subunits
have been found at the apices of the icosahedron of ϕR, but it is
not known if they are identical (70). Two distinct coat protein subunits unlinked by disulfide bonds have been isolated from ϕX174
(154); no internal protein appears to be bound to the DNA. Mutant strains containing electrophoretically distinct capsids have
been isolated; one of them possesses two proteins different from
those in the wild type (567). Such strains may be crossed with
wild type ϕX174, and phages can be formed which possess either
genotype in hybrid capsids (322). This phenomenon, known as
"phenotypic mixing," suggests that, in assembling the ϕX174 coat,
the four types (at least) of protein may be withdrawn from a
common pool (322). The two different protein subunits, wild type
or mutant, complement each other in determining infectivity on a

given bacterial strain. The significance of these data in determining possible mechanisms of adsorption and DNA transfer has been discussed by Hutchison and his collaborators (322).

Studies on *E. coli* strain C infected with ϕX174 revealed that infected cells continue to divide until shortly before lysis, and make RNA, DNA, and protein until at least 16 minutes after infection at the rates characteristic of uninfected cells (616a). Lysis occurs shortly after 26 minutes. Virus structural protein, however, begins to appear about 8 minutes after infection, increases rapidly until 18 to 20 minutes, and then stops. As Fig. 38 shows, formation of mature virus begins at about 15 minutes, is about 20% of the maximum at 18 minutes, and continues until lysis (616a). The gross picture therefore is that the multiplication of this virus appears to affect host function but slightly for over half of the latent period. At the level of protein accumulation we see an increasing displacement of synthesis to virus protein; the accumulation of virus protein is clearly a relatively late function whose kinetics of formation is consistent with the picture of deposition of virus protein from a general pool, as noted above. The nature of the lesions

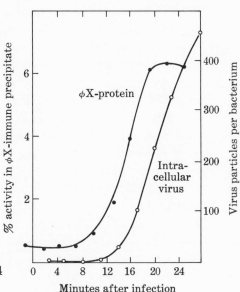

Figure 38. Appearance of virus protein and intracellular virus after infection with bacteriophage ϕX174 (616a).

leading to an abrupt arrest of many synthetic steps relatively early in maturation is not clear. The cells also become resistant to superinfection by ϕX174 at this time.

The Structure and Synthesis of Virus DNA   Sinsheimer (670) showed that ϕX174 contains a single molecule of single-stranded DNA. It is organized as a ring (206) and has a molecular weight of 1.7×10^6, about 5500 nucleotides. A similar value has been estimated by electron microscopy of a derived double-stranded DNA (100), but a slightly smaller value has also been reported (372). It is estimated that a DNA of this general size could specify about ten polypeptide species as a maximum (745). Since seven complementation groups of conditional lethal mutants have been specified for ϕX174 and S13, at least 70% of the phage genes have been detected; that is, at least 70% of the virus DNA has been accounted for (745).

The phages discussed earlier contain double-stranded linear DNA. As we shall see in Chapter 6, known DNA-dependent RNA polymerases operate best on double-stranded molecules. In this respect the injected chromosome of T4, for example, is therefore structurally suited for the synthesis of mRNA, which serves for translation into polypeptide chains. The *E. coli* RNA polymerase synthesizes a complementary RNA strand if offered a single DNA strand, but the RNA products consist of small pieces. Since the small DNA phages contain but a single strand of DNA, they must form a double-stranded structure before efficient RNA and protein synthesis can be effected in infected cells. In short, DNA synthesis should precede protein synthesis in these systems. It does indeed, but a closer examination of this phenomenon soon leads us into unexpected difficulties.

Once inside the cell, the single-stranded ring is quickly converted into a double-stranded ring, called the replicative form or RF (673, 372, 100). This form replicates semiconservatively (166). Using the RF, the single-stranded viral RNA is synthesized by making a complementary copy of the DNA strand complementing the virus-like DNA strand (166). It was originally thought that the synthesis of RF stops when single-stranded virus DNA is made; however, it has recently been shown that RF is synthesized throughout infection and seems to undergo a rapid turnover (445). The viral DNA (275), its complementary strand (617, 665), and the RF (275) can all initiate infection in bacterial spheroplasts. The fact that the complementary strand is infectious has interesting implications for RF structure and the initiation of DNA replication (617).

An *in vitro* synthesis of the covalently linked circular double-stranded DNA (RF) from single-stranded circular virus DNA has most recently been performed by Kornberg and his collaborators (260a). This important result was accomplished by the use of purified DNA polymerase (513) in conjunction with polynucleotide ligase which joined the aligned ends of the unlinked DNA molecule (260). Both enzymes were of bacterial origin. The synthesized covalent complementary circle, isolated from the duplex formed *in vitro,* has apparently been shown to be infectious (260a).

The separation of RF and analysis of its structure have been pursued actively (53, 85, 672, 334, 332, 615). Such studies have not only helped to clarify steps in biosynthesis of RF but have also merged in important ways with the study of the double-stranded circular DNA found in some animal tumor viruses, mitochondrial DNA, and so on. The problem of the mechanism of RF synthesis has also been explored quite seriously. It was found initially that the synthesis of RF was not blocked by 5-methyltryptophan (503) or by 30 μg of chloramphenicol per milliliter (673). This result was considered to fit the hypothesis that the formation of RF is accomplished entirely by the bacterial DNA polymerase and ligase, as suggested recently also by the enzymatic evidence. Bacterial mutants have been obtained which can adsorb φX174 and convert viral DNA into RF, but cannot replicate RF (164, 143). A similar result is obtained by ultraviolet irradiation of the host before infection (501a), and it has been asked if replication of RF does not also involve a bacterial function.

Mutants of φX174 (671) and S13 (743) have recently been obtained which have been blocked in the multiplication of RF although not in the formation of a single RF per mutant genome (671). The replication of RF can be blocked by 100 μg of chloramphenicol per milliliter (743) or by infection of an amino acid auxotroph (671) in the absence of the amino acids. These data have been interpreted to mean that a new virus-induced protein is required in RF replication but not in the initial conversion of viral DNA into RF, and that such replication is relatively resistant to chloramphenicol (671, 743). It can be imagined that the formation of the initial RF permits the production of RNA to determine the synthesis of a new, although unknown, RF replicase, which acts cooperatively with a function provided by the host cell.

In normal infection, RF increases in amount almost immediately for about 8 minutes, at which time single-stranded DNA, as well as viral antigen, begins to appear. Throughout this process, synthesis of host DNA continues for about 10 to 15 minutes, at which time a virus-induced protein is thought to inhibit this activity (443a). Of some value in dissociating these phenomena has been the finding that pretreatment with mitomycin C of a mutant bacterial strain deficient in its host-cell reactivation system blocks host DNA synthesis without affecting synthesis of virus DNA and virus development (444).

The host DNA polymerase, as well as the synthesis of RF DNA, can be inhibited readily by the antibiotic phleomycin, which seems to bind to regions of DNA rich in adenine-thymine pairs. The addition of this antibiotic after 8 minutes permits inhibition of replication of host DNA and inhibition of RF but not of single-stranded viral DNA (570). It is not clear how this report fits the recent result which suggests that production of single-stranded viral DNA goes hand in hand with turnover of RF (445).

It is generally agreed from kinetic experiments that RF is not a material precursor of single-stranded viral DNA (502, 166). This result is generally interpreted to mean that a second new type of virus-induced DNA polymerase must exist. It would operate somewhat like a DNA-dependent RNA polymerase, conservatively producing a third DNA strand on the double-stranded RF template. Although three classes of mutants of ϕX174 (and possibly three in

S13 as well) (745) are known to be blocked in the production of single-stranded viral DNA (671, 444, 178), no direct evidence has yet been obtained for this postulated new type of DNA polymerase. Chloramphenicol at 30 μg per ml, unable to block RF synthesis, prevents synthesis of viral DNA (743), apparently confirming the deduction that a new and as yet unknown virus-induced protein is required at this step.

In Fig. 39 is presented a recent diagram of the multiplication cycle of φX174 containing the alternating sequence of the various types of DNA that are formed. The diagram records the unusual phenomenon that the multiplication of RF and of viral DNA proceeds at a single "site," a result recently described by Sinsheimer (671) and Stone (703). It appears that, when parent viral DNA

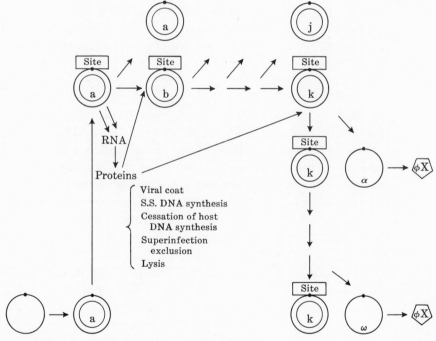

Figure 39. An outline of stages in the replication of bacteriophage φX174 (671).

is converted into an RF, it must become associated with a special bacterial site before it can function. Only one of several ^{32}P-labeled virus particles replicates under conditions of multiple infection (703). Also, ^{32}P decay in parental virus in infected cells completely inactivates the ability to produce a plaque, despite the presence of other derived RF particles (671). Such results are also consistent with the observation that the distribution of mutational events in reversion of φX174 amber mutants was almost random, and not clonal as found for T2 (165). The latter result also suggests that synthesis of viral DNA is being effected from only one of the RF templates available.

The hypothesis has been offered (703) that the special site may require a DNA polymerase situated at a particular spot on the bacterial membrane; however, the low sensitivity of the formation of this activity to chloramphenicol suggests that we may be dealing with peptides made by a path different from that for most bacterial proteins. A similar low sensitivity to this antibiotic has been recorded for synthesis of mucopeptides in the bacterial cell wall and for an early step in replication of the bacterial chromosome (415).

The Release of the Virus   The hypothesis that the multiplication site for the virus DNA might be on the bacterial membrane assumes even greater significance in view of the report that φX174 can multiply in spheroplasts and is liberated from these bodies without lysis (246). A similar statement had appeared some years earlier in a discussion of the liberation of M13 virus from intact bacteria (313). The problem of the release of φX174 at least, if not of its multiplication, seems to merge, then, with the same problems for the filamentous DNA phages, which are discussed below. It had been suggested fairly early that release of the virus precedes cell disruption (194), but this could not be confirmed in studies of phage release in single cells (323). Nevertheless, this possibility has continued to gain support.

The use of φX174 mutants, summarized in Table 13, has revealed some interesting physiological relations of lysis. Three physiological

Table 13. The Six Known Genes of φX174 (671, 444)

Complementation Group	Function
I	Prevents lysis only, cells become enlarged
II	Prevents maturation and lysis, defective nonadsorbing particles form
III	Controls a coat protein, RF made but does not accumulate, no viral DNA made
IV	Controls a coat protein, RF made, no viral DNA made
V	No viral DNA made
VI	Controls replication of RF

The Seven Known Genes of Phage S13 (745)

Complementation Group †	Function
I	Controls a coat protein, no viral DNA made
II	RF made, no viral DNA made
IIIA	RF made, no viral DNA made
IIIB	Controls a coat protein, RF made, no viral DNA made
IV	Controls replication of RF
V	Prevents lysis only, cells become enlarged
VI	RF made

† The genetic map of S13 has been shown to be circular (28a), unlike that of λ, which is linear despite its transformation into a circular molecule after infection (547).

classes of mutants have been described (322, 671) which give some insight to this question. One class, comprised of complementation groups III to VI, may be blocked in synthesis of viral DNA or of protein, but it does lyse. Thus, mature phage is not required for lysis. A second class (complementation group II), involving a single gene of unknown function, affects production of both mature phage and lysis. With a third class (complementation group I), mature phage can be made; however, the cells do not lyse or multiply but elongate to contain very large numbers of virus particles (322, 671).

Although no lytic enzyme can be demonstrated in normal infection (482), the genetic evidence suggests that a virus-induced function, presumably a virus-induced protein, is essential to lysis. This is confirmed by the discovery of a chloramphenicol-sensitive step subsequent to the synthesis of RF, which is also essential to lysis (482). The evidence, both genetic and physiological, indicates that this protein, involved in lysis and as yet unidentified, is unrelated to any virus structural component. It is interesting to note that synchronized infected cells lyse in such a way as to suggest that lysis may require a particular stage in cell division (482).

The S13 Phage   Many of the types of mutants which have been described for ϕX174 (see Table 13) appear to exist also in the closely related S13 phage studied by the Tessmans and their collaborators (745, 743, 742, 747, 744). Mutants of group V affecting lysis in S13 are apparently of the same type as the group I mutants in ϕX174. The lists of mutants for both phages differ at present in some respects, including the numbering system. It is difficult at this time for anyone not in this field to attempt a detailed comparison of the mutant lists, particularly as the exact sites of action of the virus genes are not understood for most mutants. With both viruses, some genes are known for coat proteins, but the nature and function of the other gene products have not been clarified. The life cycle of these viruses, although consistent with the general sequence of synthesis of early proteins, synthesis of DNA, and synthesis of late proteins, evidently involves reactions which have not yet been identified or explored by biochemists. Several of these reactions also appear to involve the participation of an organized polymer-synthesizing site on the bacterial membrane. The involvement of the membrane in the multiplication of ϕX174 and S13 has so far been indicated very indirectly and tentatively. The next group of viruses, to be discussed briefly, asserts this role of the bacterial membrane in an unequivocal manner.

The Filamentous DNA Phages   In 1963 reports appeared on filamentous DNA phages, the f1, fd, and M13 phages which infect male strains of *E. coli* (454, 830, 312, 489, 311, 313). The fd phage was reported to be liberated by the host cell without destruction of the cell (311). A similar phenomenon was also described for the related M13 phage (313), and in the same communication it was indicated that ϕX174 and an RNA phage can be liberated without lysis at low temperatures. The unusual limited host range of the filamentous DNA phages, as well as of the fr RNA phages, has suggested that the phenomenon may relate to the special surface physiology of male bacteria endowed with the specialized adsorptive appendages, the F pili. Recent observations have shown that the f1 phages actually attach to the tip of F pili, whereas the RNA phages attach laterally along the pilus (94). Indeed, a terminal fragment of a sheared f1 particle can also adsorb to the male pilus and can inject its small piece of DNA (200a). It also appeared that a continued study of these phages might help to clarify problems of polymer syntheses in bacterial walls and membrane. The system obviously confronts us most sharply with the general problem of how structures external to the bacterial membrane are in fact synthesized and extruded.

The fd phage is shaped like a flexible rod 8000 Å by 50 Å and contains a single-stranded DNA similar in molecular weight to that of ϕX174 (489). The DNA isolated from the virus was also shown to exist as a stable ring (490) and is thought to resemble a circle of string pulled out from opposite sides of its circumference (488). The strands do not appear to be in a base-paired conformation (488). The ring seems to be enclosed in a tube of α-helices, according to measurements of optical rotatory dispersion (158). Studies of ultraviolet dichroism of oriented virus particles have been used to assess the relation of the planes of DNA bases and aromatic acids to the longitudinal axis of the virus (50).

A monomeric coat protein, which aggregates readily, has been isolated from the virus (375). Aggregation of the protein may proceed as far as rod-like structures adsorbable to bacteria sensitive to phage fd and to ϕX174; these aggregates block adsorption of fd but not of ϕX174. Nevertheless, the aggregate rods do not have the physical properties of normal virus (375).

In the presence of fd DNA completely denuded of coat protein, irregular complexes are formed by the aggregation of protein subunits. If the virus DNA contains as little as 3% of its normal associated protein, however, the isolated protein can combine with the DNA to give some normal virus particles (376). The residual virus capsid associated with the DNA appears to serve as a nucleus for the re-formation of some normal infective particles.

These important studies of the structure and synthesis *in vitro* of the fd virus have now been climaxed by the extraordinary result that the rod-like fd phage and icosahedral ϕX174 phage can show a phenomenon somewhat related to phenotypic mixing when they multiply together in a common bacterium (377). The phenomenon is designated "genomic masking" to indicate that viral nucleic acid is incorporated into heterologous virus capsids, as a result of mixed infection, as contrasted to true "phenotypic mixing," which is now used to designate coexistence of proteins from different viruses in a common shell. *E. coli* strain C (F^+) preinfected with fd and superinfected with ϕX174 was found to release ϕX174 before lysis. Pools of both types of DNA were found, including a double-stranded intermediate of fd DNA, possibly akin to the ϕX174. Density centrifugation of lysates revealed two bands of apparently normal ϕX174 and fd, but each virus population contained particles in which homologous capsids were wrapped around heterologous DNA.

The study of the physiology of replication among these filamentous viruses has been pursued to a greater extent with the related M13 virus (313); this virus is serologically related (625) to both fd and the f1 phage (454, 830). Double-stranded circular "replicative forms" of phage-specific DNA have been isolated from infected cells (595, 596), but the relation of these forms to the multiplication cycle has not yet been explored in detail. Studies of a related filamentous phage record the absence of intact phage within the infected cell, although this compartment contains considerable virus DNA. The internal pool of coat protein is quite small, and intact phage is apparently released as soon as it is formed (369a).

M13, as well as the other related phages, has been shown to be subject to host-controlled modification of a molecular nature as yet unknown (15). In addition, a careful study of conditional lethal mutants of M13 has begun to reveal many interesting physiological and genetic phenomena (578). For example, progeny of crosses by two complementary mutants contain diploid particles which are twice as long as the normal particle but contain two separable haploid DNA molecules (624).

Six complementation groups of mutants have been found (580); see Table 14. Of the six genes, only gene 2 has been unequivocally characterized as related to an early function. *Ts* mutants for five of the groups are known, and temperature shift experiments have indicated the time at which the gene function is blocked. It was determined thereby that genes 1, 3, 4, and 5 control late functions; the *am* mutant for gene 6 also behaved like a late function. As

Table 14. Results of Infecting Nonpermissive Host Cells with M13 Amber Mutants † (580)

	Wild Type Phage	Amber Mutants in Gene					
Result		1	2	3	4	5	6
Production of infective DNA	+	+	−	+	+	+	+
Production of serum blocking power	+	−	−	+	−	−	+
Survival of infected host cells	+ (reduced growth rate)	−	+ (growth rate un- changed)	−	−	−	−

† Experiments were carried out in broth at either 30°C or 37°C.

presented in the table, infection with a gene 2 mutant blocked DNA synthesis, whereas infection with the others did not. Genes 1, 4, and 5 appear to control synthesis of phage coat protein (serum blocking power) when DNA synthesis can proceed.

It was striking that infection slowed bacterial multiplication but did not kill cells. In the absence of phage DNA synthesis (infection with a gene 2 mutant) the bacterial growth rate was unimpaired. A block in the other virus genes completely blocked cellular multiplication, however; the cells were killed. In some way the production of viral DNA which cannot be packaged in virus completely jammed the crucial sites and mechanisms in the apparatus essential to bacterial division. With these phages we have come full circle; that is, continuing virus multiplication is essential for bacterial survival. These systems appear to provide remarkable opportunities for the study of the interplay of bacterial membrane, chromosome and virus.

As applied to medicine, that science [Chemistry], I acknowledge, is yet in its infancy; but it is the infancy of Hercules.

THOMAS COOPER, 1818 (146)

Chapter 6

THE EXPRESSION OF A VIRAL GENOME

In the last several chapters I have discussed mainly the correlation between viral genes and their respective gene products, expressed in different stages of the multiplication cycle. The T-even phages have provided a wealth of experimental material for these genetic and biochemical studies of the relation between DNA as genes and proteins as gene products. The multiplication cycle itself has tended to be expressed in terms of a sequence of syntheses of various enzymes, viral DNA, and virus proteins. However, it was precisely in the study of the study of T-even phage physiology that the existence (778) of messenger RNA and its postulated role (329, 75) as the intermediary between DNA and protein were first recognized. The history of the origin of the concept of a messenger RNA and the RNA and the choice of the phage system to test this concept experimentally has been related by Jacob (327). Although Volkin and Astrachan (778) did not coin the term "messenger RNA," they nevertheless had suggested that the synthesis of virus-induced RNA is essential for the production of bacteriophage. In this chapter, in an effort to understand and to explain the course of virus multiplication and the sequential expression of the virus genome, I discuss the large body of data accumulated since the mid-1950s on the origin, structure, utilization, and degradation of the RNA produced in T-even virus infection. The postulated position of such RNA in the flow of genetic information in T4 development is presented in Fig. 40.

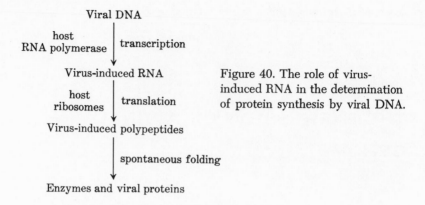

Figure 40. The role of virus-induced RNA in the determination of protein synthesis by viral DNA.

Such a discussion of mRNA will not represent the entirety of virus multiplication, as many reactions, virus assembly for example, do not appear to require RNA synthesis. Nevertheless, the protein components generated in infection may be either direct primary products of translation of RNA, like lysozyme, or perhaps derivatives of such primary products, as polypeptides or the head protein may be. Despite the existence of the latter group of complexities, for the most part the production of intact virus particles requires the generation of numerous interacting proteins whose existence is set by the production of translatable messages.[20] Obviously, we must begin to try to understand the principles of this process.

Before starting on the proposed survey of RNA physiology in T4 infection, we may ask whether the schema presented in Fig. 40 is rigorously proved. Ideally we would like to be able to effect each of the steps in the schema separately with purified enzymes and templates in systems studied *in vitro*. The *in vitro* synthesis of the coat polypeptide of an RNA phage, starting with virus RNA and an appropriate system of ribosomes and soluble components, has

[20] It may be well to keep in mind, however, that in bacteria some RNA made on DNA, that is, tRNA and possibly ribosomal RNA, may not serve as messages. Although this situation is possibly not relevant to the T-even virus infections, it appears that some viruses, possibly including the T-even group, may direct the synthesis of new tRNA species, as discussed in Chapter 4.

been described (527, 93). It has even been shown that such an *in vitro* product can be assembled into intact RNA phage particles (378). In these instances, however, intact virus RNA was used as the preformed message.

Such stepwise *in vitro* synthesis has not yet been so clearly accomplished in the DNA-based phage system. Nevertheless, not only do numerous elements of indirect evidence suggest the validity of the messenger hypothesis in phage infection, but also several more direct experiments have perhaps begun to provide the desired support. In one instance a complex *in vitro* system containing virus DNA, *E. coli* RNA polymerase, *E. coli* ribosomes, and many other components has been reported to be capable of incorporating amino acids into material precipitable by phage antiserum (758, 759). In this study serious efforts were made to minimize the degradation of virus-induced RNA and to ensure that other RNA molecules would not be translated. Nevertheless, this report, indicating that an *in vitro* system is capable of generating messenger RNA for a late function, that is, virus structural protein, is quite startling and requires some clarification.

In a very recent report (626) it has been stated that mRNA isolated late in infection by T4 can be translated *in vitro* in a protein-synthesizing system derived from infected or uninfected *E. coli* to give rise both to peptides characteristic of head protein and to phage lysozyme. These activities were not obtained with mRNA made early in infection. In additonal experiments, special efforts were made to exclude the tRNA of infected cells from the preparations of late mRNA. Such mRNA fractions had not lost their activity (249a). These important findings seem to indicate not only that phage-induced RNA does code for phage proteins but also that the RNA message for lysozyme can be isolated essentially intact, and that new types of tRNA and amino acid-activating enzymes are not necessary to translate codons present in phage mRNA into some late proteins.

The Effect of T-Even Phage in Stopping Bacterial Syntheses   The arrest of synthesis of bacterial RNA and protein has been very useful in studying the small amount of RNA made during infection. It will be recalled that in my early studies I could not detect any RNA accumulation after infection and, lacking appropriate tools, discounted the observed slight ^{32}P incorporation into an RNA fraction (109, 110, 111). A small and indeed crucial fraction containing newly made RNA, mRNA, was proved to exist by Volkin and Astrachan in 1956 (778). In 1961, after the impetus of the messenger hypothesis (329), it was shown that no wholly new ribosomes are synthesized after T-even phage infection (75). In other infections, as with SP8 (485), ϕX174 (616a), or λ (741), RNA synthesis may continue initially at a normal rate, and much of this newly made RNA consists of normal bacterial constituents, including ribosomal RNA. Thus the T-even phage systems really provided a unique opportunity for the analysis of the nature of the RNA made after virus infection. Nevertheless, this opportunity was not seized for many years, indeed not until the state of theory became ripe for the appropriate experiments.

It has undoubtedly been very helpful to have such an unusual system available for the study of mRNA production, but the problem of how T-even infection abruptly arrests the production of bacterial RNA (534), ribosomal RNA, and messages alike has been badly neglected until fairly recently. To my mind this is a very important problem. Although it had been known since 1953 that host DNA was but slowly converted into an acid-soluble form (307), it was not until 1962 that Nomura and his colleagues tested the notion that bacterial genes were damaged immediately and irreparably by infection (535). These workers demonstrated that phage-infected Hfr males could transfer functional bacterial chromosomal markers to recipient bacteria for as long as 10 to 20 minutes after infection. They concluded therefore that the immediate damage to the bacterial genes examined was not extensive. In more recent experiments it has been shown that the rapid inhibition of host RNA synthesis also occurs with phage mutants unable to cause degradation of host DNA (310).

It had been shown that the addition of chloramphenicol before infection with T4 permitted the synthesis of host RNA (778), including tRNA and ribosomal RNA (536), as well as bacterial DNA and mRNA (297, 537), at the same time as viral mRNA (549). A comparison of the synthesis of RNA in normal and in infected *E. coli* with and without chloramphenicol is presented in Table 15. From these results many workers have concluded that the synthesis of a virus-specific protein, as yet unidentified, is required for the inhibition of RNA synthesis (17, 560, 536, 434, 741, 740).

The latter hypothesis presents some difficulties because the arrest of host synthesis on infection is extraordinarily rapid and complete. Such an inhibitory protein would have to be among the earliest of the "early early proteins." Furthermore, mutants unable to effect this inhibition have not yet been obtained (434). Actually, when both virus mRNA and host RNA were produced in the presence of chloramphenicol, it was shown that the syntheses of host DNA and host mRNA are severely inhibited by phage even in the absence of protein synthesis (535, 549). Reexamination of this point also revealed that inhibition of bacterial nucleic acid synthesis in infected *E. coli* pretreated with chloramphenicol is markedly in-

Table 15. Synthesis of Various Nucleic Acids in E. coli B Infected by Phage T4 (or T2) and Effects of Chloramphenicol (CM) (549, 297, 537)

	Synthesis † of					
	Host DNA	Host mRNA	rRNA	tRNA	Phage DNA	Phage mRNA
Uninfected *E. coli*						
No CM	+	+	+	+	−	−
CM	+	+	+	+	−	−
T4 infected *E. coli*						
No CM	−	−	−	+ ‡	+	+
CM before infection	+ ‡	+ ‡	+	+	−	+
CM after infection	−	−	−	−	+	+

† + means that the amount synthesized is of the order of magnitude comparable to that synthesized by control culture; − means nearly complete inhibition.
‡ See (297, 537, 318).

creased by increasing the multiplicity of infection (537). This result was confirmed by Terzi (740) who found that T4 infection normally does not turn off host RNA synthesis completely in Shigella. However, inhibition of host synthesis in this organism is increased by increasing multiplicity. The hypothesis has therefore been modified to suggest that T4 has two mechanisms to inhibit host synthesis; one requires a newly synthesized protein and does not operate in Shigella; the other mechanism, of an unknown nature, is thought to operate in both hosts.

I wish to present a simple hypothesis to explain these data; my hypothesis is predicated on the notion that chloramphenicol may have effects other than that of affecting protein synthesis. In our studies on infection of amino acid auxotrophs we observed that the synthesis of bacterial RNA is arrested, despite the absence of the required amino acid (645), in contrast to its continuance in the presence of chloramphenicol. I therefore believe that protein synthesis is not essential to the arrest of synthesis of bacterial RNA. I also think that the assumption that chloramphenicol acts exclusively on protein synthesis is unwarranted. The hypothesis that I wish to offer suggests that infection with the T-even phage separates the transcribing apparatus, presumably in the bacterial membrane, from the bacterial genome and that this effect is among those inhibited by chloramphenicol. It is supposed that this effect is produced by the rapid osmotic equilibration of the inside of the bacterium and the external medium as a result of the puncturing of the bacterial membrane by the injection apparatus of the virus. Naturally, such an effect would be increased by increasing the multiplicity of infection. I suspect that, in some direct or indirect way, chloramphenicol may affect the stability of the structural relations of bacterial membrane and chromosome.

In support of this hypothesis, we note that cells infected with a T-even phage swell rapidly. In 1948 Doermann (173) examined infected cultures in a nephelometer and showed, as presented in Fig. 41, that infection produced an immediate drop of turbidity. After about 20 minutes the turbidity was restored to its original level, to be followed immediately by lysis in infection with r strain.

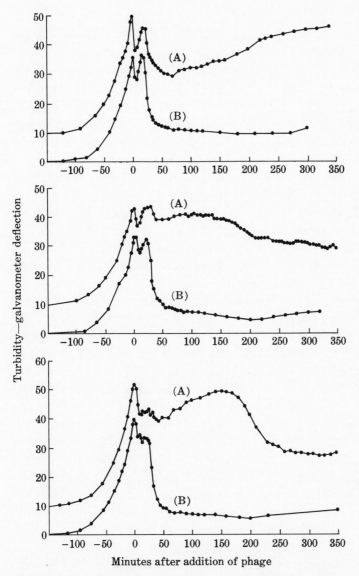

Figure 41. Turbidimetric comparison (173) of lysis induced by T2r and T2r+ (top), T4r and T4r+ (center), and T6r and T6r+ (bottom) (173). The A curves represent the turbidity of the r+-infected culture. In all cases, the A curves are scaled up ten units on the turbidity axis. The B curves represent the turbidity of the r-infected culture. The multiplicity of infection in these experiments varied from 3.3 to 5.4.

I attribute the initial drop in the light-scattering properties of the bacteria to the rapid swelling of the infected cells.

The results of infection with osmotically shocked T2 ghosts, however, show that, although such particles adsorb, only a small proportion (10% to 35%) of the particles kill. Nevertheless, adsorption of ghosts arrests bacterial multiplication and markedly inhibits protein and RNA synthesis for about 80 minutes, after which time the cells resume their normal metabolic activity (223). Since a ghost cannot induce synthesis of a specific protein, I similarly attribute these effects to osmotic equilibration, as described above. However, the absence of virus development, including the absence of synthesis of virus-induced nucleases, does not irreversibly damage the bacterial chromosome. I suggest that this structure eventually reestablishes its structural relations with the membrane to resume normal function.

In developing this hypothesis I have relied most heavily on the studies with phage ghosts by French and Siminovitch (223). Identical results have not been obtained by other workers (301, 302), but it appears that there are difficulties in reproducing preparations of phage ghosts exactly. In any case the differences in results are minor with respect to the inhibitory activities of these particles and to the reversibility of the effects observed (301, 302).

I know of only one experiment at present which argues, as yet weakly, against the hypothesis. It appears that T2 inactivated by poly-L-lysine adsorbs to *E. coli* strain B and injects its DNA without contributing genes in mixed infection (651). Nevertheless, cells treated with such phage alone are not killed and are only somewhat inhibited in production of β-galactosidase. It would be important to know, among many other physiological factors, if such "infected" cells do leak metabolites. In the experiment of Nomura and his collaborators (535) in which host genetic material is transferred to a recipient after infection, it is noteworthy that mating and transfer leading to synthesis of β-galactosidase must be begun before infection. These workers state that, after phage addition before mating, no enzyme synthesis is obtained, "presumably because of damage to the cell surface, which prevents effective mating." In interpreting this experiment, I would suggest that prior infection prevents the transfer of the now disconnected donor chromosome, whereas infection of the donor after mating cannot disconnect the chromosome from the membrane and chromosome of the bacterial recipient.

Curiously, the study of the arrest of synthesis of host DNA in these early phenomena of infection has largely been neglected, despite some few data (535, 549, 537). This is one area in which a study of incorporation of cytosine into DNA would be quite useful. It would obviously be important to know if the synthesis of host DNA and that of RNA are inhibited coordinately by infection. Although it is suggested (549) that host DNA synthesis is inhibited to a far greater extent in chloramphenicol-pretreated infected cells, this is not proved by the data presented so far (549, 535). Indeed, the reverse has been indicated in (537). In the proof or disproof of the hypothesis I have presented, which makes much of the presumed structural integration of chromosome and membrane, it is quite possible that a knowledge of the fate of the synthesis of bacterial DNA will be at least as significant as the data on synthesis of bacterial RNA.

It may be asked why a notion as simple as this had not been formulated earlier. Whether it is correct or not will obviously be determined experimentally, and such an experimental proof must go far in establishing the existence of the postulated structure and the conditions for its disruption. It will be recalled that for about twenty years the concept, derived from early electron microscopy, of a central nucleoid detached from the bacterial membrane dominated bacterial cytochemistry and bacterial physiology. As long as the bacterial DNA was thought to exist as this detached nucleoid, there was no need to think in terms of the disruption of organized structure, as I have suggested. It did not seem to matter that the early concept necessarily carried with it images of transforming DNA and of the DNA of lysogenic phage happily swimming through the cytoplasm in search of the right region of the bacterial chromosome. The recently developed view that chromosome and membrane unite at key peripheral sites not only has important implications for DNA synthesis and probably for RNA synthesis as well, it will also require significant rethinking of ideas about the mechanisms of transformation and lysogeny. Undoubtedly, the study of the multiplication of M13 virus will also be one of the most important biological tools for the study of this inadequately documented cytological concept.

On the Discovery of Virus-Induced RNA   When ^{32}P is incorporated into T2-infected cells, a small amount (1% to 3% of the P of the total RNA) is incorporated into the RNA fraction and behaves like RNA. Such an amount could not have been detected without the use of isotopes. Degradation of the RNA and fractionation revealed the presence of ^{32}P-containing ribose nucleotides which could have been derived only from RNA (778). In this fractionation the newly formed labeled nucleotides were diluted by the preformed nonradioactive ribonucleotides of the uninfected cell. The isotope contents of the four ribonucleotides were found to exist in ratios similar to the ratios of the deoxynucleotides of virus DNA and were quite dissimilar from the ratios of the nucleotides in host RNA, as can be seen in Table 16. This led to the idea that virus-induced RNA mimics virus DNA and therefore represents copies of virus genes instrumental in effecting virus function.

Table 16. Ratios of Incorporation of ^{32}P in RNA of T2-Infected E. coli Contrasted with Host and Virus Nucleic Acids (778)

Nucleotides	Distribution of Bases in E. coli Bases (%)	Distribution of ^{32}P in T2- E. coli RNA (%)	Distribution of Bases in T2 DNA (%)
Cytosine †	23	18	17
Guanine	31	22	18
Uracil †	23	30	32.5
Adenine	23	30	32.5

† Virus DNA contains thymine, instead of uracil, and cytosine is replaced by 5-hydroxymethylcytosine.

There are several reasons for believing that this result is a fortunate accident and is really atypical. As we shall see below, the RNA produced in T-even phage infection is derived primarily from transcription of only a single strand. Why should the derived RNA have base ratios suggesting base pairing? It appears that the strand read has an average composition like that of total phage DNA. The same type of result was obtained in T7 infection (773). However, some phages contain DNA with strands of differing density which are separable after denaturation and, in the case of the *B. subtilis*-SP8 infection, the RNA made is complementary only to a pyrimidine-rich strand (484, 485). A similar deviation in the composition of T4 mRNA was first detected by Bautz and Hall (35).

Furthermore the ratios of the components found in this RNA may vary considerably as a function of the time of the radioactive pulse (773, 644, 220). In our own studies we found that the initial molar ratio of newly formed nucleotides of uracil to cytosine may be over 3 and may fall, over 60 minutes, to 1.5, instead of the ratio of about 2 expected from the first experiments. In other words the chemical analyses that helped to generate the first notions of mRNA were the consequence of considerable chance.

We know now that the RNA made early represents early functions only. There is no obvious reason for expecting the average composition of one strand of early RNA to simulate the composition of phage DNA as a whole. In fact, as noted above, its ratio of uracil to cytosine is somewhat high. Indeed, it has been observed in several instances, λ phage for example, that early RNA products are relatively high in adenine and thymine (674, 737, 107).

It may be mentioned that a recent slight alteration of the technique of centrifuging RNA in density gradients of $CsSO_4$ should be useful in facilitating the characterization of different categories of RNA. The addition of 1% formaldehyde has eliminated the aggregation and precipitation noted with many RNA samples in solutions of $CsSO_4$ (456). This might be useful in defining RNA complementary to one of two DNA strands which differ in density.

On the Turnover of Virus-Induced RNA   When ^{32}P is selectively incorporated into RNA for a short interval and incorporation of highly radioactive ^{32}P is stopped by dilution of the ^{32}P with ^{31}P, DNA continues to incorporate ^{32}P while the isotope content of the labeled RNA falls almost reciprocally. Thus the ^{32}P ribonucleotides appear to be precursors of deoxyribonucleotides at some level of phosphorus compounds, a reaction sequence which we have demonstrated in cell-free extracts (128) and discussed in part in Chapter 4.

For these results to be obtained it is necessary to effect a rapid equilibration of isotopic precursors and the nonisotopic diluent. Actually, the late conversion of label in RNA into DNA is rather slow, as is the loss of label from the RNA fraction. This result could easily reflect either a slowing of turnover late in infection or the existence of an active labeled pool of radioactive nucleotides relatively unable to equilibrate with exogenous ^{31}P orthophosphate. We have had such results in our work with radioactive uracil and can improve equilibration and apparent reciprocal turnover by infecting with a sufficiently large number of particles to permit a sharp loss of the intracellular pool; see Fig. 13 (221). In Fig. 42 an experiment is presented on turnover in cells infected at a multiplicity permitting such equilibration. Actually, little is known of the size of the nucleotide pool at different stages of infection, and of the rates at which different components contribute to this pool. That a nucleotide derived from the turnover of RNA may be reutilized for RNA synthesis, despite an attempt to dilute it by addition of an exogenous metabolite, has been clearly demonstrated by Nierlich (532) and by Haselkorn and his co-workers (287). This result is of the greatest importance in interpreting some experiments of Edlin, to be discussed later, which purported to show that early RNA synthesized in the presence of fluorouracil contained messages for late functions (192). The conclusions drawn were incorrect because they did not consider the subsequent reutilization of the fluorouridylate derived from turnover of early RNA in the synthesis of late messages (287, 192).

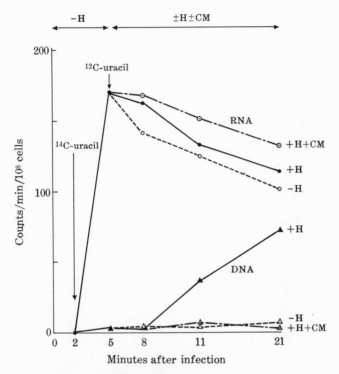

Figure 42. RNA turnover in presence and absence
of protein synthesis (645). H = histidine; CM =
chloramphenicol.

Is Virus-Induced RNA a Message?   In Chapter 5 we discussed
some of the difficulties in demonstrating an informational role of
RNA by nutritional techniques. One unusual organism, *E. coli* strain
W, could be shown to be almost totally dependent on exogenous
uracil in the synthesis of dCMP hydroxymethylase (573). Also, in
an experiment with Sekiguchi (645) presented in Fig. 35, we found
that a uracil deficiency produced a delay in synthesis of dCMP
hydroxymethylase and a far greater lag in synthesis of thymidylate
synthetase, a relatively late early enzyme. The uracil, used for synthesis of the essential mRNA's in these instances, is presumed to
result from the degradation of preformed RNA.

In the same experiment, lysozyme production was almost totally inhibited in the absence of exogenous uracil. This result could be interpreted as stemming from the generation of an even more severe uracil deficiency, because uracil was deposited as HMC and thymine in DNA, or by the inhibition of DNA synthesis itself, or both. The experiments of Protass and Korn (585), in showing that actinomycin D inhibits lysozyme synthesis without affecting DNA synthesis, appeared to have demonstrated a role for mRNA in the synthesis of a late protein. However, the recent experiment of Korn (386), showing some unusual effects of actinomycin D on maturation, raises some doubts about the validity of such a simple interpretation.

Important experiments showing that RNA made after infection is transferring information for protein synthesis depend on the use of the analogue, 5-fluorouracil (FU). This compound is incorporated into RNA during infection (650); it is not incorporated into DNA. Benzer and Champe (52, 99) demonstrated the phenotypic

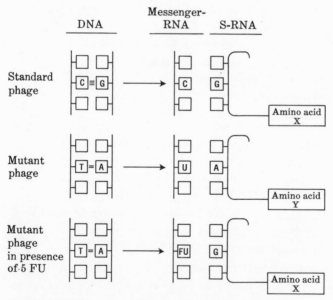

Figure 43. Proposed mechanism for the specific action of 5-fluorouracil (FU) (99).

reversion of rII mutants in the presence of the analogue. They suggested (Fig. 43) that FU was incorporated in place of uracil into the mRNA from the mutant gene and that it was translated as cytosine which coded for functional protein. If the mutant site contains a guanine-cytosine pair, the mutant does not usually respond to FU. If, on the other hand, the mutant site contains an adenine-thymine pair, as determined by mutagenic techniques, no more than half of the mutants respond to FU. This result was interpreted to suggest that only one strand of mRNA is made from the double-stranded DNA, that is, that an mRNA is the complementary copy of only a single DNA strand, as had been suggested by Bautz and Hall (35). I also made this point earlier in the discussion of mRNA produced in SP8 infection. Further evidence in the T4 system for this important conclusion is discussed below.

The most direct evidence for the informational content of RNA has been mentioned earlier in describing experiments showing that RNA isolated late in infection codes in an *in vitro* system for the syntheses of head protein peptides and of phage lysozyme (626).

Is mRNA Made by a Virus-Induced Enzyme?

Is mRNA Made by a Virus-Induced Enzyme?   If mRNA synthesis were necessary for protein synthesis, and a new virus-induced enzyme, a new DNA-dependent RNA polymerase, were necessary for synthesis of mRNA, virus synthesis could not start. Despite this obvious contradiction, it had been common for some years to imagine precisely this, that a new enzyme was required as a result of the difficulty of synthesis of virus-induced mRNA in chloramphenicol-pretreated infected cells. In 1963, however, we showed that normal functional virus-induced mRNA could be made after T6 infection of a bacterium starved for an amino acid and incapable of protein synthesis (140, 645).[21] Such RNA is made in these cases without the apparent synthesis of ribosomal RNA. Thus the

[21] That mRNA could be synthesized at almost a normal rate in the absence of protein synthesis was surprising enough at that time, since most workers usually stated that the absence of protein synthesis prevented all RNA synthesis. It now appears that the so-called amino acid control on RNA synthesis is directed mainly to the control of synthesis of ribosomal RNA and tRNA.

arrest of synthesis of ribosomal RNA in infection does not require protein synthesis.

Although the physiological evidence and the rigor of our logic strongly support the concept that the host DNA-dependent RNA polymerase must be the functional entity early in infection, recent studies of this enzyme in extracts of infected cells have produced considerable confusion. It was reported initially that several enzymes of RNA metabolism were not altered by infection. For example, we had shown that the level of polynucleotide phosphorylase in extracts is not affected by infection (644). Ortiz and his associates (558) confirmed this result and reported only a slow decline in the level of DNA-dependent RNA polymerase (to about 50% of its initial level in 30 minutes). These workers did describe the very rapid disappearance during infection of another enzyme which is very active in incorporating ATP into an acid-insoluble product. Their results are presented in Fig. 44. The effect is evoked by T-even phage and T5 but not by T3 or λ. The former infections produce a soluble inhibitor of the enzyme, polyriboadenylate polymerase. There is no indication at present why this bacterial enzyme activity, whose function is quite unknown (285, 286), should be so uniquely extinguished by infection.

Re-examination of the level of activity of DNA-directed RNA polymerase in several laboratories (369, 676) led to reports that this enzyme was rapidly inactivated by infection to perhaps 10% to 20% of the initial level. However, this decrease in activity was too slow to account for the immediate block in formation of bacterial mRNA. Sköld and Buchanan (676) suggested that the observed decrease might possibly relate to the arrest of synthesis of early enzymes and might point to a requirement for a new RNA polymerase for transcription of late functions. Their laboratory has also reported the presence of a preexisting protein inhibitor of the polymerase (551). Furth and Pizer (233) were unable to find a comparable inhibitor in uninfected cells but did observe in infected cells an inhibitor whose properties seemed to resemble degraded nucleic acid more than a protein. Difficulties have been

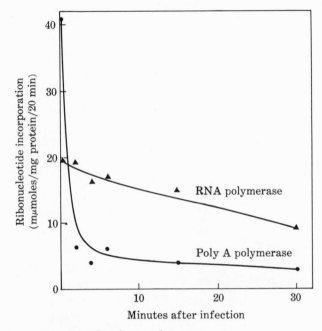

Figure 44. RNA polymerase and poly A polymerase
after T2 infection of *E. coli* (558).

observed with the polymerase assay as a result of an ATP deficiency during incubation (551). We can therefore ask at present
whether the decrease in polymerase observed in various laboratories
represent real decreases in the enzyme or artifacts of analysis. Hara
and Mitsui (284) have studied the course of inactivation of RNA
polymerase and have suggested that after T-even phage infection
the multiunit enzyme is detached from host DNA and dissociates
to inactive subunits. There are no data at present to suggest that
a new virus-induced RNA polymerase does appear after infection.*

* NOTE ADDED IN PROOF: In a recent study of the RNA polymerase from infected and normal bacteria it was found that the purified enzymes from the
two sources are immunochemically identical. However, differences were observed in activities on various DNA templates and in the electrophoretic
properties of one protein subunit disassociated from the enzyme by alkaline
6M urea (785a). The basis of these differences is as yet undetermined.

Some Properties of Virus-Induced mRNA   The work of Volkin and Astrachan (776) showed virus-induced RNA to be associated largely with sedimentable fractions. Nomura and his colleagues (534) and Brenner and his colleagues (75) demonstrated that this material is attached largely to preexisting ribosomes. Indeed, such RNA has recently been found almost entirely in polysomes (292) associated with the bacterial membrane (276, 127). The Russian investigators have reported that both mRNA synthesis and synthesis of phage DNA is associated with the cytoplasmic membrane, where the DNA of the parental phage is found as well (831).

We have observed that between 75% and 80% of the isotopic label contained in this RNA fraction is associated with ribosomes (644); a value of 63% is recorded by Nomura and his collaborators (534). The RNA could be released from the ribosomes by incubation at low Mg^{++} concentration ($10^{-4} M$) or by disruption of the ribosomal complex with phenol (534).

This RNA was found to be fairly large and heterogeneous, although the gradual drift upward in sedimentation constant (324, 622) indicates that more recent studies have been more successful in preserving the RNA during isolation. Nevertheless, it should be noted that no one knows how large or how heterogeneous messenger populations of this system should be, and it would therefore be important to have controls for such isolations. For example, now that dCMP hydroxymethylase (molecular weight 68,000), a head protein (molecular weight about 80,000), and lysozyme (molecular weight about 19,000) have been characterized, it would be most useful to have the RNA characteristic of these proteins as physical markers during isolations of early and late RNA, respectively. Although this has not yet been done, experiments reported earlier on the ability of isolated RNA populations to code for specific proteins suggest that it may soon be feasible (27, 626).

A fractionation of early and late mRNA in T4 infection has indicated that the fractions taken after 8 minutes contain a significant amount of low-molecular-weight species of mRNA. Such a material is present in far lower concentration in early mRNA. The low-molecular-weight material does not appear to be a random degradation product of the high-molecular-weight species of mRNA (27). It seems reasonable to ask if such a low-molecular-weight late mRNA is not the species reported to permit the *in vitro* synthesis of lysozyme (626).

Nomura and his co-workers (534) showed that virus-induced RNA possesses a higher electrophoretic mobility in starch gels than does the RNA of uninfected cells. We have confirmed this interesting result, which probably bears on the secondary structure of free mRNA as compared to free ribosomal RNA. In Fig. 45 we can see that the RNA made in infected cells unable to synthesize protein also possesses this characteristic (645).

In 1961 Hall and Spiegelman (280) demonstrated the complementarity of sequence of such RNA and denatured virus by hybridization techniques, which their group has done much to develop. In this initial study RNA-DNA hybrids were separated by density gradient centrifugation. The essentially complete inhibition of synthesis of bacterial RNA was demonstrated once again, as well as the specificity of the reaction between T2 RNA and strands of denatured T-even DNA. Ribonuclease was introduced to minimize RNA contaminations (822), and the absence of complementary RNA-RNA complexes resistant to ribonuclease can be taken as an indication that only a single DNA strand is transcribed *in vivo*, that is, an indication of asymmetric transcription.

This result was particularly significant at that time because the genetic studies had suggested the formation of only a single RNA strand. Nevertheless, the initial enzymatic studies with purified RNA polymerase and virus DNA had revealed formation of RNA complementary to both DNA strands (242, 97). In the recent past this apparently contradictory result was shown to be in error. That RNA polymerase copies only a single DNA strand *in vitro* is a relatively recent observation (369, 462, 264, 145) which has lagged behind the observations of the asymmetry of transcription *in vivo* (754, 296, 244).

It is now known that damage to the template DNA leads to the production of symmetrical transcription *in vitro* (264, 145), perhaps by introducing new initiation points. In studies with isolated RF of

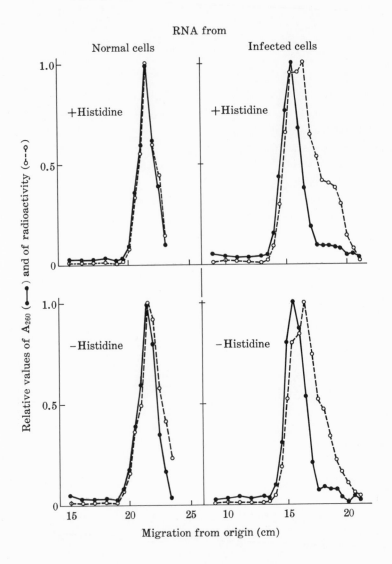

Figure 45. The electrophoretic properties of RNA
made in normal and in T6-infected *E. coli* strain
THU in the presence and absence of the required
amino acid, histidine (645).

φX174 it was found that ruptured rings led to symmetric transcription *in vitro*. On the other hand, intact, presumably undamaged, double-stranded rings produced only the RNA made *in vivo*. Such RNA is complementary to the DNA strand which has been synthesized complementary to virus DNA (100). This finding of asymmetric transcription is therefore similar to results with T-even phage DNA.

The initial centrifugal methods of isolation could handle only small amounts of material, whereas the electrophoretic method did not effect complete separations. To improve these isolations Bautz and Hall introduced column chromatographic methods based on hybrid formation between RNA and DNA fixed to cellulose in the column (35, 34). Although the isolated RNA was shown to represent a copy of only a single DNA strand and to serve in stimulating amino acid incorporation into polypeptides in ribosomal systems, it apparently aggregated readily to give functionally inactive complexes (34). By adsorbing RNA with virus DNA carrying deletions such as those in the rII region it was possible to enrich and isolate RNA distinctive for the rII character. Chemical and physical data on the rII RNA have not yet been published. Such rII mRNA has recently been used to hybridize with sonicated T4 DNA and thereby to isolate bits of rII-specific DNA. The DNA fragments were shown to have appropriate transforming activity for the selected marker (504).

The chromatographic method was further simplified by Bolton and McCarthy (65) who immobilized denatured DNA in agar. They used this technique and numerous variants of it to explore the specificity of hybridization, the nature of gene products, and evolutionary relationships among DNA fragments (64). The technique has also been modified by studying hybrid formation on nitrocellulose membranes (544); the fixation of denatured DNA is improved by drying (252) or is prevented by pretreatment with albumin (163). Only RNA hybridized over considerable polynucleotide lengths is retained after ribonuclease treatment, and complications derived from the reannealing of DNA have also been minimized (163). Competition tests and saturation tests have also been devised which determine whether two given preparations of RNA contain the same or different polynucleotide sequences complementary to DNA (544, 279). Such tests are obviously useful in the comparison of the RNA made early and late in infection; the results of such tests are discussed below.

Hybridization has also been important in determining which strand of the double-stranded DNA is read early in infection. Strand separation and isolation have been possible with the DNA of several phages. The RNA made *in vitro* in *B. megatherium* infected by α phage was shown to hybridize solely with the heavy pyrimidine-rich strand of α DNA (19, 244). A similar result has been noted earlier for the RNA made *in vivo* in infection of *B. subtilis* by SP8 (484, 485).

It is not possible to discount the importance of the hybridization techniques for detecting the existence of homologous sequences of RNA or DNA in cells or viruses. The results of these techniques, although not always easily interpretable in their quantitative aspects, are nonetheless usually unequivocal, even as are the immunochemical methods for proteins, in demonstrating the existence of specific relationships among these polymers. At present, hybridization serves as a major approach to the determination of the nature of synthesis of nucleic acid in infected cells because it permits the products of preexisting cellular genomes and those of virus genomes to be distinguished. The recent detection of virus-induced RNA by this method in tumors produced by certain adenoviruses attests to the continued survival and function of elements of virus genomes in some tumors (230) and provides, for example, a potential test of the virus etiology of human cancers.

The Degradation of Messages   In Chapter 4 I described the interconversion of the 5′-nucleotides of virus-induced RNA and deoxyribonucleotides in cell-free extracts, which apparently reproduces the interconversion of such RNA and DNA exemplified in Fig. 42. Analysis of the initial degradative steps by our laboratory and others has revealed some complications which have not yet been resolved.

The mRNA made after infection was labeled with ^{14}C-uracil. Since the bulk of the virus-induced RNA was on the ribosomes, this purified subcellular fraction was used as the starting material (644, 645). Omission of Mg^{++} permitted the activation of a ribonuclease which gave rise to 3′-phosphates from the labeled virus-induced mRNA. However, in the presence of $5 \times 10^{-3}\ M\ Mg^{++}$, essentially no degradation was observed. Addition of 0.01 M potassium phosphate in the presence of Mg^{++} permitted an extensive degradation of the mRNA but not of the ribosomal RNA. Analysis of the products revealed that at least two-thirds of the nucleotides produced were nucleoside diphosphates, containing the same ratio of labeled uracil to cytosine as existed in the intact mRNA. Because the remaining acid-soluble products were almost entirely 5-nucleotides, ribonuclease was excluded as a significant agent in the degradation. It appeared therefore that the purified ribosomal preparation contained active polynucleotide phosphorylase and a phosphodiesterase which degraded mRNA in the presence of inorganic orthophosphate. In the *in vitro* system the first enzyme was the most active (644).

As supporting evidence of a role for polynucleotide phosphorylase in the degradation, in addition to the requirement for orthophosphate and the production of nucleoside diphosphates, it was found that supplementation of the system by purified polynucleotide phosphorylase accelerated the degradation. Furthermore, formation of nucleoside diphosphates was inhibited by 6-azauridine diphosphate, an inhibitor of this enzyme (644).

It is possible that these enzymes are contaminants on the ribosomes since the enzymes are also present in supernatant fluids. Hardy and Kurland concluded that a number of enzymes, including polynucleotide phosphorylase and poly A polymerase, which have been reported to exist in ribosomes, are probably adsorbed contaminants (286), although this is difficult to prove. In any case, it was of interest that polynucleotide phosphorylase, which had most frequently been thought of and studied in a synthetic capacity, was now implicated in the degradation of mRNA. Comparable results were obtained with the pulse-labeled RNA of uninfected bacteria in which mRNA was similarly sensitive to degradation by this enzyme. The bulk of the RNA present in ribosomes, the ribosomal RNA made in long-term pulse labeling, was resistant in this form, whereas free ribosomal RNA was also readily degraded (644).

These reactions can be represented as follows:

$$(XMP)_n + nP_i \rightleftharpoons nXDP - \text{polynucleotide phosphorylase}$$

$$(XMP)_n \xrightarrow[H_2O]{K^+} nXMP - \text{phosphodiesterase}$$

An RNA-5'-phosphodiesterase optimally active in 0.1 M potassium ion was then isolated from the supernatant fraction of *E. coli* by Spahr and Schlessinger (686). The enzyme is mainly an exonuclease but was reported to have some endonuclease activity. Both degradative enzymes are found in many microorganisms (781, 359). Initially, optimal K^+ concentrations were not used in testing this enzyme in our systems. On checking this point, as presented in Fig. 46, it can be seen that the incubation of extracts in 0.1 M KCl facilitates degradation of RNA more than does 0.01 M KCl, but degradation occurs at about twice the rate and extent in 0.01 M phosphate. Degradation was most extensive in potassium phosphate. The products in 0.1 M KCl were essentially all nucleoside monophosphate, whereas, in 0.01 M potassium or sodium phosphate, 75% of the products were diphosphates (645).

Nevertheless, despite the evident role of both enzymes in extracts, it has not been clear whether one or both enzymes operate to degrade messages in intact cells. The production of nucleoside diphosphates is obviously useful in preparing RNA nucleotides for synthesis of deoxyribonucleoside diphosphates, while the K^+ requirement of the phosphodiesterase is evidently suited to the internal environment of the bacterium. Recent enzymatic studies have confirmed this general picture but have not answered the question of the relative importance of these mechanisms of degradation of mRNA *in vivo* (234, 235).

Two approaches to the mechanism of the degradation *in vivo* have been followed. Mutant strains have been isolated which have been thought to be deficient in ribonuclease and in polynucleotide

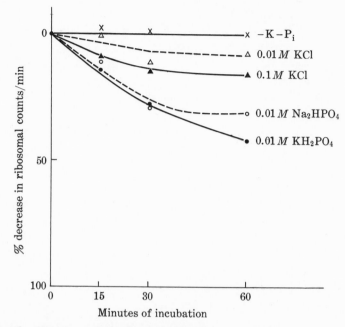

Figure 46. The enzymatic degradation of labeled phage-induced RNA associated with *E. coli* ribosomes (645). Ribosomes were isolated from *E. coli* strain THU exposed to ^{14}C-uracil for 13 minutes after infection. Ribosomes were incubated at 37°C in 0.05 M tris, pH 7.5, plus 5×10^{-3} M MgCl$_2$ containing compounds as indicated.

phosphorylase, and these strains have been shown to degrade mRNA (371). Nevertheless, the "phosphorylase-deficient" strain was shown to contain a significant amount of the enzyme [at least a quarter of the level in strain B (747a)] by test of phosphorolysis of poly A. Therefore this result cannot be considered to exclude polynucleotide phosphorylase as an enzymatic mechanism for the *in vivo* degradation of mRNA.

In another study a bacterial strain defective in the transport and concentration of K$^+$ was used to determine the stability *in vivo* of T4 mRNA in the presence and absence of this cation. Infection in the absence of K$^+$ permits synthesis of RNA but not of protein or

DNA (105). Surprisingly, the K+ requirement for DNA synthesis was independent of that for synthesis of virus-induced enzymes (105). The RNA made in infection in the absence of K+ was largely ribosomal RNA, as in pretreatment with chloramphenicol (106). It was therefore necessary to accumulate mRNA containing ^{14}C-uracil after infection in the presence of K+ and to study the subsequent fate of this material in the presence of ^{12}C-uracil in both the presence and absence of K+. In the presence of K+, ^{14}C-uracil was displaced by ^{12}C-uracil in a manner comparable to that represented in Fig. 42. In the absence of K+ the radioactivity of the mRNA actually increased and then remained constant. This could indicate either that there is a requirement for K+ in RNA degradation or that the label from degraded RNA had to be used for newly formed DNA to avoid masking by resynthesis of RNA (106). The use of actinomycin D to prevent the resynthesis of new RNA has been helpful in the study of messenger degradation (69), but in this instance it introduces new problems in the interpretation of already complicated experiments (106).

Although chloramphenicol inhibits the disappearance of label in such chase experiments (106), it can be seen in Fig. 42 that it does not do so merely because protein synthesis does not take place. The absence of an essential amino acid, preventing protein synthesis, even accelerates degradation of mRNA slightly. In any case, although the experiment showing uracil turnover in RNA upon K+ depletion is suggestive, the system is complex and does not provide an unequivocal result. It appears that clear answers about the degradation *in vivo* of mRNA will depend on the isolation of mutant strains completely lacking the two enzymes implicated in messenger destruction so far.[22]

The Control of Synthesis of mRNA in Infected Cells   Two major hypotheses concerning the sequence of synthesis of the major classes

[22] At least three phosphodiesterases active on RNA, in addition to those mentioned above, appear to be present in *E. coli*. They include a cyclic phosphodiesterase and two other recently discovered enzymes, one of which prefers double-stranded RNA (685, 439).

of virus-induced RNA are presented in Fig. 47. In Fig. 47a we see a model which suggests that all genes can be transcribed early in infection, but that only RNA molecules derived from genes for early functions can be translated early. The model in Fig. 47b proposes that only the genes for early functions are transcribed and translated early. Genes for late functions are transcribed only after DNA synthesis, mainly from progeny DNA.

The very first experiments bearing on these models tended to support that given in Fig. 47a (see 119). For example, a mutant requiring adenine and arginine and infected in the presence of adenine alone is capable of making complete phage when adenine is removed and arginine is added (774, 775). The interpretation of this result suggested that the RNA made early is adequate for both early and late functions. However, this interpretation did not take into account RNA turnover and the possible availability of adenine from early RNA for the synthesis of late RNA.

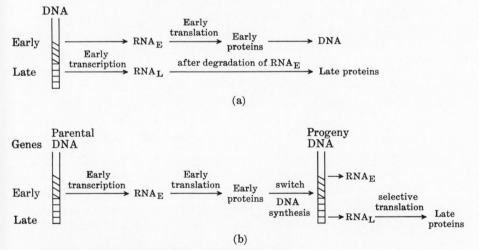

(a)

(b)

Figure 47. Hypotheses concerning the course of synthesis and utilization of phage-induced RNA. (a) All classes of RNA are synthesized early and translated sequentially. (b) Various classes of RNA are synthesized sequentially.

In an early test of these hypotheses Kano-Sueoka and Spiegelman (352) compared the column chromatographic behavior and size distribution in sucrose density gradients of RNA made in infection during early and late pulses. Since duplicate samples of RNA labeled at 3 to 5 minutes were essentially identical but differed markedly from RNA made at 13 to 15 minutes, it was concluded that the genome is transcribed sequentially, as suggested in Fig. 47b.

These workers, having observed that essentially identical classes of RNA are made early in the presence or absence of chloramphenicol, incorporated chloramphenicol into the infected systems 1 minute before adding isotope. In subsequent experiments they added chloramphenicol early or late and then compared the classes of RNA made later. It was found that the RNA made late, after relatively early addition of the antibiotic, was similar to early RNA (688). The authors interpreted this result to suggest that protein synthesis is necessary for *any* sequential transcription to occur. This result does not demand this conclusion; as we shall see below, the transcription of several cistrons, for example, those for dCMP hydroxymethylase and thymidylate synthetase, at different times before the inception of DNA synthesis does not require protein synthesis.

Our work on this problem began during a study of the lethal action of streptomycin (698, 697) on polyauxotrophic strains of *E. coli* requiring thymine, uracil, and an amino acid for growth (140, 645). Such strains, when starved for an amino acid, were found to be capable of synthesis of mRNA (699, 140, 645). The synthesis of this fraction of RNA appears to be under amino acid control to a far lesser degree than the synthesis of ribosomal RNA and tRNA (365, 518). It seemed to us that such a system should be most useful in studying the production and properties of the RNA produced early in infection. On infection in the absence of the amino acid histidine, which prevented synthesis of an early enzyme, synthesis of RNA was but slightly inhibited. As shown in Table 17, this RNA was comparable to normal virus-induced RNA in base composition, distribution on ribosomes, metabolic lability, turnover (see Fig. 42), and electrophoretic mobility (see Fig. 45). As men-

Table 17. Distribution and Base Ratios of Labeled RNA in Normal and T6r⁺-Infected Cells † (645)

Cells	Conditions	Radioactivity in Ribosomes (% of total)	[¹⁴C]RNA on Ribosomes	
			Amount of Labeled RNA (% total RNA)	UMP/CMP
Normal	+ histidine	89	10	1.3
	− histidine	86	1.4	1.6
	+ histidine + chloramphenicol	72	6.9	1.4
T6r⁺- infected	+ histidine	79	2.1	2.5
	− histidine	75	1.0	3.2
	+ histidine + chloramphenicol	77	0.9	3.4

† Bacteria $(1 \times 10^9$ cells/ml) were incubated in 100 ml each of the following media: basal medium containing thymine alone; basal plus histidine (20 μg/ml); basal plus histidine plus chloramphenicol (40 μg/ml). T6r⁺ phase was added to 3 samples after incubation for 5 minutes (multiplicity of 8 phages/bacterium). [¹⁴C]Uracil (0.5 μC/μmole) was added to all samples after incubation for 7 minutes (final concentration of uracil, 0.1 μmole/ml). The reaction was stopped after incubation for 20 minutes.

tioned earlier, virus-induced RNA produced under comparable conditions in the absence of protein synthesis is not only found mainly in ribosomes, but is also present in organized polysomes (292). Hauge has also added the observation that such RNA is as hybridizable to phage DNA as is the RNA made under conditions of protein synthesis (292). It appears then that virus-induced mRNA is made in the absence of protein synthesis and is present in polysomes apparently ready to code for the synthesis of specific proteins.

When histidine was returned to the infected cell, which had accumulated untranslated mRNA on its ribosomes, the synthesis of

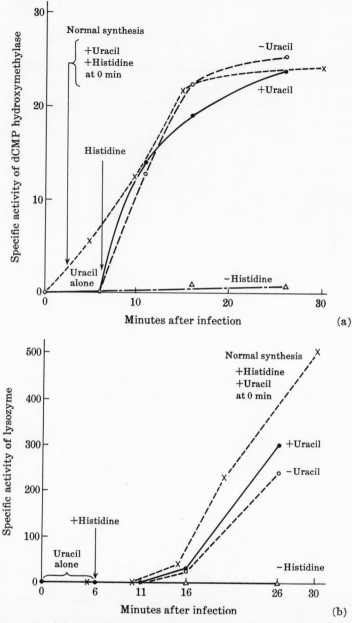

Figure 48. (a) Stimulated formation of an early enzyme, dCMP hydroxymethylase, in *E. coli* strain THU preincubated with uracil after infection (645). (b) Lack of effect of preincubation with uracil on production of the late enzyme, lysozyme (645). Formation of lysozyme in the same experiment.

dCMP hydroxymethylase proceeded at a rate at least twice that of the normal initial rate, as presented in Fig. 48a. Nevertheless, the highest levels of enzyme were comparable in all instances, an indication that the operation of the control mechanism switches off synthesis of early enzymes in these cases too. It can be seen in Fig. 48b that the preformation of early RNA and its deposition on the ribosomes (at least 75% of the total) did not hasten the time course of appearance of a late enzyme, lysozyme. This experiment, then, strongly suggests that the RNA made in the absence of protein synthesis is functional and represents the transcribed product of early cistrons only. Thus the phage genome appears to be transcribed sequentially, producing RNA for early proteins before that for late protein.

In this infected bacterium, thymidylate synthetase appears about 5 minutes after dCMP hydroxymethylase (Fig. 49a). Figure 49b shows that the preformation of RNA essentially eliminated this lag in synthesis of dTMP synthetase and that both enzymes were made without lag immediately after addition of histidine. This experiment shows that protein synthesis is not required for the transcription of different early cistrons. On the other hand, if preformation of RNA exceeded the time necessary for the normal formation of late mRNA and proteins, a lag in lysozyme formation still occurred after addition of histidine (Fig. 49c). Thus the transcription of the genome relating to lysozyme requires not only the transcription of cistrons relating to early enzymes but some steps involving protein synthesis as well.

Is protein synthesis rather than the production of phage DNA required for the initiation of production of late proteins? We have noted that early enzymes continued to be synthesized in infection with phages unable to stimulate synthesis of virus DNA: ultraviolet-irradiated phage, selected *am* and *ts* mutants. It could then be imagined that the lag after addition of histidine is required for DNA synthesis only, since synthesis of virus DNA required the prior formation of certain early enzymes. It had been reported that 5-fluorodeoxyuridine (FUDR) prevented net synthesis of DNA but not that of virus particles containing late structural proteins. At

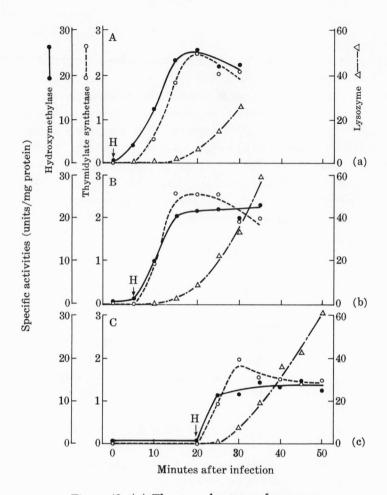

Figure 49. (a) The normal pattern of appearance
of two early enzymes, dCMP hydroxymethylase
and thymidylate synthetase, and a late enzyme,
lysozyme in *E. coli* strain THU infected by T6r+
(645). Histidine (H) was added at 0 minutes.
(b) The stimulated formation without lag of the
two early enzymes in infected THU preincubated
with uracil for 5 minutes. Histidine (H) was
added at 5 minutes. (c) The stimulated formation
without lag of the two early enzymes and the delay
in lysozyme formation after preincubation with
uracil for 20 minutes. Histidine (H) was added at
20 minutes.

first this result suggested that DNA synthesis was not required, that this hypothesis was incorrect (779). Nevertheless, since host DNA provided thymine for phage growth, it did not seem likely that FUDR was capable of blocking synthesis of virus DNA completely. Actually, we were able to show that uracil is incorporated into DNA during infection in the presence of FUDR; that is, some DNA multiplication does occur (645). Thus a requirement for DNA synthesis could still be imagined to be essential for the production of late enzymes.

This point was then tested in another system. Phage was irradiated with ultraviolet light and used to infect cells under conditions in which DNA synthesis did not occur. Although dCMP hydroxymethylase synthesis continues, there is indeed a total lack of production of lysozyme (645). It has been quite difficult to obtain specific chemical inhibitors of DNA synthesis which will totally prevent synthesis of virus DNA. 5-Azacytidine appears to block DNA synthesis, but not so completely as would be desirable, and some synthesis of lysozyme occurs (175). Lysozyme production may attain up to 70% of the normal rate, although phage yield may be no more than 3 infectious particles per cell and intracellular phage DNA equivalents may be no more than 6 to 10. Nevertheless, an agent such as FUDR can be used to reduce DNA pools for the study of such functions as genetic recombination (224).

The separation of transcription and translation in infected cells has also been studied with combinations of 5-methyltryptophan to block protein synthesis and with actinomycin D to block synthesis of mRNA. The tryptophan analogue, 5-methyltryptophan, interrupts protein synthesis and is readily reversed by tryptophan (130). A similar effect of the analogue is observed in the production of dCMP hydroxymethylase, and reversal by tryptophan is in fact followed by a burst of enzyme appearance (212), as if mRNA had been stored. Actinomycin D is a potent inhibitor of DNA-dependent RNA polymerase in gram-positive organisms, but the antibiotic requires the elimination of cell wall components to permit penetration and activity in *E. coli*. We have noted earlier the additional effect of actinomycin D on some maturation steps in T4 infection. Despite

these complexities, mRNA synthesis was studied in the presence of
the tryptophan analogue plus Mg^{++}, and translation of the mRNA
to protein was tested in the presence of actinomycin D to eliminate
continuing synthesis of mRNA. It was observed that the rate and
amount of enzyme synthesis were proportional to the time of the
presumed synthesis of mRNA (274). Thus, as we saw previously,
mRNA could be stored in the absence of protein synthesis. It
appeared that little utilizable mRNA for early functions could be
stored in different systems for longer than 20 minutes after protein
synthesis. These complex experiments have been interpreted to suggest that the arrest of synthesis of early proteins results from an
inactivation of early mRNA by a protein generated late in infection
(274).

On Late and Early mRNA and Proteins   The curves showing
appearance of phage lysozyme presented in Figs. 48 and 49 show the
maximal level of early lysozyme in infected cells. It is definitely less
than 0.5% of the final level. Similar results, determined immunochemically, have been obtained for virus structural proteins (380).
Unfortunately, no one has attempted to show that 0 molecules of
a late protein are produced early, a point relevant to the problem
of the availability of mRNA derived from "late" genes. In any case,
it is evident that the bulk of synthesis of late proteins occurs late,
after some DNA is made. In addition to the evidence of our experiment with ultraviolet-irradiated phage (645), Levinthal and his
collaborators (434) state that all phage mutants which are totally
unable to make DNA are also unable to make detectable amounts
of late proteins. Also, as discussed in the preceding section, expression of stored early mRNA revealed the production of early
proteins early.

Nevertheless, some workers have attempted to detect the early
presence of mRNA for late functions. One set of ingenious experiments by Edlin using intact cells revealed effects on the production
of late proteins by incorporating 5-fluorouracil into early mRNA
(192). However, as we have remarked earlier, the turnover of
mRNA permitted the reutilization of fluorouridylate which could

not be eliminated by flooding the system with uracil (532, 287). Although these experiments of Edlin are now known to be misleading because of this turnover phenomenon, he had also suggested (192) that late mRNA is made early in proportion to the number of gene replicas, is relatively stable, and is eventually expressed after degradation of early mRNA. Several additional experiments suggest that such a gene dosage theory cannot be correct. It can be seen in Fig. 49C that no detectable lysozyme is produced if mRNA is accumulated for 20 minutes before protein synthesis. In experiments with fluorescent antibodies for virus precursor proteins which could readily detect one phage equivalent in single infected cells, no such proteins were detected before DNA synthesis started. This was true even if the cells infected with many amber mutants incapable of DNA synthesis were observed for 60 minutes (647). The synchrony of appearance of virus protein also argued against the gene dosage hypothesis. Once again the trigger was DNA synthesis.

At the present time a single phenomenon suggests the possibility that the synthesis of late virus proteins may not require normal replication of the virus genome. Numerous bacteria carrying defective prophages may be induced to give rise to organized particles devoid of DNA, which are bactericidal and possess a characteristic phage morphology. In one such case Marmur and his collaborators found that the "phage" induced in *B. subtilis* contains host DNA capable of bacterial transformation and lacks a DNA which can be thought of as viral (641, 718). The particle does not replicate in any known host. These authors suggest that this "phage," designated the PBSX particle, is a transitional evolutionary form between episome and phage. The particle was produced despite the presence of mitomycin C and FUDR in the medium. From this, these authors suggest that the synthesis of PBSX does not require DNA synthesis (641). In short, they suggest that synthesis of virus structural proteins does not require synthesis of virus DNA. At the moment I do not find such evidence convincing, but I do believe that the problem is of sufficient importance to warrant careful study. For the present I prefer to imagine that some limited replication of true PBSX DNA has taken place but that defectiveness is defined precisely in the inability of the virus proteins to package the viral DNA. The identification of the true PBSX DNA may perhaps be sought by hybridization after the identification of a virus-specific mRNA, an RNA which does not hybridize with the DNA of *B. subtilis* cured of PBSX.[23]

On the Hybridization of Early and Late mRNA   Since 1964 numerous groups of workers have studied the complementarity of mRNA, isolated from infected cells, with denatured virus DNA. Nygaard and Hall (544) showed that at least 80% of such RNA complexes with phage DNA to the extent of about 0.3 μg RNA per μg DNA. The RNA isolated in infection was tested for the ability to inhibit complex formation by various classes of RNA with DNA, such inhibition being taken as evidence that common sequences exist in the two types of RNA. By this type of test it was found that T2 RNA made between 0 and 6.5 minutes after infection partially inhibited complex formation between denatured T2 DNA and the RNA made between 15 and 19 minutes. Preincubation of DNA with early RNA caused a decrease of about 50% in the amount of labeled late RNA capable of forming complexes, whereas preincubation with late RNA almost completely prevented the formation of complexes with late RNA and early RNA. It was concluded that early RNA does not contain numerous sequences transcribed late, whereas late RNA contains essentially all sequences of RNA made early (279). In other words, early transcription within the cell produces early RNA only, whereas early RNA, as well as new classes of RNA, is also transcribed late in infection. That such new classes of RNA produced late can determine synthesis of late proteins has apparently been demonstrated by Salser and his collaborators (626), as noted earlier.

[23] Many organisms which have been found to suffer "thymineless death" give rise to defective phage particles which are bactericidal (662, 509). Thymine deficiency is an active inducer of lysogenic bacteria (508). It has not yet been possible to find a characteristic base composition for the mRNA produced during thymineless death (663), but new species of such RNA might be sought by hybridization techniques.

The result that only early RNA is made early evidently supports the model in Fig. 47b and contradicts the model in Fig. 47a. However, the result that early RNA is also made late now provides a serious problem concerning the arrest of early protein synthesis. Are these results correct? These data have been extensively confirmed by Geiduschek and his collaborators (240, 243), as well as by Khesin and the Russian group, who were among the first to show differences between early and late mRNA (367, 657). Khesin has reported that he finds a marked decrease in the production of early RNA between 7 and 8 minutes after infection (see Fig. 1 of 366). This result appears quantitatively different from those of other workers, and it will be greatly interesting to know if this result indeed connotes even a partial shutoff in the transcription of early genes.

In any case some early RNA is produced late in infection, and we must ask why it does not appear to be translated. Recent studies (29, 228a) have shown that the polysomes obtained from cells disrupted late in infection do contain both early and late messages. An exclusion mechanism does not appear to operate in the competition of these RNA classes for the ribosomes.*

Both Geiduschek (240) and Khesin (366) have also reported that infection with *am* mutants which block DNA synthesis prevents the transcription of late genes. Khesin has obtained a similar result by addition of chloramphenicol to a normally infected system at 4 minutes or earlier (366). If the antibiotic were added at 9 minutes, it is stated that further decrease of synthesis of early RNA did not occur and late RNA continued to be made at a less than maximal rate. Chloramphenicol added at this time seemed to fix the pattern of synthesis of both types of RNA.

These striking evidences of sequential transcription *in vivo* have led these groups to attempt to determine the nature of the products

---

* NOTE ADDED IN PROOF: In a recent detailed study of the hybridization of mRNA with T4 DNA it was concluded that at least three classes of early mRNA molecules are formed in succession during the first 5 minutes of infection (63a). Many of these RNA species are reduced severalfold in the period of synthesis of late mRNA. Late and early mRNA have similar rates of degradation *in vivo*.

during transcription of phage DNA *in vitro* with an isolated DNA-dependent RNA polymerase of *E. coli*. As noted in an earlier section, an *in vitro* synthesis, which transcribes asymmetrically, that is, transcribes only one strand of the double-stranded DNA, was shown fairly recently. Khesin and his collaborators were in fact the first to demonstrate this important result and to report that such RNA made *in vitro* consisted of early classes only (369). That the *in vitro* system operating on native T2 or T4 DNA produces early RNA alone has been amply confirmed (243). Such an *in vitro* product contains essentially all RNA classes found in the *in vivo* product and little else; both types of transcription use the same DNA strand at any one locus. The loci characteristic of late functions are clearly unavailable for transcription by isolated RNA polymerase. According to the Russian group (368), shearing of virus DNA to double-stranded pieces of molecular weight about 3×10^5 not only produces transcription of both strands in the *in vitro* system but also leads to the copying of late genes.

It might be imagined that the formation of late RNA is under the control of organized cell structure, even as the orderly replication of DNA is postulated to be. To underline this potential difficulty we note that both newly injected DNA and newly synthesized mRNA are localized in the bacterial membrane (831). According to Khesin (366, 368), when spheroplasts making late mRNA are lysed, the disrupted cells switch entirely to the synthesis of early mRNA.

It appears that newly injected phage DNA is organized to permit expression of early functions alone and to restrict the transcription of late functions. Neither the level of methylation of the bases nor that of glucosylation of HMC in phage DNA appears to affect detectably the initiation or quality of the products of transcription in an *in vitro* synthesis of mRNA (542, 63, 514).

On the Lysozyme Message   Bautz and his collaborators have studied the kinetics of appearance of two specific fractions of mRNA purified by the use of hybridization with virus DNA containing large specific gene deletions. Their work has led to a startling and unexpected result. The purification of T4 mRNA corresponding to the rII region was undertaken as an approach to the product of an early cistron (37). This specific product was indeed found to be synthesized continuously between 2 and 20 minutes after infection (36, 355), amounting to about 1% to 2% of the total hybridizable RNA isolated at various times. This result is an apparent confirmation of the reports on the continuous transcription of early genes. The mRNA corresponding to the late function, the e (endolysin) or lysozyme gene, was similarly isolated and studied. The surprising result was that this mRNA also can be found early in infection, although at only about 0.1% to 0.2% of the total early hybridizable RNA. Such mRNA is also found on infection of a nonpermissive host with an early *am* mutant (355).

The kinetics of appearance of the two mRNA's are presented in Fig. 50. It can be seen in Fig. 50a that the rate of production of rII RNA increases slowly and declines slowly in normal infection (T4W). In infection with the *am* mutant this RNA continues to be formed. On the other hand, as presented in Fig. 50B, the product of the e gene is reported as maximal at 3 minutes and almost disappears by 6 minutes. In normal infection the e mRNA develops a second increase which does not occur in infection with the mutant.

Bautz and his colleagues (36) have calculated that only one lysozyme messenger per infecting phage genome is probably present 3 minutes after infection. They suggested therefore that the infecting phage genome may be transcribed once and that mRNA for late functions is nontranslatable and represses synthesis of further copies by a feedback control of transcription. Eventually, however, their own repetition and extension of the earlier competition experiments led them to abandon this hypothesis and to adopt the view that the lysozyme gene is rather unique among late functions with respect to early transcription (355). In extending their studies they showed that the strand of the e gene transcribed early is similar to that transcribed late, since early lysozyme mRNA did not hybridize with that made late. Their most recent hypothesis on the origin of lysozyme RNA introduces an interesting notion to our inquiry; alluding to genetic studies, they propose that the lysozyme gene is transcribed counterclockwise, as is the early function rII gene.

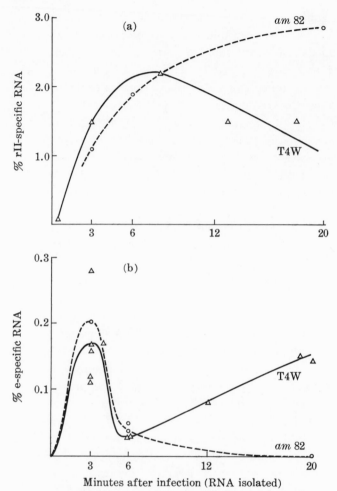

Figure 50. The kinetics of appearance of mRNA specific for (a) the rII (early) and (b) the e (late) genes (355).

This is believed to be a direction opposite that of the transcription of other late function genes such as those for phage coat and tail fibers (355). This has recently been stated to be the case (706a).

The direction of transcription can in principle be determined rigorously by extension of the elegant genetic and chemical studies of Terzaghi and his co-workers (739, 548). These workers have characterized mutant lysozymes induced by phage whose e genes have been genetically defined. Their studies have not only defined precisely the nature of proflavine-induced mutations as additions or deletions of a single nucleotide in virus DNA but have also defined the direction of translation of a nucleotide sequence. It may be supposed that these methods will eventually be applicable to other genes and their gene products. They suppose that this direction of transcription of the e gene in some way relates to its position among early function genes, as can be seen in Fig. 51. If mere position among early or late functions is critical, however, we are compelled

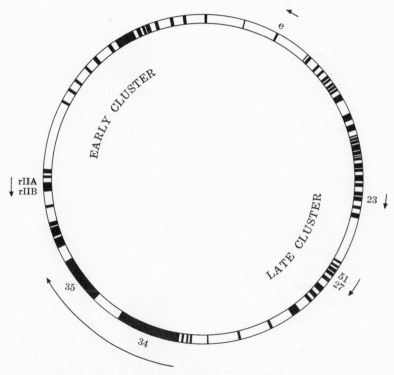

Figure 51. Suggested directions of transcription of the rII and e genes, as compared to those for other late functions (355).

to ask about the direction of transcription for the several groups of early functions, such as that represented by dCMP hydroxymethylase situated between e and rII, and the gene for dTMP synthetase situated between those for head and tail proteins. Obviously, the data are inadequate on this matter, but this important possibility, that different groups of genes may be transcribed from different strands, clearly raises many questions.

In addition to the question of the nature of transcriptive control which has permitted the lysozyme message to appear before it is needed, we are left with the problem of why this early message is not translated. No reason has yet been given for these effects. It will obviously be important to test a presumably early lysozyme mRNA in the *in vitro* system of Salser and his associates (626) to learn if such a potentially functional molecule truly exists.

Repressors, Operons, and Polycistronal RNA   The theories of Jacob and Monod concerning the controls of groups of bacterial genes (330) have also been based on the properties of certain virus systems, such as the λ system. The concept of repression of the transcription of a group of genes (an operon) on DNA included the postulate of the existence of the product of a regulator gene, a specific repressor molecule. In one model of the molecular mode of action of the repressor, it is capable of specific reaction with a portion of the genome. Just recently this postulate has received important experimental support. Proteins ("repressors") have been isolated which appear to fulfill many of the requirements in repression of the operon for lactose utilization (251) and in repression of the development of λ bacteriophage, including the property of reacting specifically with native λ phage DNA (588, 589). However, no strong evidence has yet been obtained to indicate that comparable operons or regulator genes producing specific repressors operate in the development of the T-even phages. It is possible that it may not be necessary to invoke such a hypothesis to understand these systems.

The concept of operons has led to the postulation of polycistronal RNA. Although the existence of such bacterial products has not been rigorously supported by isolation and demonstration of multiple activities, the existence of the large multifunctional RNA of the RNA viruses is frequently invoked as a possible model for the behavior of such molecules. Numerous observations have indicated that the translation of virus RNA is a very complex matter leading to the sequential and often partial expression of its coded information. It has therefore been necessary to consider the possibility that much of the control of biosynthesis is effected through mechanisms of translation of polycistronal RNA. It is interesting that a phenomenon similar to that of repression has also been observed to operate in controlling the translation of the RNA of the MS2 coliphage (193, 721). With this RNA as a messenger RNA in cell-free extracts, preincubation of RNA with coat protein (presumably a late function in this system) inhibits the production of non-coat protein (presumably early functions) more than that of coat protein. The late proteins thereby control and minimize the late expression of early functions which have already been expressed.

The clustering of genes for certain groups of early functions and late functions in the T-even phages suggests that functional operons may exist to yield polycistronal RNA. The high sedimentation rates of phage-induced mRNA also suggest that much of this material may be polycistronal, and therefore may code for several proteins. We have discussed in Chapter 4 the existence of such a cluster of contiguous and functionally related genes for dCMP deaminase (cd locus), dTMP synthetase (td locus), and DHFA reductase (wh locus). It is not known, however, if this group of genes is transcribed coordinately to produce a polycistronal RNA. In discussing this question earlier (120) I have pointed to some data suggesting that the production of synthetase and that of the reductase may be more closely linked than are the production of the synthetase and that of the hydroxymethylase, but have noted the inconclusiveness of the data. In Chapter 4 I have also noted the existence of apparently dissimilar controls operating to switch off the deaminase and the DHFA reductase. Indeed, there may be a chemical reason to believe that dCMP deaminase may not be produced via a polycistronal message. It may be recalled from Chapter 4 that this protein sticks to the ribosomes. It can then be imagined that it would be necessary to produce numerous messages to permit production of numerous deaminase molecules on different ribosomes. If this proves to be the case, it would be grossly inefficient for the infected cell to be compelled to produce excess RNA for the other genes as well. The postulated stickiness of the deaminase, observed *in vitro*, may represent an inefficiency also; it remains to be seen if this can be detected *in vivo*.

Although this system seems well suited to the study of the existence of an operon, these functions are not essential, and conditional lethal mutants blocked in these functions have not yet been obtained. The possibility of coordinate translation with the RNA derived from appropriate *am* mutations would undoubtedly provide an interesting opportnuity for study. Stahl and his colleagues (690, 525) have pointed to the existence of "polarity" mutations in certain *am* mutants. Thus the activity of gene 35 is depressed by the existence of an *am* mutation in gene 34. The effect of proximity of the mutations on complementation has led these workers to suggest that some gene pairs in T4 are cotranscribed. A similar polarity effect in expression of two genes for coat proteins in S13 has also been described (746).

Nevertheless, the existence of so many separate *am* mutations among early functions leading to blocks in a single function suggests rather strongly that at least these functions are not integrated into operons. The fact that *am* mutant N1122m leads to a "coordinate" block in production of both dCMP hydroxymethylase (gene 42) and DNA polymerase (gene 43) (811) might suggest that these genes function in an operon. On the other hand, the fact that *am* mutants are known for each of these functions separately (786) may be taken to suggest that the expressions of these functions are not so linked through an RNA containing a nonsense codon; indeed *am* N122m has recently been reported to be a double mutant (786).

The binding of RNA polymerase to viral DNA has been measured as another approach to the problem of the existence of operons in viral DNA. The *E. coli* enzyme is large enough to be seen by electron microscopy and is stated to exist in a structure comprised of six subunits arranged in a hexagon with a cross section of 120 to 130 Å (144). The observed attachment sites of the enzyme on the DNA of polyoma and human papilloma viruses were about 8 and 11 to 13, respectively, values consistent with one enzyme molecule per cistron (150). These results suggest the absence of operons in these DNA viruses. A similar result was obtained by studying the binding of enzyme to T7 DNA to produce nonfilterable complexes (150, 341). It was observed that denaturation of T7 DNA produces many more binding sites (341). On the other hand, λ DNA has many fewer binding sites for the enzyme than these other samples (341), and it may well be that, as already suggested by the existence of a repressor, λ DNA is organized more completely into coordinately controlled operons. Native T4 DNA has been reported to contain sites sufficient for simultaneous synthesis of 180 molecules of RNA (73). This value seems extraordinarily high considering that it is about 10 times greater than the number of early proteins detected so far. Since early RNA made *in vivo* appears to be essentially identical with early RNA made *in vitro*, it appears unlikely that there are sites on the native DNA which do not become available to the enzyme *in vivo*. The significance of this value for phage physiology remains to be determined.

The finding that much of the RNA made on the double-stranded RF DNA of φX174 is very large, possibly as long as the DNA itself, suggests a polycistronic nature for this material (295, 757).

On the Problem of Gene Selection   The problem of the precise mode of action of a DNA-dependent RNA polymerase is being slowly analysed but is still far from being well understood. It is now known that the β-γ P atoms of a nucleoside triphosphate are retained on the first nucleotide made during RNA synthesis. The RNA chains grow by addition of nucleotides to the 3'-hydroxyl group of the nucleoside end, eliminating the β-γ P atoms as pyrophosphate from the entering nucleoside triphosphate.[24] The syn-

[24] In the recent study by Mitra and his collaborators (513) of the replication of the circular single-stranded M13 DNA by highly purified DNA polymerase of *E. coli*, they found that the initiating termini were 5'-monophosphates of

thesis is thus said to proceed from the 5′ to the 3′ end of the molecule, even with T-even and RF DNA (478, 74, 757). A similar mechanism and direction operate during RNA synthesis by RNA polymerase induced by an RNA phage (31). This is the same direction as the ribosomal translation of RNA (739), and it defines the RNA end providing an initial amino end in the growth of a polypeptide.

As a consequence of this direction of transcription and translation, RNA molecules tend not to be degraded until the nucleoside ends are released. The presence of 3′-phosphoryl ends markedly inhibits the action of polynucleotide phosphorylase and numerous exonucleases. Furthermore, it can be imagined that the newly formed RNA can be integrated directly into ribosomes to generate polysomes (from 70S particles or separate 50S + 30S particles?) and to form the integrated transcription-translation complex postulated by Stent (694). It should be noted, however, that a notion added to this hypothesis, that translation (and protein synthesis) is a major control on RNA synthesis, does not appear to apply to T-even phage infection, since the rate of formation of RNA-charged ribosomes is but slightly decreased in the absence of protein synthesis (644).

The studies with the isolated polymerase have also indicated that RNA ends containing ATP and GTP are preferentially formed, the former being in several-fold excess for T-even DNA (478, 74). These experiments suggest that initiation occurs on a strand containing particular pyrimidines, and indeed an asymmetric distribution of pyrimidine-rich clusters has been observed in strands of DNA from numerous organisms, including the phages (728, 402). These clusters have been detected by means of a selective interaction of various base-rich strands of denatured DNA with polynucleotides containing hypoxanthine and guanine (poly IG) or U (poly U). Such interactions result in isolable DNA-polyribonucleotide complexes

each of the four deoxynucleotides. Not only is the terminal pyrophosphoryl group of the initial deoxynucleoside triphosphate eliminated in this system, but also no specific nucleotide locus for initiation appears to exist on this circular template.

from which the free DNA strands can be isolated, as described earlier for phages α and SP8. It appears that a strand of T-even phage DNA containing thymidine-rich clusters is precisely the strand transcribed initially both by RNA polymerase *in vitro* and during the early stage of infection (728). It has been suggested that such clusters are the initiation points for the formation of RNA messages. In the case of λ DNA, which contains cytosine-rich clusters on both strands, it has been shown that both strands are indeed transcribed during infection, presumably from the initiation sites provided by these clusters (738).*

These newer techniques are being used very actively in the study of transcription of the intact and fragmented λ genome. For example, early λ mRNA is also rich in adenine and is referable to one-half of one strand (674) which has in fact been isolated (107, 317). We can expect the analysis of these relations to be developed in great detail in defining the apparently complex sequence of events during λ multiplication.

On Translation and the Problem of Message Selection   The translation of mRNA to form many proteins in *E. coli* is initiated by N-formylmethionine, which is subsequently removed from the polypeptide chain *in vivo*. The translation of RNA messages from RNA phages has shown a similar requirement in the synthesis of both coat protein (384, 829, 273) and early proteins (546, 771). Factors isolated from *E. coli* ribosomes help to effect a binding of formylmethionine-tRNA specifically to ribosomes and thus to facilitate the initiation of translation of messages containing the appropriate codon (623). It has also been shown that similar factors in the presence of ribosomes facilitate both the synthesis of RNA transcribed from T4 DNA by RNA polymerase and the translation of such presumably early RNA (603). These results suggest that the formation of a transcription-translation complex containing DNA,

---

* NOTE ADDED IN PROOF: Summers and Szybalski (720a) report that more than 99% of the RNA made in T3 and T7 infections are transcribed from only one of the two DNA strands. The transcribed strand has cytosine clusters, whereas the untranscribed strand is devoid of cytosine or thymine clusters.

RNA polymerase, mRNA, and ribosomes may indeed govern the rate of transcription in infected cells. This view is also supported by the fact that *E. coli* containing few ribosomes, as a result of depletion of Mg^{++}, has only a very low rate of synthesis of mRNA on infection in a medium of adequate Mg^{++} content (526). Another implication of these data (603) is that early T-even phage proteins are also initiated by formylmethionine. This inference has not yet been tested directly, however.

Synthetic messages lacking the formylmethionine codons (AUG and UUG) are translated. On the basis of various competitive phenomena, a series of hypotheses concerning the presence and absence of these codons in early and late RNA respectively and postulated competitive advantages derived therefrom can be imagined to explain the apparent absence of translation of early RNA produced late. However, the observation that both early and late RNA are found on ribosomes late in infection indicates that late RNA does not merely win out in competing for ribosomes (29). Nevertheless, an interesting recent experiment may bear on a possible requirement for N-formylmethionine early in infection.

Recent experiments strongly suggest a possible requirement for N-formyl methionine and formyl groups throughout infection. It has been observed that trimethoprim, an inhibitor of dihydrofolate reductase, blocks synthesis of N-formylmethionyl-tRNA (512). Protein synthesis is blocked in *E. coli* by trimethoprim in a medium rich in thymine, purine, amino acids, and other compounds whose synthesis is dependent on THFA. Protein synthesis is rapidly reinitiated in the presence of the inhibitor by infection with T2, T4, and T5, however, but not with λ (512). Phage-induced DHFA reductase is known to be less sensitive to trimethoprim than is the bacterial enzyme. Protein synthesis is also reinitiated for a brief period by infection with a wh mutant of T4. In this instance, the inception of DNA synthesis arrested protein synthesis; the latter could be extended to produce complete phage by exogenous supply of thymine and adenine, or by arrest of DNA synthesis by fluorodeoxyuridine (512). There appears to be a fine adjustment of formyl supply dependent on the rates of synthesis of thymidylate, purine, and protein. The mechanism of protein initiation seems to be unchanged after T-even infection.

A phenomenon described by Rutter and his colleagues in 1950 (621) bears re-examination in the light of these more recent data. Sulfanilamide-inhibited *E. coli,* which grows at 30% of the normal rate in rich media, is unable to support multiplication of T-even phages in such media but can support multiplication of T1, T3, and T7. In this sulfanilamide-inhibited system, the folate deficiency cannot be relieved by increase of DHFA reductase, but perhaps it is not exacerbated by infection with T1, T3, and T7 which do not require significant net synthesis of DNA components. On the other hand, some viruses, possibly exemplified by a virulent T-odd phage, may not require formylmethionine to initiate synthesis of their characteristic proteins. It is difficult to see how the presence of the folic acid and dihydrofolate reductase associated with the phage tail plate (769a) and thereby probably excluded from entrance into the cell can be invoked to explain any of these phenomena.

On the Organic Cations   In recent years the histones, found associated with DNA in the chromosomes of eucaryotic cells, are being investigated as possible repressors of genetic function. Bachrach and Friedmann (22) are evidently exploring the possible role of the basic internal protein of T-even phage with this in mind. The problem of specificity is of overwhelming importance in such postulates, but conclusive evidence to support the concept of histone specificity has not yet been obtained. That specific protein-DNA interactions may exist is implicit in the existence of RNA and DNA polymerases and protein repressors, although these substances are anionic at neutral pH (589). Nevertheless, preferred reactivities of synthetic basic polypeptides with polynucleotide regions have been detected. For example, polylysine has a strong preference for adenine-thymine rich regions of DNA (428).

Bacterial DNA is not known to be associated with histones, however; indeed, the neutralizing cations for this crucial structure have never been defined. Gram-negative bacteria, such as *E. coli,* are rich in smaller basic molecules, the polyamines, putrescine and spermidine, whose structures are

$$H_2N—(CH_2)_4—NH_2$$
1,4-Diaminobutane
(putrescine)

$$H_2N—(CH_2)_5—NH_2$$
1,5-Diaminopentane
(cadaverine)

$$H_2N—(CH_2)_4—NH—(CH_2)_3—NH_2$$
Spermidine

$$H_2N—(CH_2)_3—NH—(CH_2)_4—NH—(CH_2)_3—NH_2$$
Spermine

As described in our recent papers (594, 134, 137), in bacteria these cations can neutralize about a fifth to a quarter of the nucleic acid phosphorus and can exist in distinctly separable compartments; that is, spermidine appears to be entirely associated with cell structure, whereas putrescine exists in a more readily soluble state. Both the bacterial polyamine, spermidine, and the derived polyamine, spermine, found in eucaryotic cells, help to stabilize numerous bacterial structures, including membrane, ribosomes, as well as DNA. We have imagined as a result of our studies of the stabilization of ribosomes by spermidine (135) that Mg^{++} and spermidine both serve as important species of bacterial cement.

The physiological relations of these compounds had largely been neglected until recently. To those workers who had considered the problem of the cations at all, it did not seem likely that these small polybasic molecules could react specifically with the nucleic acids. However, we had shown that spermidine had structural effects on ribosomes which could not be duplicated by putrescine (135). The recent interesting crystallographic work of Liquori and his associates (449) has demonstrated that spermidine can fit very snugly across the narrow groove of DNA, holding very tightly indeed to three phosphate groups and thereby stabilizing the DNA chain. Putrescine is far less effective in fulfilling the chemical and geometric requirements for reacting with DNA. Spermidine and spermine have even been found to affect the secondary structure of single-stranded polyuridylate, as shown by the considerable shift in the melting temperature of this compound in the presence of these specific cations (726).

The well-known effects of spermidine in stimulating the reinitiation of RNA synthesis *in vitro* (137) have now been extended to the demonstration that the intracellular spermidine concentration, modified by intracellular putrescine concentration, relates not only to the quantity of RNA synthesized but also to the control of the synthesis of ribosomal RNA particularly (134). Thus, relaxed strains of *E. coli*, which can synthesize ribosomal RNA in the absence of amino acids required for growth, have a markedly disturbed pattern of polyamine synthesis, even in the absence of RNA synthesis. These strains are characterized by unusually high rates of spermidine synthesis and unusually low rates of putrescine biosynthesis. The latter appears to be inhibited by the high levels of intracellular spermidine (134).

In view of these few instances of active physiological roles of the polyamines in bacterial activity, it has seemed appropriate to reexamine the possible role of polyamines in phage multiplication, although no evidence for spermidine specificity in association with phage DNA has been obtained as yet. The existence of these cations in large amount in T-even phages was detected by Hershey (305), and their structures were established by Ames and his co-workers (7). The unusual concentrations of these bases in the T-even phages are presented in Table 18 (6), where it can be seen that putrescine and spermidine can neutralize almost 40% of the

Table 18. Cation Content of T4 Phage (6)

Cation	Phage Incubated in	
	$MgCl_2$ (meq/eq P)	$CaCl_2$ (meq/eq P)
Putrescine^{++}	250	290
Spermidine^{+++}	75	87
Ca^{++}	<2	96
Mg^{++}	340	360
Na^+	90	30
K^+	60	<30
Total meq per eq P	815	863

phage phosphorus. The finding of the large amounts of the bases in these phages can be attributed to the relative impermeability of the phage head proteins, unlike the situation in many other viruses. A permeable mutant of T4 (osmotic-shock resistant) exchanges its polyamines with Mg^{++} without apparent inactivation (6). Furthermore, the unnatural polyamine, spermine, replaces spermidine in bacteria and phage if added to the growth medium. These results, which suggest that the polyamines in phage are nonspecific cations, underlined the earlier conclusion of Hershey (305) that the compounds do not fulfill a genetic role as does the DNA in the phage. Nevertheless, it must be recalled that phage DNA lacking polyamines is transferred from virus to a bacterium containing these substances. Detailed comparisons of the development of phages deficient in polyamines and rich in these materials were not made (6); it is possible that differences in growth patterns might have been detected. Actually no one has rigorously compared the products of RNA polymerase on phage DNA derived from such polyamine-rich and polyamine-deficient phage. It must be asked if the presence or absence of spermidine on phage DNA may not affect the transcription of particular genes. The question is not easily answered, because the assays must be done under conditions in which the polyamines are not displaced.

That organic bases do have significant effects in phage physiology has been noted on a few occasions. The diamidine, pentamidine, was reported to stimulate production of T1 DNA and phage in *E. coli* (8). Certain steroidal diamines are more mutagenic on, and more inhibitory at low concentration to, the development of T-even phages than for RNA phages (477). When the compounds are added to T-even infected cells before the inception of DNA synthesis (before 7 minutes), lysozyme synthesis is blocked. When the steroidal diamines are added at 10 minutes, DNA synthesis is stopped selectively. Tails can be produced in such a system, but functional heads cannot be formed. It is possible, as Mahler and Baylor have suggested (477), that functional heads result from an absence of functional DNA rather than of protein. It appears likely that DNA is the primary target of these compounds.

Cells infected by T-even phage leak large amounts of putrescine

(204); this leakage is eventually arrested in normal infection. The loss of putrescine is not stopped, however, on infection by rII mutants whose multiplication cycle is abortive in *E. coli* K12(λ). The multiplication of such rII mutants can be rescued in K12(λ) in large part by addition of high concentrations of spermidine, spermine, or Mg^{++} (204, 78) at crucial periods during the latent period. The mechanism of these effects is obscure. Nevertheless, high concentrations of the polyamines do not inhibit DNA, RNA, and protein synthesis in these infected cells and appear to contribute in some way to the repair of the bacterial membrane.

Bachrach has studied the inhibitory activity of enzymatically oxidized spermidine and spermine on virus multiplication. In these compounds both primary amino groups of spermine are replaced by aldehyde groups, or one amino group of spermidine, derived from the aminopropyl moiety, is so replaced. These products are probably not formed in *E. coli* since labeled polyamines can often be recovered quantitatively from such systems. The substances inhibit the growth of numerous bacterial species and inactivate numerous phage species (23), although T2 is somewhat less sensitive than T5. In T5 infection the killed phages adsorb and inject their DNA, to which the oxidized polyamine is attached. Although the cells do not make DNA, they do not degrade viral DNA, however, and can be induced to make β-galactosidase (24). Cells infected with T5 inactivated by oxidized spermine are unable to produce viral mRNA (25), and it was shown that addition of oxidized spermine directly to uninfected cells preferentially inhibits production of mRNA (26). Such an effect has recently been extended to the inhibition of mRNA in various types of infection (21). Bachrach thus appears to have discovered a substitute, active on intact gram-negative bacteria, for actinomycin D which permits him to distinguish between the production of early and late mRNA (21).

Shalitin and Sarid (652, 649) have studied the effects of the polyamines on production of early and late enzymes. They report that polyamines enhance rescue of early mutants and inhibit rescue of late mutants. The polyamines also inhibit production of late enzymes and other late functions in normal infection. Since these substances inhibit DNA synthesis at the concentrations tested, the effects on late functions seem easily interpretable. Putrescine at quite high concentrations, although inhibitory to synthesis of DNA and late proteins, does not inhibit the synthesis of two early enzymes; however, it does reduce the rate of RNA synthesis slightly.

Although Hershey had demonstrated some synthesis of the polyamines during infection, even in the presence of chloramphenicol (305), the quantitative relations of this synthesis to that of phage DNA were not clear from his work. As a prelude to attempting to detect more specific effects of the polyamines on the physiology of infection, we have determined the accumulation of the polyamines in T6r$^+$-infected cells (137). Figure 52 shows that after an initial lag in synthesis the accumulation of polyamines in the infected cells between 20 and 60 minutes parallels accumulation of DNA. These rates are similar to those for the synthesis of putrescine and spermidine in uninfected cells, and it may be supposed that a synthesis of new enzymes for these functions does not take place (137). Before 20 minutes there is a release of putrescine into the medium which is then taken up again into the cells. Very little spermidine passes into the medium initially. Infected cells

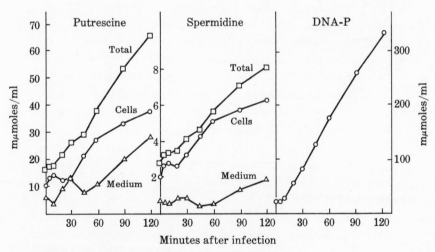

Figure 52. The accumulation of polyamines in both cells and medium as compared to DNA synthesis of a T6r$^+$-infected culture (137).

obviously leak both polyamines after 60 minutes. We imagine that the initial lag in spermidine synthesis may arise from the release of reutilizable spermidine from disrupted bacterial structures, ribosomes and bacterial DNA.

Although this net increase in polyamines in infection is not surprising, this is the first instance in which polyamine synthesis appears to be tied to DNA accumulation. In all systems examined previously, spermidine accumulation paralleled RNA content and not DNA. Thus phage infection provides a new biological system for study of the significance of polyamine synthesis.

We have attempted to learn if the availability of spermidine affects the course of synthesis of virus DNA, as it does for synthesis of ribosomal RNA. Although it is commonly reported that amino acid deficiency imposed after the inception of DNA synthesis does not limit this synthesis, we thought that a limitation of the spermidine precursor, methionine, might limit DNA synthesis. The cells were infected in the presence of just enough methionine to permit synthesis of early proteins and the beginning of DNA synthesis. When methionine was exhausted, spermidine production stopped sharply. DNA synthesis also stopped when the system ran out of spermidine but unfortunately, perhaps necessarily, lysis also began early. It may well be that the apparent inhibition of DNA synthesis in this instance stems entirely from early lysis; these two manifestations of methionine and spermidine limitation have not yet been separated (137). Early lysis generally may be related to a deficiency of spermidine, which may stabilize membranes. It will be recalled that T3 lyses quite early and contains an enzyme which destroys S-adenosyl methionine, the spermidine precursor.

Our recent work on polyamines in phage infection was undertaken initially to test the notion that spermidine covers transcription sites on parental DNA. This possible "repressor" might be removed later as a result of the action of an enzyme, such as an acetylase produced early in infection. Experiments to test this remote possibility are still in progress.

Why Does the Synthesis of Early Proteins Stop? We have proposed (644, 120) that the separation of strands for the replication of virus DNA can in itself prevent the transcription of early functions, since a double-stranded template is essential to normal function of RNA polymerase. We know now that some synthesis of early RNA occurs after DNA synthesis starts. Therefore we conclude that, although strand separation in itself may be a molecular switch for transcription on parental DNA, the elimination of this template for the transcription of early RNA is not a physiological determinant in this system. Evidently, early genes in progeny DNA can be transcribed to some extent to form early messages. We ask, then, if it is true that such messages are not translated as well as late messages, if indeed there is a total arrest in the synthesis of early proteins.

In several instances a plateau is not obtained in the curves of net increase of certain virus-induced proteins. Among these instances are those of the internal antigen of the T-even phages and of the deoxycytidylate deaminase in infection of *B. subtilis* by phage 2C (565). Nevertheless, it appears clear that, in almost all instances, the curve of net accumulation does achieve a maximum. In too many instances, however, a significant decrease can be detected late in the extracts of infected cells, and we are compelled to ask if the apparent plateau or development of a maximum is not the consequence of synthesis and degradation in the cells or extract. In Chapter 4 we presented circumstantial evidence to suggest that maturation in T-even phage infection may require some proteolysis, and indeed I remarked on this in my earliest work (109, 110). Not only may such proteolysis contribute to lysis, but also we can imagine that decreases in enzyme activity may represent active degradation of the enzymes as a result of proteolysis.

We do not suppose, however, that the numerous instances of arrest of early enzymes really reflect an artifactual uncontrolled balance of synthesis and degradation. We think that, even if synthesis of early enzymes has not stopped completely, a very high percentage of such synthesis has stopped. Indeed, experiments of Khesin (366), alluded to earlier, suggest that the level of synthesis of early RNA is controlled even as late as 9 minutes after infection by some chloramphenicol-sensitive process. Nevertheless, no one has yet designed experiments to test the proportions of the early enzyme present in an extract at 25 minutes after infection that have been synthesized after extracts show maximal activity, that is, between 20 and 25 minutes. Although the gel electrophoresis experiments on the early and late proteins formed in short pulses of amino acid incorporation strongly suggest gross replacement of early synthesis by late synthesis, the data have not yet appeared in such form as to prove that there is absolutely no synthesis of early enzymes at late intervals (434, 220). If it is assumed that the peaks have been identified, it is unlikely that the scanning of gel electrophoretic patterns can reduce the base lines to zero; it seems likely that the proof of this point will require some preliminary purification of particular proteins.

In a recent study of infection with a *ts* T4 mutant unable to make dCMP hydroxymethylase active at 44°, neither DNA nor lysozyme was made at 44°. Nevertheless, the activity of thymidylate synthetase leveled off after 10 to 15 minutes, as in normal infection (500). This result argues against the possibility that a late function degrades early proteins at a rate sufficient to produce the observed plateau. In addition, Mathews and Kessin noted that protein synthesis continued actively after the specific enzyme activity had attained a constant level. They asked if the synthesis of the synthetase does not continue at a decreased rate, matching total protein synthesis, and suggested that an appreciable rate of early enzyme synthesis may in fact occur throughout normal infection.

In any case, there does appear to be a major reduction in the synthesis of early proteins and, at least in the relative proportion of early messages, at the time of DNA replication. It must be asked if the process of beginning these changes in the expression of early functions is not tied solely to the elimination of double-stranded parental DNA in order to begin DNA replication. No phage mutants are yet known which stop these early syntheses without being tied to another function which controls DNA replication; that is, the synthesis of a specific protein controlling early RNA synthesis is not yet indicated. As we suggested as a result of our experiments with ultraviolet-irradiated phage, the inability of DNA strands to separate and replicate may still be the main reason for the continuation of the synthesis of early mRNA derived from parental DNA.

The phenomenon of continued enzyme synthesis in certain situations in which DNA synthesis is blocked helps to eliminate another unlikely hypothesis on the arrest of early enzyme synthesis. It will be recalled that the dCMP deaminase of T4-infected cells was isolated after autolysis of a ribosomal fraction. The data thus included the possibility that a high percentage of the bacterial ribosomes could have been jammed by this enzyme. However, continued synthesis of early enzymes to three or four times the normal level in infection by ultraviolet-irradiated phage or various mutants indicates that all of the ribosomes were not so jammed at the usual time of early enzyme arrest in normal infection. It may be asked, however, if the arrest of early enzyme synthesis at three or four times the normal level does not relate to this unusual property of the deaminase. It would be interesting to compare various aspects of protein synthesis in infection with cd$^-$ and cd$^+$ strains from this point of view.

It seems to us that the main problem connected with the apparent arrest of synthesis of early proteins is that early messages formed late do not appear to be translated as well as late messages. Since both early and late RNA can be found on ribosomes, the problem is not that of affinity for these structures but that of producing polypeptides from the bound messages. It will be important to see, then, if early RNA, isolated late, can actually be used to code for a specific early protein. It appears also that early and late RNA have similar half-lives of about 3.5 minutes at 37° (271a). It will be of interest to see if in the late RNA differences in half-life can be detected for that controlling lysozyme and that controlling a suitable early enzyme, as might be expected for the survival of used and unused messages.

Why Do Late Functions Start?   In 1962 Séchaud and Streisinger (642) showed that bacteria infected by two different h$^+$ mutants incapable of producing h tail fibers became capable of forming h tail fiber protein as a result of recombination. Recombination of mutant DNA molecules was presumed to occur entirely in a pool of replicating DNA in which recombination was stimulated by ultraviolet irradiation of the infected bacteria. The concept of a replicating pool is probably comparable to imagining replication of bacterial DNA occurring in a central nucleoid. We might equally suppose, in line with the more modern interpretation concerning the site of replication of the bacterial chromosome, that both replication and recombination of viral DNA also take place at the bacterial membrane. In any case the formation of h recombinants was markedly increased by irradiation after 10 minutes of infection, after the formation of the replicated virus DNA and progeny DNA. These experiments indicated that information for synthesis of the tail fiber proteins (and lysozyme as well) can be made from replicated DNA and not from parental DNA exclusively, although the possibility that a parental strand may contribute to synthesis of late proteins has not been excluded. These authors also suggested that the technique would be a good one with which to study production of early proteins, as it might determine if the mRNA for early proteins made on progeny DNA can actually be translated. In any case, the various pieces of information concerning the origin of late proteins are not contradictory. No late message appears early (with the exception of lysozyme mRNA), late message and late proteins are preceded by DNA synthesis, and replicated DNA permits synthesis of late mRNA.

Parental DNA is so organized that it does not permit transcription of late functions, and we may propose numerous reasons for this. It can be supposed that such sites are covered, for example, by internal protein or polyamines; although unlikely, this possibility has not been carefully excluded. The DNA may lack appropriate initiation sites for the RNA polymerase; such initiation sites may be afforded by nicking the DNA specifically with nucleases. Another type of hypothesis suggests that one of the early enzymes is a new type of DNA-dependent RNA polymerase which can initiate syntheses at initiation sites unavailable to the original bacterial enzyme. Such a possibility has been invoked to account for transcription of late functions in λ infections (177), but such a polymerase has not yet been detected in any DNA system. Evidence for new proteins participating in transcription of late λ genes has been obtained (675). In any case, no increase in RNA polymerase has been detected in T-even phage infection, early or late.

Unfortunately, this result would be more convincing if RNA polymerase activity were not decreased.

As noted earlier, disruption of cell structure late in infection has been reported (366) to prevent transcription of late functions and to increase transcription of early functions. Although this does argue against the idea of a new polymerase, to my mind it need not argue against the notion of new initiation sites in the transcribed DNA. It can be imagined that in an intact cell the bulk of the unpackaged viral DNA in the replicative pool is unnicked and is withheld from the host RNA polymerase active in the membrane on a limited number of appropriately nicked progeny DNA molecules. Such membrane-bound templates for late transcription may never enter into replication, since phage DNA contains few if any single-stranded breaks and much of the DNA in the vegetative pool may never serve as a template for transcription; see introduction to discussion in (156). Cell disruption might now saturate the RNA polymerase with unnicked progeny DNA. This situation might define some of the difficulties involved in isolating a system capable of synthesizing late mRNA *in vitro*.*

It is easy to see that we know very little about the site and mechanism of transcription of late genes. The concept that transcription is effected in an organized complex of specially prepared replicated DNA and host membrane containing the RNA polymerase only serves to pose the problem in terms comparable to that suggested for the replication, recombination, and manipulation of DNA generally. The sequence of observed syntheses can perhaps be viewed most easily (and naively) in terms of the processing of parental and progeny DNA on a well-ordered membranous belt line whose branch points throw off numerous products capable of the most unexpected feats of self-assembly.

---

* NOTE ADDED IN PROOF: The synthesis of late mRNA has now been detected in an *in vitro* system containing membrane components, DNA and RNA polymerase (683a). Such synthesis requires the addition of a factor correlated with the functioning of T4 gene 55, mutants of which make early mRNA, early proteins, and DNA, but not late mRNA. Whether this gene product effects its control of late RNA transcription by acting as a nickase or by some other mechanism has not yet been determined.

CONCLUSIONS AND EPILOGUE

Our work leading to the discovery of virus-induced enzymes began with what seemed to be a simple problem, the analysis of T-even phage DNA. We unexpectedly discovered a new simple compound, a pyrimidine, into whose nature, structural relations, and origins we inquired. We pursued the exaggerated metabolism of a freak of biochemistry, in the tradition of chemical investigation in pathology, and began to find numerous phenomena of more general interest. They included another major approach to the genetic control of protein synthesis with special significance for virology, possibly even for the therapy of virus diseases. Explorations in other virus systems have revealed not only the generality of the phenomenon of virus-induced increase or acquisition of enzymatic equipment, but also the variability of the mechanisms developed in such metabolic expansions and the enormous fertility and number of evolutionary solutions from one virus infection to another. Finally, the problem of the origin of the enzymes and other proteins in our phage systems has merged with many key problems of developmental biology, posing numerous questions found not only in other virus systems but also in more complex systems of bacteria, plants, and animals.

This description of the present state of our work and interests, as well as those of many hundreds of investigators throughout the world, has revealed the enormous complexity of even such apparently simple biological material as a virus. I have also stated that we cannot handle these problems of virus multiplication without understanding the structure and organized activity of the host bacterium with which the virus interacts. Furthermore, the infected bacterium has new properties of metabolism and organization, which are different from those of either of the interacting components alone. The pursuit of the origin of our biochemical freak has exposed innumerable significant problems which will occupy the attention of biochemists and biologists for many years to come.

It has been evident also that the progress of science not only reveals new specific and general truths but also shows how little we do know. The true scope of the task set by Hopkins for biochemistry in the understanding of virus multiplication is just beginning to be defined. For the first time in two decades of biochemical virology, we can begin to see the nature of our problem in terms of specific ordered structures and reaction sequences. Some thirty years ago, Hopkins himself and some of his students spoke in such terms about energy metabolism and integrated metabolic sequences. However, chemical hints concerning the structural and enzymatic nature of replication and information transfer only recently became available, in no small part through the contributions of these very studies on the T-even phages. There is no end of problems in homogeneous systems, and they apparently include many steps in the self-assembly of the viruses, but the genuinely difficult questions that now impede our progress in virology are the understanding of the sites, mechanisms, and integration of DNA replication, RNA transcription and translation in the integrated molecular components of the intact membranes, chromosomes, and ribosomes of cells. In the past decade the virologist has necessarily become both biochemist and geneticist. In the next decade it seems reasonable to expect that he will have to become organic chemist, polymer chemist, electron microscopist, cytologist, and cell physiologist. In the period to come, he may, with much effort, solve his present problems, but what unpredictable discoveries will then have emerged?

REFERENCES

1. Abbott, M. T., R. J. Kadner, and R. M. Fink. *J. Biol. Chem.*, **239**, 156 (1964).
2. Abbott, M. T., E. K. Schandl, R. F. Lee, T. S. Parker, and R. J. Midgett. *Biochim. Biophys. Acta*, **132**, 525 (1967).
3. Abrams, R., and S. Duraiswami. *Biochem. Biophys. Res. Commun.*, **18**, 409 (1965).
4. Adams, M. H., and B. H. Park. *Virology*, **2**, 719 (1956).
4a. Alegria, A. H. *Biochim. Biophys. Acta*, **149**, 317 (1967).
5. Alikhanian, S. I., C. N. Grinberg, V. N. Krylov, A. N. Maisourian, and M. G. Oganesian. *J. Genetics*, **59**, 283 (1966).
6. Ames, B. N., and D. T. Dubin. *J. Biol. Chem.*, **235**, 769 (1960).
7. Ames, B. N., D. T. Dubin, and S. M. Rosenthal. *Science*, **127**, 814 (1958).
8. Amos, H., and E. Vollmayer. *J. Bact.*, **73**, 178 (1957).
9. Anfinsen, C. B. *Fed. Proc.*, **20**, 634 (1961).
10. Anraku, N., and J. Tomizawa. *J. Mol. Biol.*, **11**, 50 (1965).
11. ———. *J. Mol. Biol.*, **12**, 805 (1965).
12. Aposhian, H. V. *Biochem. Biophys. Res. Commun.*, **18**, 230 (1965).
12a. ———. Personal communication.
13. Aposhian, H. V., and A. Kornberg. *J. Biol. Chem.*, **237**, 519 (1962).
14. Aposhian, H. V., and G. Y. Tremblay. *J. Biol. Chem.*, **241**, 5095 (1966).
15. Arber, W. *J. Mol. Biol.*, **20**, 483 (1966).
16. Arber, W., and G. Kellenberger. *Virology*, **5**, 458 (1958).
17. Astrachan, L., and E. Volkin. *Biochim. Biophys. Acta*, **32**, 449 (1959).
18. Atwood, K. C., and F. Mukai. *Proc. Nat. Acad. Sci.*, **39**, 1027 (1953).
19. Aurisicchio, S., E. Dore, C. Frontali, F. Gaeta, and G. Toschi. *Biochim. Biophys. Acta*, **80**, 514 (1964).
20. Avery, O. T., C. M. Macleod, and M. McCarty. *J. Exp. Med.*, **79**, 137 (1944).
21. Bachrach, U. *4th Meeting European Biochemists, Oslo, July 1967*, Abstract 15.
22. Bachrach, U., and A. Friedmann. *Biochem. Biophys. Res. Commun.*, **26**, 596 (1967).

23. Bachrach, U., and J. Leibovici. *Israel J. Med. Sci.*, 1, 541 (1965).
24. ———. *Biochem. Biophys. Res. Commun.*, 19, 357 (1965).
25. ———. *J. Mol. Biol.*, 19, 120 (1966).
26. Bachrach, U., and S. Persky. *Biochem. Biophys. Res. Commun.*, 24, 135 (1966).
27. Baguley, B. C., P. L. Bergquist, and R. K. Ralph. *Biochim. Biophys. Acta*, 138, 51 (1967).
28. Baker, B. R. *J. Med. Chem.*, 10, 912 (1967).
28a. Baker, R., and I. Tessman. *Proc. Nat. Acad. Sci.*, 58, 1438 (1967).
29. Baldi, M. I., and R. Haselkorn. *J. Mol. Biol.*, 27, 193 (1967).
30. Baltimore, D., and R. M. Franklin. *J. Biol. Chem.*, 238, 3395 (1963).
31. Banerjee, A. K., L. Eoyang, K. Hori, and J. T. August. *Proc. Nat. Acad. Sci.*, 57, 986 (1967).
32. Barner, H. D., and S. S. Cohen. *J. Bact.*, 68, 80 (1954).
33. ———. *J. Biol. Chem.*, 234, 2987 (1959).
34. Bautz, E. K. F. *Cold Spring Harbor Symp. Quant. Biol.*, 28, 205 (1963).
35. Bautz, E. K. F., and B. Hall. *Proc. Nat. Acad. Sci.*, 48, 400 (1962).
36. Bautz, E. K. F., T. Kasai, E. Reilly, and F. A. Bautz. *Proc. Nat. Acad. Sci.*, 55, 1081 (1966).
37. Bautz, E. K. F., and E. Reilly. *Science*, 151, 328 (1966).
38. Bautz, F. A. *Genetics*, 53, 913 (1966).
39. Bawden, F. C., and N. W. Pirie. *Proc. Roy. Soc.*, 123B, 274 (1937).
40. Bawden, F. C., N. W. Pirie, J. D. Bernal, and I. Fankuchen. *Nature*, 138, 1051 (1936).
41. Beck, W. S., and J. Hardy. *Proc. Nat. Acad. Sci.*, 54, 286 (1965).
42. Becker, A., M. Gefter, and J. Hurwitz. *Fed. Proc.*, 26, 395 (1967).
43. Becker, A., and J. Hurwitz. *Fed. Proc.*, 25, 276 (1966).
44. ———. *J. Biol. Chem.*, 242, 936 (1967).
44a. Becker, A., G. Lyn, M. Gefter, and J. Hurwitz. *Proc. Nat. Acad. Sci.*, 58, 1996 (1967).
45. Beijerinck, M. W. *Verh. Akad. Wetensch. Amsterdam*, II, 6, No. 5, 1 (1898).
46. Bello, L. J., and M. J. Bessman. *Biochim. Biophys. Acta*, 72, 647 (1963).
47. ———. *J. Biol Chem.*, 238, 1777 (1963).
48. Bello, L. J., M. J. Van Bibber, and M. J. Bessman. *J. Biol. Chem.*, 236, 1467 (1961).
49. ———. *Biochim. Biophys. Acta*, 53, 194 (1961).
50. Bendet, I. J., and J. E. Mayfield. *Biophys. J.*, 7, 111 (1967).

51. Benzer, S. *Harvey Lectures,* **Ser. 56** (1960–61).
52. Benzer, S., and S. P. Champe. *Proc. Nat. Acad. Sci.,* **47,** 1025 (1961).
53. Benzinger, R., R. Jaenisch, and P. H. Hofschneider. *J. Mol. Biol.,* **21,** 493 (1966).
54. Bertani, L. E., A. Haggmark, and P. Reichard. *J. Biol. Chem.,* **236,** PC 67 (1961).
55. Bessman, M. J. *J. Biol. Chem.,* **234,** 2735 (1959).
56. Bessman, M. J., and L. J. Bello. *J. Biol. Chem.,* **236,** PC 72 (1961).
57. Bessman, M. J., I. R. Lehman, J. Adler, S. B. Zimmerman, E. S. Simms, and A. Kornberg. *Proc. Nat. Acad. Sci.,* **44,** 633 (1958).
58. Bessman, M. J., and M. J. Van Bibber. *Biochem. Biophys. Res. Commun.,* **1,** 101 (1959).
59. Biswas, C., J. Hardy, and W. S. Beck. *J. Biol. Chem.,* **240,** 3631 (1965).
60. Blakley, R. L. *J. Biol. Chem.,* **240,** 2173 (1965).
61. ———. *Fed. Proc.,* **25,** 1633 (1966).
62. Bobek, M., J. Farkaš, and F. Šorm. *Coll. Czech. Chem. Commun.,* **30,** 3134 (1965); **32,** 3581 (1967).
62a. Boezi, J. A., R. L. Armstrong, and M. De Backer. *Biochem. Biophys. Res. Commun.,* **29,** 281 (1967).
63. Bogdanova, E. S., and R. B. Khesin. *Conference of Kurchatov's Institute of Atomic Energy, Moscow, June 1966.*
63a. Bolle, A., R. H. Epstein, W. Salser, and E. P. Geiduschek. *J. Mol. Biol.,* **31,** 325 (1968).
64. Bolton, E. T. *Cancer Res.,* **26,** 1964 (1966).
65. Bolton, E. T., and B. J. McCarthy. *Proc. Nat. Acad. Sci.,* **48,** 1390 (1962).
66. Borek, E., A. Ryan, and J. Rockenbach. *Fed. Proc.,* **13,** 184 (1954).
67. Borek, E., and P. R. Srinivasan. *Ann. Rev. Biochem.,* **35,** 275 (1966).
68. Bosch, L., E. Harbers, and C. Heidelberger. *Cancer Res.,* **18,** 335 (1958).
69. Bose, S. K., and R. J. Warren. *Biochem. Biophys. Res. Commun.,* **26,** 385 (1967).
70. Bradley, D. E. *J. Gen. Microbiol.,* **31,** 435 (1963).
71. Breitman, T. R., and R. M. Bradford. *J. Bact.,* **93,** 845 (1967).
72. ———. *Biochim. Biophys. Acta,* **138,** 217 (1967).
73. Bremer, H., M. Konrad, and R. Bruner. *J. Mol. Biol.,* **16,** 104 (1966).

74. Bremer, H., M. W. Konrad, K. Gaines, and G. S. Stent. *J. Mol. Biol.*, **13**, 540 (1965).
75. Brenner, S., F. Jacob, and M. Meselson. *Nature*, **190**, 576 (1961).
76. Brenner, S., G. Streisinger, R. W. Horne, S. P. Champe, L. Barnett, S. Benzer, and M. W. Rees. *J. Mol. Biol.*, **1**, 281 (1959).
77. Brenner, S., A. O. W. Stretton, and S. Kaplan. *Nature*, **206**, 994 (1965).
78. Brock, M. L. *Virology*, **26**, 221 (1965).
79. Brossmer, R., and E. Röhm. *Angewandte Chemie (Internat. Ed.)*, **2**, 742 (1963).
80. ———. *Angewandte Chemie (Internat. Ed.)*, **3**, 66 (1964).
81. ———. *Z. Naturforsch*, **21b**, 942 (1966).
82. Brown, G. L., and A. V. Martin. *Nature*, **176**, 971 (1956).
83. Brown, N. C., A. Larsson, and P. Reichard. *J. Biol. Chem.*, **242**, 4272 (1967).
84. Burgi, I., and A. D. Hershey. *J. Mol. Biol.*, **4**, 313 (1962).
85. Burton, A., and R. L. Sinsheimer. *J. Mol. Biol.*, **14**, 327 (1965).
86. Burton, K. *Biochem. J.*, **61**, 473 (1955).
87. Burton, K., M. R. Lunt, G. B. Peterson, and J. C. Siebke. *Cold Spring Harbor Symp. Quant. Biol.*, **28**, 27 (1963).
88. Butler, V. P., S. M. Beiser, B. F. Erlanger, S. W. Tanenbaum, S. Cohen, and A. Bendich. *Proc. Nat. Acad. Sci.*, **48**, 1597 (1962).
89. Buttin, G., and A. Kornberg. *J. Biol. Chem.*, **241**, 5419 (1966).
90. Cairns, J., G. S. Stent, and J. D. Watson (eds.). *Phage and the Origins of Molecular Biology*, Cold Spring Harbor Laboratory of Quantitative Biology, 1966.
91. Campbell, A. *Virology*, **9**, 293 (1959).
92. ———. *Virology*, **14**, 22 (1961).
93. Capecchi, M. R. *J. Mol. Biol.*, **21**, 173 (1966).
94. Caro, L. G., and M. Schnös. *Proc. Nat. Acad. Sci.*, **56**, 126 (1966).
95. Carusi, E. A., and R. L. Sinsheimer. *J. Mol. Biol.*, **7**, 388 (1963).
96. Cassidy, P., F. Kahan, and A. A. Alegria. *Fed. Proc.*, **24**, 222 (1965).
97. Chamberlin, M., and P. Berg. *Proc. Nat. Acad. Sci.*, **48**, 81 (1962).
98. Champe, S. P. *Ann. Rev. Microbiol.*, **17**, 87 (1963).
99. Champe, S. P., and S. Benzer. *Proc. Nat. Acad. Sci.*, **48**, 532 (1962).
100. Chandler, B., M. Hayashi, M. N. Hayashi, and S. Spiegelman. *Science*, **143**, 47 (1964).
101. Chaproniere-Rickenberg, D. M., H. R. Mahler, and D. Fraser. *Virology*, **23**, 96 (1964).
102. Chargaff, E. *Experentia*, **6**, 201 (1950).

102a. Chrispeels, M. J., R. F. Boyd, L. S. Williams, and F. C. Neidhardt. *J. Mol. Biol.*, **31**, 463 (1968).

103. Cline, R. E., R. M. Fink, and K. Fink. *J. Am. Chem. Soc.*, **81**, 2521 (1959).

104. Cocito, C., and A. D. Hershey. *Biochim. Biophys. Acta*, **37**, 543 (1960)

105. Cohen, P. S., and H. L. Ennis. *Virology*, **27**, 282 (1965).

106. ———. *J. Bact.*, **92**, 1345 (1966).

107. Cohen, S. N., U. Maitra, and J. Hurwitz. *Molecular Biology of the Viruses, Symposium of Edmonton, Canada*, New York, Academic Press, 1967, p. 159.

108. Cohen, S. S. *J. Biol. Chem.*, **156**, 691 (1944).

109. ———. *Cold Spring Harbor Symp. Quant. Biol.*, **12**, 35 (1947).

110. ———. *J. Biol. Chem.*, **174**, 281 (1948).

111. ———. *J. Biol. Chem.*, **174**, 295 (1948).

112. ———. *Bact. Rev.*, **13**, 1 (1949).

113. ———. *Nature*, **168**, 746 (1951).

114. ———. *Cold Spring Harbor Symp. Quant. Biol.*, **18**, 221 (1953).

115. ———. *Chem. Pathways Metabolism*, **1**, 173 (1954).

116. ———. In *The Chemical Basis of Heredity*, W. D. McElroy and B. Glass (eds.), Baltimore, Johns Hopkins University Press, 1956.

117. ———. *Science*, **123**, 653 (1956).

118. ———. *Fed. Proc.*, **20**, 641 (1961).

119. ———. *Ann. Rev. Biochemistry*, **32**, 83 (1963).

120. ———. *Genetics Today. Proc. XI Internat. Congress Genetics*, Pergamon Press, 1964, p. 151.

121. ———. *Prog. Nucleic Acid Res. and Mol. Biol.*, **5**, 1 (1966).

122. Cohen, S. S., and T. F. Anderson. *J. Exp. Med.*, **84**, 511 (1946).

123. ———. *J. Exp. Med.*, **84**, 525 (1946).

124. Cohen, S. S., and R. Arbogast. *J. Exp. Med.*, **91**, 637 (1950).

125. Cohen, S. S., and H. D. Barner. *Proc. Nat. Acad. Sci.*, **40**, 885 (1954).

126. ———. *J. Biol. Chem.*, **226**, 631 (1957).

127. ———. *J. Biol. Chem.*, **237**, PC 1376 (1962).

128. Cohen, S. S., H. D. Barner, and J. Lichtenstein. *J. Biol. Chem.*, **236**, 1448 (1961).

129. Cohen, S. S., J. G. Flaks, H. D. Barner, M. R. Loeb, and J. Lichtenstein. *Proc. Nat. Acad. Sci.*, **44**, 1004 (1958).

130. Cohen, S. S., and C. B. Fowler. *J. Exp. Med.*, **85**, 771 (1947).

131. ———. *J. Exp. Med.*, **87**, 259 (1948).

132. ———. *J. Exp. Med.*, **87**, 275 (1948).

133. Cohen, S. S., M. Green, and H. D. Barner. *Biochim. Biophys. Acta*, **22**, 210 (1956).

134. Cohen, S. S., N. Hoffner, A. M. Jansen, M. Moore, and A. Raina. *Proc. Nat. Acad. Sci.*, **57**, 721 (1967).

135. Cohen, S. S., and J. Lichtenstein. *J. Biol. Chem.*, **235**, 2112 (1960).

136. Cohen, S. S., J. Lichtenstein, H. D. Barner, and M. Green. *J. Biol. Chem.*, **228**, 611 (1957).

137. Cohen, S. S., and A. Raina. *Rutgers Symposium. Organizational Biosynthesis,* 1967, p. 157.

138. Cohen, S. S., and L. Roth. *J. Bact.*, **65**, 490 (1953).

139. Cohen, S. S., and D. B. M. Scott. *Science*, **111**, 543 (1950).

140. Cohen, S. S., M. Sekiguchi, J. L. Stern, and H. D. Barner. *Proc. Nat. Acad. Sci.*, **49**, 699 (1963).

141. Cohen, S. S., and W. M. Stanley. *J. Biol. Chem.*, **144**, 589 (1942).

142. Cohen, S. S., and L. L. Weed. *J. Biol. Chem.*, **209**, 789 (1954).

143. Colley, D. G., and C. E. Dowell. *Virology*, **31**, 168 (1967).

143a. Colowick, S. P. Personal communication.

144. Colville, A. J. E., E. F. J. van Bruggen, and H. Fernándéz-Morán. *J. Mol. Biol.*, **17**, 302 (1966).

145. Colville, A. J. E., L. C. Kanner, G. P. Tocchini-Valentini, M. T. Sarnat, and E. P. Geiduschek. *Proc. Nat. Acad. Sci.*, **53**, 1140 (1965).

146. Cooper, T. *A Discourse on the Connexion between Chemistry and Medicine.* University of Pennsylvania, 1818.

147. Coval, M., V. Miller, and H. VanVunakis. *Fed. Proc.*, **19**, 410 (1960).

148. Cowie, D. B., and P. Szafranski. *Carnegie Institution Year Book,* **65**, 121 (1966).

149. Crawford, L. V. *Virology*, **7**, 359 (1959).

150. Crawford, L. V., E. M. Crawford, J. P. Richardson, and H. S. Slayter. *J. Mol. Biol.*, **14**, 593 (1965).

151. Cummings, D. J., V. A. Chapman, S. S. DeLong, and L. Mondale. *J. Virology*, **1**, 193 (1967).

152. Cummings, D. J., and L. Mondale. *J. Bact.*, **93**, 1917 (1967).

153. Cummings, D. J., and T. Wanko. *J. Mol. Biol.*, **7**, 658 (1963).

154. Dann-Markert, A., H. F. Deutsch, and W. Zillig. *Virology*, **29**, 126 (1966).

155. Davison, P. F., and D. Freifelder. *Biopolymers*, **2**, 15 (1964).

156. ———. *J. Mol. Biol.*, **16**, 490 (1966).

157. Davison, P. F., D. Freifelder, R. Hede, and C. Levinthal. *Proc. Nat. Acad. Sci.*, **47**, 1123 (1961).

158. Day, L. A. *J. Mol. Biol.*, **15**, 395 (1966).

159. Delbrück, M. *J. Gen. Physiol.*, **23**, 643 (1940).
160. Delihas, N. Ph.D. dissertation, Yale University, 1960.
161. ———. *Virology*, **13**, 242 (1961).
162. DeMars, R. I., S. E. Luria, H. Fisher, and C. Levinthal. *Ann. Inst. Pasteur*, **84**, 113 (1953).
163. Denhardt, D. T. *Biochem. Biophys. Res. Commun.*, **23**, 641 (1966).
164. Denhardt, D. T., D. H. Dressler, and A. Hathaway. *Proc. Nat. Acad. Sci.*, **57**, 813 (1967).
165. Denhardt, D. T., and R. B. Silver. *Virology*, **30**, 10 (1966).
166. Denhardt, D. T., and R. L. Sinsheimer. *J. Mol. Biol.*, **12**, 647 (1965).
167. DeWaard, A. *Biochim. Biophys. Acta*, **87**, 169 (1964).
168. ———. *Biochim. Biophys. Acta*, **92**, 286 (1964).
169. DeWaard, A., A. V. Paul, and I. R. Lehman. *Proc. Nat. Acad. Sci.*, **54**, 1241 (1965).
170. Diener, T. O., and W. B. Raymer. *Science*, **158**, 378 (1967).
171. Dirksen, M., J. C. Hutson, and J. M. Buchanan. *Proc. Nat. Acad. Sci.*, **50**, 507 (1963).
172. Dirksen, M., J. S. Wiberg, J. F. Koerner, and J. M. Buchanan. *Proc. Nat. Acad. Sci.*, **46**, 1425 (1960).
173. Doermann, A. H. *J. Bact.*, **55**, 257 (1948).
174. ———. *J. Gen. Physiol.*, **35**, 645 (1952).
175. Doskocil, J., and F. Šorm. *Biochim. Biophys. Acta*, **145**, 780 (1967).
176. Doughty, C. C., and J. A. Mann. *J. Bact.*, **93**, 1089 (1967).
177. Dove, W. F. *J. Mol. Biol.*, **19**, 187 (1966).
178. Dowell, C. E., and R. L. Sinsheimer. *J. Mol. Biol.*, **16**, 374 (1966).
179. Duckworth, D. H., and M. J. Bessman. *J. Biol. Chem.*, **242**, 2877 (1967).
180. Dunn, D. B., and J. D. Smith. *Biochem. J.*, **68**, 627 (1958).
181. Durham, L. J., A. Larsson, and P. Reichard. *European J. Biochem.*, **1**, 92 (1967).
182. Duschinsky, R., E. Pleven, and C. Heidelberger. *J. Am. Chem. Soc.*, **79**, 4559 (1957).
183. Earhart, C. F., and F. C. Neidhardt. *Virology*, **33**, 694 (1967).
184. Ebisuzaki, K. *J. Mol. Biol.*, **5**, 506 (1962).
185. Eddleman, H. L., and S. W. Champe. Personal communication.
186. ———. *Virology*, **30**, 471 (1966).
187. Edgar, R. S. In *Phage and the Origins of Molecular Biology*, J. Cairns, G. S. Stent, and J. D. Watson (eds.), Cold Spring Harbor Laboratory of Quantitative Biology, 1966.
188. Edgar, R. S., G. H. Denhardt, and R. H. Epstein. *Genetics*, **49**, 635 (1964).

189. Edgar, R. S., and I. Lielausis. *Genetics,* **49,** 649 (1964).
190. ———. *Genetics,* **52,** 1187 (1965).
191. Edgar, R. S., and W. B. Wood. *Proc. Nat. Acad. Sci.,* **55,** 498 (1966).
192. Edlin, G. *J. Mol. Biol.,* **12,** 363 (1965).
193. Eggen, K., and D. Nathans. *Fed. Proc.,* **26,** 449 (1967).
194. Eigner, J., A. H. Stouthamer, I. Van der Sluys, and J. A. Cohen. *J. Mol. Biol.,* **6,** 61 (1963).
195. Ellis, E. L., and M. Delbrück. *J. Gen. Physiol.,* **22,** 365 (1939).
196. Epstein, R. H., A. Bolle, C. M. Steinberg, E. Kellenberger, E. Boy de la Tour, R. Chevalley, R. S. Edgar, M. Susman, G. H. Denhardt, and A. Lielausis. *Cold Spring Harbor Symp. Quant. Biol.,* **28,** 375 (1963).
197. Erikson, R. L., and W. Szybalski. *Virology,* **22,** 111 (1964).
198. Erlanger, B. F., and S. M. Beiser. *Proc. Nat. Acad. Sci.,* **52,** 68 (1964).
199. Evans, E. A., Jr. *Ann. Inst. Pasteur,* **84,** 129 (1953).
200. Falaschi, A., and A. Kornberg. *Proc. Nat. Acad. Sci.,* **54,** 1713 (1965).
200a. Fareed, G., K. A. Ippen, and R. C. Valentine. *Biochem. Biophys. Res. Commun.,* **35,** 275 (1966).
201. Fareed, G. C., and C. C. Richardson. *Proc. Nat. Acad. Sci.,* **58,** 665 (1967).
202. Fattig, W. D., and F. Lanni. *Genetics,* **51,** 157 (1965).
203. Ferrari, W., G. L. Gessa, B. Loddo, and M. L. Schivo. *Virology,* **26,** 154 (1965).
204. Ferroluzzi-Ames, G., and B. N. Ames. *Biochem. Biophys. Res. Commun.,* **18,** 639 (1965).
205. Feynman, R. *Science,* **153,** 699 (1966).
206. Fiers, W., and R. L. Sinsheimer. *J. Mol. Biol.,* **5,** 424 (1962).
207. Fink, R. M., R. E. Cline, R. B. Henderson, and K. Fink. *J. Biol. Chem.,* **221,** 425 (1956).
208. Flaks, J. G., and S. S. Cohen. *Biochim. Biophys. Acta,* **25,** 667 (1957).
209. ———. *Fed. Proc.,* **17,** 220 (1958).
210. ———. *J. Biol. Chem.,* **234,** 1501 (1959).
211. ———. *J. Biol. Chem.,* **234,** 2981 (1959).
212. Flaks, J. G., J. Lichtenstein, and S. S. Cohen. *J. Biol. Chem.,* **234,** 1507 (1959).
213. Fleming, W. H., and M. J. Bessman. *J. Biol. Chem.,* **240,** PC 4108 (1965).
214. ———. *J. Biol. Chem.,* **242,** 363 (1967).

214a. Foft, J. W., W.-T. Hsu, and S. B. Weiss. *Fed. Proc.*, **27**, 341 (1968).

215. Foster, R. A. C. *J. Bact.*, **56**, 795 (1948).

216. Fraenkel-Conrat, H. *J. Am. Chem. Soc.*, **78**, 882 (1956).

217. Frankel, F. R. *J. Mol. Biol.*, **18**, 109 (1966).

218. ———. *J. Mol. Biol.*, **18**, 127 (1966).

218a. Frankel, F. R. *Proc. Nat. Acad. Sci.*, **59**, 131 (1968).

219. Franklin, R. M., and D. Baltimore. *Cold Spring Harbor Symp. Quant. Biol.*, **27**, 175 (1962).

220. Freda, C. Ph.D. dissertation, University of Pennsylvania, 1967.

221. Freda, C., and S. S. Cohen. *J. Bact.*, **92**, 1670 (1966).

222. Freese, E. B., and E. Freese. *Proc. Nat. Acad. Sci.*, **57**, 650 (1967).

223. French, R. C., and L. Siminovitch. *Can. J. Microbiol.*, **1**, 757 (1955).

224. Frey, M. C., and N. E. Melechen. *Virology*, **25**, 620 (1965).

225. Friedkin, M. *The Kinetics of Cellular Proliferation*, New York City, Grune and Stratton, 1959, p. 97.

226. ———. *Fed. Proc.*, **18**, 230 (1959).

227. Friedkin, M., E. J. Crawford, E. Donovan, and E. S. Pastore. *J. Biol. Chem.*, **237**, 3811 (1962).

228. Friedkin, M., and A. Kornberg. In *The Chemical Basis of Heredity*, W. D. McElroy and B. Glass (eds.), Baltimore, Johns Hopkins Press, 1956, p. 609.

228a. Friesen, J. D., B. Dale, and W. Bode. *J. Mol. Biol.*, **28**, 413 (1967).

229. Fujimoto, D., P. R. Srinivasan, and E. Borek. *Biochemistry*, **4**, 2849 (1965).

230. Fujinaga, K., and M. Green. *Proc. Nat. Acad. Sci.*, **57**, 806 (1967).

231. Fukasawa, T., K. Jokura, and K. Kurahashi. *Biochim. Biophys. Acta*, **74**, 608 (1963).

232. Fukasawa, T., and S. Saito. *J. Mol. Biol.*, **8**, 175 (1964).

233. Furth, J. J., and L. I. Pizer. *J. Mol. Biol.*, **15**, 124 (1966).

234. Futai, M., Y. Anraku, and D. Mizuno. *Biochim. Biophys. Acta*, **119**, 373 (1966).

235. Futai, M., and D. Mizuno. *J. Biochemistry*, **59**, 521 (1966).

236. Garen, A. *Virology*, **14**, 151 (1961).

237. Garen, A., S. Garen, and R. C. Wilhelm. *J. Mol. Biol.*, **14**, 167 (1965).

238. Gefter, M. L., A. Becker, and J. Hurwitz. *Proc. Nat. Acad. Sci.*, **58**, 240 (1967).

239. Gefter, M. L., R. Hausmann, M. Gold, and J. Hurwitz. *J. Biol. Chem.*, **241**, 1995 (1966).

240. Geiduschek, E. P. *Bull. Soc. Chim. Biol.*, **47**, 1571 (1965).

241. Geiduschek, E. P., F. A. Eiserling, and R. H. Epstein. Referred to in *Principles of Biomolecular Organization*, Ciba Foundation, 1965.
242. Geiduschek, E. P., T. Nakamoto, and S. B. Weiss. *Proc. Nat. Acad. Sci.*, **47**, 1405 (1961).
243. Geiduschek, E. P., L. Snyder, and M. Sarnat. *J. Mol. Biol.*, **19**, 541 (1966).
244. Geiduschek, E. P., G. P. Tocchini-Valentini, and M. T. Sarnat. *Proc. Nat. Acad. Sci.*, **52**, 486 (1964).
245. Gellert, M. *Proc. Nat. Acad. Sci.*, **57**, 148 (1967).
246. Gemsa, D., and S. D. Davis. *Fed. Proc.*, **26**, 364 (1967).
247. Georgopoulos, C. P. *Biochem. Biophys. Res. Commun.*, **28**, 179 (1967).
248. Geraci, G., M. Rossi, and E. Scarano. *Biochemistry*, **6**, 183 (1967).
249. Gesteland, R. F., W. Salser, A. Bolle, and R. Epstein. *4th Meeting European Biochemists, Oslo, July 1967*, Abstract 530.
249a. Gesteland, R. F. Personal communication.
250. Gierer, A., and G. Schramm. *Z. Naturforsch.*, **11b**, 138 (1956).
251. Gilbert, W., and B. Mueller-Hill. *Proc. Nat. Acad. Sci.*, **56**, 1891 (1966).
252. Gillespie, D., and S. Spiegelman. *J. Mol. Biol.*, **12**, 829 (1965).
253. Gilliland, J. M., R. E. Langman, and R. H. Symons. *Virology*, **30**, 716 (1966).
254. Giner-Sorolla, A., and L. Medrek. *J. Med. Chem.*, **9**, 97 (1966).
255. Gold, M., R. Hausmann, U. Maitra, and J. Hurwitz. *Proc. Nat. Acad. Sci.*, **52**, 292 (1964).
256. Gold, M., and J. Hurwitz. *Cold Spring Harbor Symp. Quant. Biol.*, **28**, 149 (1963).
257. Goldberg, E. B. *Proc. Nat. Acad. Sci.*, **56**, 1457 (1966).
258. Goldstein, G. A., and G. M. Brown. *Arch. Biochem. Biophys.*, **103**, 449 (1963).
259. Goulian, M. *Fed. Proc.*, **26**, 396 (1967).
260. Goulian, M., and A. Kornberg. *Proc. Nat. Acad. Sci.*, **58**, 1723 (1967).
260a. Goulian, M., A. Kornberg, and R. L. Sinsheimer. *Proc. Nat. Acad. Sci.*, **58**, 2321 (1967).
261. Graham, A. F. *Ann. Inst. Pasteur*, **84**, 90 (1953).
261a. Green, D. M. *J. Mol. Biol.*, **22**, 1 (1966).
262. ———. *J. Mol. Biol.*, **22**, 15 (1966).
263. Green, M. *Cold Spring Harbor Symp. Quant. Biol.*, **27**, 219 (1962).
264. Green, M. H. *Proc. Nat. Acad. Sci.*, **52**, 1388 (1964).
265. Green, M., H. D. Barner, and S. S. Cohen. *J. Biol. Chem.*, **228**, 621 (1957).

266. Green, M., and S. S. Cohen. *J. Biol. Chem.*, **225**, 387 (1957).
267. ———. *J. Biol. Chem.*, **225**, 397 (1957).
268. ———. *J. Biol. Chem.*, **228**, 601 (1957).
269. Greenberg, G. R. *Proc. Nat. Acad. Sci.*, **56**, 1226 (1966).
270. Greenberg, G. R., and R. L. Somerville. *Proc. Nat. Acad. Sci.*, **48**, 247 (1962).
271. Greenberg, G. R., R. L. Somerville, and S. DeWolf. *Proc. Nat. Acad. Sci.*, **48**, 242 (1962).
271a. Greene, R., and D. Korn. *J. Mol. Biol.*, **28**, 435 (1967).
272. Grossman, L., S. S. Levine, and W. S. Allison. *J. Mol. Biol.*, **3**, 47 (1961).
273. Gussin, G. N., M. R. Capecchi, J. M. Adams, J. E. Argetsinger, J. Tooze, K. Weber, and J. D. Watson. *Cold Spring Harbor Symp. Quant. Biol.*, **31**, 251 (1966).
274. Guthrie, G. D., and J. M. Buchanan. *Fed. Proc.*, **25**, 864 (1966).
275. Guthrie, G. D., and R. L. Sinsheimer. *Biochim. Biophys. Acta*, **72**, 290 (1963).
276. Haarr, L. *4th Meeting European Biochemists, Oslo, July 1967*, Abstract 143.
277. Haber, K. *Biochem. Biophys. Res. Commun.*, **23**, 502 (1966).
278. Hadorn, E. *Developmental Genetic and Lethal Factors*, New York, John Wiley and Sons, 1961.
279. Hall, B. D., A. P. Nygaard, and M. H. Green. *J. Mol. Biol.*, **9**, 143 (1964).
280. Hall, B. D., and S. Spiegelman. *Proc. Nat. Acad. Sci.*, **47**, 137 (1961).
280a. Hall, D. H. *Proc. Nat. Acad. Sci.*, **58**, 584 (1967).
281. Hall, D. H., and I. Tessman. *Virology*, **29**, 339 (1966).
282. Hall, D. H., I. Tessman, and O. Karlstrom. *Virology*, **31**, 441 (1967).
283. Hamilton, L. D., R. K. Barclay, M. H. F. Wilkins, G. L. Brown, H. R. Wilson, D. A. Marvin, H. Ephrussi-Taylor, and N. S. Simmons. *J. Biophys. Biochem. Cyt.*, **5**, 397 (1959).
284. Hara, K., and H. Mitsui. *J. Biochem. (Japan)*, **61**, 359 (1967).
285. Hardy, S. J. S., and C. G. Kurland. *Biochemistry*, **5**, 3668 (1966).
286. ———. *Biochemistry*, **5**, 3676 (1966).
287. Haselkorn, R., M. I. Baldi, and J. Doskocil. *4th Meeting European Biochemists, Oslo, July 1967*, Abstract 30.
288. Haslam, E. A., D. H. Roscoe, and R. G. Tucker. *Biochim. Biophys. Acta*, **134**, 312 (1967).
289. Hattman, S. *Virology*, **24**, 333 (1964).

290. Hattman, S., and T. Fukusawa, *Proc. Nat. Acad. Sci.*, **50**, 297 (1963).
291. Hattman, S., H. R. Revel, and S. E. Luria. *Virology*, **30**, 427 (1966).
292. Hauge, J. G. *4th Meeting European Biochemists, Oslo, July 1967*, Abstract 140.
293. Haussmann, R. *J. Virology*, **1**, 57 (1967).
294. Haussmann, R., and M. Gold. *J. Biol. Chem.*, **241**, 1985 (1966).
295. Hayashi, M. *Proc. Nat. Acad. Sci.*, **54**, 1736 (1965).
296. Hayashi, M., M. N. Hayashi, and S. Spiegelman. *Proc. Nat. Acad. Sci.*, **50**, 664 (1963).
297. Hayward, W. S., and M. H. Green. *Proc. Nat. Acad. Sci.*, **54**, 1675 (1965).
298. Hayward, R. S., and S. B. Weiss. *Proc. Nat. Acad. Sci.*, **55**, 1161 (1966).
299. Heidelberger, C., N. K. Chaudhuri, P. Danneberg, D. Mooren, L. Griesbach, R. Duschinsky, R. J. Schnitzer, E. Pleven, and J. Scheiner. *Nature*, **179**, 663 (1957).
300. d'Hérelle, F. *Compt. Rend. Acad. Sci.*, **165**, 373 (1917).
301. Herriott, R. M., and J. L. Barlow. *J. Gen. Physiol.*, **40**, 809 (1957).
302. ———. *J. Gen. Physiol.*, **41**, 307 (1957).
303. Hershey, A. D. *Ann. Inst. Pasteur*, **84**, 99 (1953).
304. ———. *J. Gen. Physiol.*, **37**, 1 (1953).
305. ———. *Virology*, **4**, 237 (1957).
306. Hershey, A. D., and M. Chase. *J. Gen. Physiol.*, **36**, 39 (1952).
307. Hershey, A. D., J. Dixon, and M. Chase. *J. Gen. Physiol.*, **36**, 777 (1953).
308. Hershey, A. D., A. Garen, D. K. Fraser, and J. D. Hudis. *Carnegie Institution Year Book*, **53**, 210 (1954).
309. Hershey, A. D., and N. E. Melechen. *Virology*, **3**, 207 (1957).
310. Hill, C. W., and H. Echols. Personal communication.
310a. Hiraga, S., K. Igarishi, and T. Yura. *Biochim. Biophys. Acta*, **149**, 41 (1967).
311. Hoffmann-Berling, H., H. Dürwald, and I. Buelke. *Z. Naturforsch.*, **18b**, 893 (1963).
312. Hoffman-Berling, H., D. A. Marvin, and H. Dürwald. *Z. Naturforsch.*, **18b**, 876 (1963).
313. Hofschneider, P. H., and A. Preuss. *J. Mol. Biol.*, **7**, 450 (1963).
314. *Hopkins & Biochemistry 1861–1947*, J. Needham and E. Baldwin (eds.), Cambridge, England, W. Heffer and Sons, Ltd., 1949.
315. Horowitz, N. H., and U. Leupold. *Cold Spring Harbor Symp. Quant. Biol.*, **16**, 65 (1951).

316. Hosoda, J. *Biochem. Biophys. Res. Commun.*, **27**, 294 (1967).
317. Hradecna, Z., and W. Szybalski. *Virology*, **32**, 633 (1967).
318. Hsu, W., J. W. Foft, and S. B. Weiss. *Proc. Nat. Acad. Sci.*, **58**, 2028 (1967).
319. Hudnik-Plevnik, T. A., and N. E. Melechen. *J. Biol. Chem.*, **242**, 4118 (1967).
320. Hung, P. P., and L. R. Overby. *Fed. Proc.*, **26**, 733 (1967).
321. Huppert, J., and L. Blum-Émerique. *Compt. Rend. Acad. Sci.*, **264**, 226 (1967).
321a. Hurwitz, J., *J. Biol. Chem.*, **234**, 2351 (1959).
321b. Hurwitz, J., A. Becker, M. L. Gefter, and M. Gold. *J. Cell Physiol.*, Supp. 1, **70**, 181 (1967).
322. Hutchinson, C. A., M. H. Edgell, and R. L. Sinsheimer. *J. Mol. Biol.*, **23**, 553 (1967).
323. Hutchinson, C. A., and R. L. Sinsheimer. *J. Mol. Biol.*, **7**, 206 (1963).
324. Ishihama, A., N. Mizuno, M. Takai, E. Otaka, and S. Osawa. *J. Mol. Biol.*, **5**, 251 (1962).
325. Israel, J. V., T. F. Anderson, and M. Levine. *Proc. Nat. Acad. Sci.*, **57**, 284 (1967).
326. Iwanowski, D. *Bull. Acad. Imp. Sci. Petrograd*, **3**, 67 (1892).
327. Jacob, F. *Science*, **152**, 1470 (1966).
328. Jacob, F., C. R. Fuerst, and E. L. Wollman. *Ann. Inst. Pasteur*, **93**, 724 (1957).
329. Jacob, F., and J. Monod. *J. Mol. Biol.*, **3**, 318 (1961).
330. ———. *Cold Spring Harbor Symp. Quant. Biol.*, **26**, 193 (1961).
331. Jacob, F., and E. L. Wollman. *Ann. Inst. Pasteur*, **90**, 282 (1956).
332. Jaenisch, R., P. H. Hofschneider, and A. Preuss. *J. Mol. Biol.*, **21**, 501 (1966).
333. Janion, C., and D. Shugar. *Acta Biochem. Polonica*, **12**, 337 (1965).
334. Jansz, H. S., and P. H. Pouwels. *Biochem. Biophys. Res. Commun.*, **18**, 589 (1965).
335. Jesaitis, M. *Nature*, **178**, 637 (1956).
336. ———. *J. Exp. Med.*, **106**, 233 (1957).
337. ———. *Bact. Proc.*, 45 (1959).
338. ———. *J. Gen. Physiol.*, **44**, 585 (1961).
339. ———. *J. Exp. Med.*, **121**, 133 (1965).
340. Jesaitis, M., and W. E. Goebel. *Cold Spring Harbor Symp. Quant. Biol.*, **18**, 205 (1953).
341. Jones, O. W., and P. Berg. *J. Mol. Biol.*, **22**, 199 (1966).
342. Jorgensen, S. E., and J. F. Koerner. *J. Biol. Chem.*, **241**, 3090 (1966).

343. Josse, J., and A. Kornberg. *J. Biol. Chem.*, **237**, 1968 (1967).
344. Kahan, F., E. Kahan, and B. Riddle. *Fed. Proc.*, **23**, 318 (1964).
345. Kaiser, A. D., and D. S. Hogness. *J. Mol. Biol.*, **2**, 392 (1960).
346. Kaiser, A. D. *J. Gen. Physiol.*, **49**, No. 6, Part 2, 171 (1966`.
347. Kallen, R. G., M. Simon, and J. Marmur. *J. Mol. Biol.*, **5**, 248 (1962).
348. Kammen, H. O. *Anal. Biochem.*, **17**, 553 (1966).
349. ———. *Biochim. Biophys. Acta*, **134**, 301 (1967).
350. Kammen, H. O., and M. Strand. *J. Biol. Chem.*, **242**, 1954 (1967).
351. Kaneko, I., and R. H. Doi. *Proc. Nat. Acad. Sci.*, **55**, 564 (1966).
352. Kano-Sueoka, T., and S. Spiegelman. *Proc. Nat. Acad. Sci.*, **48**, 1942 (1962).
353. Kano-Sueoka, T., and N. Sueoka. *J. Mol. Biol.*, **20**, 183 (1966).
354. Kára, J., and R. Weil. *Proc. Nat. Acad. Sci.*, **57**, 63 (1967).
355. Kasai, T., and E. K. F. Bautz. *Rutgers Symposium, Organizational Biosynthesis*, 1967, p. 111.
356. Katz, W., and W. Weidel. *Z. Naturforsch.*, **16b**, 363 (1961).
357. Kaye, A., and E. Winocour. *J. Mol. Biol.*, **24**, 475 (1967).
357a. Keck, K., H. R. Mahler, and D. Fraser. *Arch Biochem. Biophys.*, **86**, 85 (1960).
358. Keilin, D. *The History of Cell Respiration and Cytochromes*, Cambridge University Press, 1966.
359. Keir, H. M., R. H. Mathog, and C. E. Carter. *Biochemistry*, **3**, 1188 (1964).
360. Kellenberger, E., In *Phage and the Origins of Molecular Biology*, J. Cairns, G. S. Stent, and J. D. Watson (eds.), Cold Spring Harbor Laboratory of Quantitative Biology, 1966.
361. ———. In *Principles of Biomolecular Organization*, Ciba Foundation, p. 192, 1965.
361a. Kellenberger, E., F. A. Eiserling, and E. Boy de la Tour. *J. Ultrastructure Res.*, **21**, 335 (1968).
361b. Kellenberger, E. *Virology*, **34**, 549 (1968).
362. Kellenberger, E., J. Séchaud, and A. Ryter. *Virology*, **8**, 478 (1959).
363. Kellenberger, G., and E. Kellenberger. *Virology*, **3**, 275 (1957).
364. Kendrew, J. C. *Scientific American*, **216**, 141 (March 1967).
365. Kepes, A. *Biochim. Biophys. Acta*, **76**, 293 (1963).
366. Khesin, R. B. *International Congress of Microbiology, Moscow*, 15 (1966).
367. Khesin, R. B., and M. F. Shemiakin. *Biokhimiya*, **27**, 761 (1962).
368. Khesin, R. B., M. F. Shemyakin, I. A. Bass, O. B. Astaurova, S. G. Kamzolova, N. A. Kiseljev, and V. F. Manyakov. *Conference of Kurchatov's Institute of Atomic Energy, Moscow, June 1966.*

369. Khesin, R. B., M. F. Shemyakin, Zh. M. Gorlenko, S. L. Bogdanova, and T. P. Afanas'eva. *Biokhimiya,* **27,** 1092 (1962).

369a. Kihara, N. K., K. Furuse, and I. Watanabe. *Proc. Japan Acad.,* **43,** 773 (1967).

370. Kisliuk, R. L. *J. Biol. Chem.,* **227,** 805 (1957).

371. Kivity-Vogel, T., and D. Elson. *Biochim. Biophys. Acta,* **138,** 66 (1947).

372. Kleinschmidt, A. K., A. Burton, and R. L. Sinsheimer. *Science,* **142,** 961 (1963).

373. Kleinschmidt, A. K., D. Lang, D. Jacherts, and R. K. Zahn. *Biochim. Biophys. Acta,* **61,** 857 (1962).

374. Klimenko, S. M., T. I. Tikchonenko, and V. M. Andrev. *J. Mol. Biol.,* **23,** 523 (1967).

375. Knippers, R., and H. Hoffmann-Berling. *J. Mol. Biol.,* **21,** 281 (1966).

376. ———. *J. Mol. Biol.,* **21,** 293 (1966).

377. ———. *J. Mol. Biol.,* **21,** 305 (1966).

378. Knolle, P., and C. Weissmann. *4th Meeting European Biochemists, Oslo, July 1967,* Abstract 121.

379. Koch, G., and W. J. Dreyer. *Virology,* **6,** 291 (1958).

380. Koch, G., and A. D. Hershey. *J. Mol. Biol.,* **1,** 260 (1959).

381. Koerner, J. F., M. S. Smith, and J. M. Buchanan. *J. Am. Chem. Soc.,* **81,** 2594 (1959).

382. ———. *J. Biol. Chem.,* **235,** 2691 (1960).

383. Koerner, J. F., S. Varadarajan, and J. Buchanan. *J. Biol. Chem.,* **235,** 2691 (1960).

384. Kolakofsky, D., and T. Nakamoto. *Proc. Nat. Acad. Sci.,* **56,** 1786 (1966).

385. Koppel, H. C., R. H. Springer, R. K. Robins, and C. C. Cheng. *J. Org. Chem.,* **27,** 3614 (1962).

386. Korn, D. *J. Biol. Chem.,* **242,** 160 (1967).

387. Korn, D., and A. Weissbach. *J. Biol. Chem.,* **238,** 3390 (1963).

388. ———. *Virology,* **22,** 91 (1964).

389. Kornberg, A. *Enzymatic Synthesis of DNA,* New York, John Wiley and Sons, 1961.

390. Kornberg, A., S. B. Zimmerman, S. R. Kornberg, and J. Josse. *Proc. Nat. Acad. Sci.,* **45,** 772 (1959).

391. Kornberg, S. R., S. B. Zimmerman, and A. Kornberg. *J. Biol. Chem.,* **236,** 1487 (1961).

392. Kozinski, A. W. *Virology,* **13,** 124 (1961).

393. Kozinski, A. W., and M. J. Bessman. *J. Mol. Biol.,* **3,** 746 (1961).

393a. Kozinski, A. W., and Z. Z. Felgenhauer. *J. Virology,* **1,** 1193 (1967).

394. Kozinski, A. W., and P. B. Kozinski. *Proc. Nat. Acad. Sci.*, **57,** 1705 (1967).

395. Kozinski, A. W., P. B. Kozinski, and R. James. *J. Virology,* 1, 758 (1967).

396. Kozinski, A. W., P. B. Kozinski, and P. Shannon. *Proc. Nat. Acad. Sci.*, **50,** 746 (1963).

397. Kozinski, A. W., and Z. K. Lorkiewicz. *Proc. Nat. Acad. Sci.*, **58,** 2109 (1967).

398. Kozloff, L. M. *Cold Spring Harbor Symp. Quant. Biol.*, **18,** 209 (1953).

398a. Kozloff, L. M., *Ann. Rev. Biochem.*, **29,** 475 (1960).

399. Kozloff, L. M. In *Phage and the Origins of Molecular Biology*, J. Cairns, G. S. Stent, and J. D. Watson (eds.), Cold Spring Harbor Laboratory of Quantitative Biology, 1966.

399a. Kozloff, L. M., and M. Lute. *J. Mol. Biol.*, **12,** 780 (1965).

400. Kozloff, L. M., and F. W. Putnam. *J. Biol. Chem.*, **182,** 229 (1950).

401. Kravchenko, N. A. *Proc. Roy. Soc.*, **167B,** 429 (1967).

402. Kubinski, H., Z. Opara-Kubinska, and W. Szybalski. *J. Mol. Biol.*, **20,** 313 (1966).

403. Kunkee, R. E., and A. B. Pardee. *Biochim. Biophys. Acta,* **19,** 245 (1956).

404. Kuno, S., and I. R. Lehman. *J. Biol. Chem.*, **237,** 1266 (162).

405. Kutter, E. Personal communication.

406. Labaw, L. B. *J. Bact.*, **62,** 169 (1951).

407. Landy, A., J. Abelson, J. D. Smith, H. Goodman, and S. Brenner. *4th Meeting European Biochemists, Oslo, July 1967,* Abstract 117.

408. Langridge, R., and J. Marmur. *Science,* **143,** 1450 (1964).

409. Langridge, R., H. R. Wilson, C. W. Hooper, M. H. F. Wilkins, and L. D. Hamilton. *J. Mol. Biol.*, **2,** 19 (1960).

410. Lanni, F. *Perspectives Biol. Med.*, **3,** 418 (1960).

411. Lanni, Y. T. *Proc. Nat. Acad. Sci.*, **53,** 969 (1965).

412. Lanni, Y. T., F. Lanni, and M. J. Tevethia. *Science,* **152,** 208 (1966).

413. Lanning, M. C., and S. S. Cohen. *J. Biol. Chem.*, **207,** 193 (1954).

414. ———. *J. Biol. Chem.*, **216,** 413 (1955).

415. Lark, K. G. *Bact. Rev.*, **30,** 3 (1966).

416. Larsson, A., and P. Reichard. *Biochim. Biophys. Acta,* **113,** 407 (1966).

417. ———. *J. Biol. Chem.*, **241,** 2533, 2540 (1966).

418. Lauffer, M. A. *Biochemistry,* **5,** 2440 (1966).

419. Lauffer, M. A., and W. M. Stanley. *Chem. Rev.*, **24,** 303 (1939).

420. Lawley, P. D. *J. Mol. Biol.*, **24**, 75 (1967).
421. Ledinko, N. *J. Mol. Biol.*, **9**, 834 (1964).
422. Lee-Huang, S., and L. Cavalieri. *Science*, **148**, 1474 (1965).
423. Lehman, I. R. *J. Biol. Chem.*, **235**, 1479 (1960).
424. Lehman, I. R., and E. A. Pratt. *J. Biol. Chem.*, **235**, 3254 (1960).
425. Lehman, I. R., G. G. Roussos, and E. A. Pratt. *J. Biol. Chem.*, **237**, 819 (1962).
426. ———. *J. Biol. Chem.*, **237**, 829 (1962).
427. Leive, L. *Biochem. Biophys. Res. Commun.*, **18**, 13 (1965).
428. Leng, M., and G. Felsenfeld. *Proc. Nat. Acad. Sci.*, **56**, 1325 (1966).
429. Lesley, S. M., R. C. French, A. F. Graham, and C. E. Van Rooyen. *Can. J. Med. Sci.*, **29**, 128 (1951).
430. Levin, A. P., and K. Burton. *J. Gen. Microbiol.*, **25**, 307 (1961).
431. Levine, L., J. L. Barlow, and H. Van Vunakis. *Virology*, **6**, 702 (1958).
432. Levine, L., W. T. Murakami, H. Van Vunakis, and L. Grossman. *Proc. Nat. Acad. Sci.*, **46**, 1038 (1960).
433. Levinthal, C., and H. Fisher. *Biochim. Biophys. Acta*, **9**, 597 (1952).
434. Levinthal, C., J. Hosoda, and D. Shub. *Molecular Biology of the Viruses, Symposium at Edmonton, Canada*, New York, Academic Press, 1967, p. 71.
435. Levinthal, C., and C. A. Thomas, Jr. *Biochim. Biophys. Acta*, **23**, 453 (1957).
436. Levisohn, R. *Genetics*, **55**, 345 (1967).
437. Lewin, L. L. *Proc. Soc. Exp. Biol. Med.*, **124**, 39 (1967).
438. Lezius, A. G., S. Hennig, C. Menzel, and E. Metz. *4th Meeting European Biochemists, Oslo, July 1967*, Abstract 10.
439. Libonati, M., E. Vinuela, and C. Weissmann. *4th Meeting European Biochemists, Oslo, July 1967*, Abstract 576.
440. Lichtenstein, J., H. D. Barner, and S. S. Cohen. *J. Biol. Chem.*, **235**, 457 (1960).
441. Lichtenstein, J., and S. S. Cohen. *J. Biol. Chem.*, **235**, 1134 (1960).
442. Lieberman, I., A. Kornberg, and E. S. Simms. *J. Biol. Chem.*, **215**, 403 (1955).
443. Lim, R., and S. S. Cohen. *J. Biol. Chem.*, **241**, 4304 (1966).
443a. Lindqvist, B., and R. L. Sinsheimer, *J. Mol. Biol.*, **28**, 87 (1967).
444. Lindqvist, B., and R. L. Sinsheimer. *J. Mol. Biol.*, **30**, 69 (1967).
445. ———. *Fed. Proc.*, **26**, 449 (1967).
446. Lipsett, M. N. *Cold Spring Harbor Symp. Quant. Biol.*, **31**, 449 (1966).
447. Lipsett, M. N., J. S. Norton, and A. Peterkofsky. *Biochemistry*, **6**, 855 (1967).

448. ———. *Proc. Nat. Acad. Sci.*, **55**, 1169 (1966).
449. Liquori, A. M., L. Constantinos, V. Crescenzi, V. Elia, E. Giglio, R. Puliti, M. DeSantis Savino, and V. Vitagliano. *J. Mol. Biol.*, **24**, 113 (1967).
450. Little, J. W. *J. Biol. Chem.*, **242**, 679 (1967).
451. Little, J. W., I. R. Lehman, and A. D. Kaiser. *J. Biol. Chem.*, **242**, 672 (1967).
452. Loeb, M. R., and S. S. Cohen. *J. Biol. Chem.*, **234**, 360 (1959).
453. ———. *J. Biol. Chem.*, **234**, 364 (1959).
454. Loeb, T. *Science*, **131**, 932 (1960).
455. Loeffler, F., and P. Frosch. *Zent. Bakter.* I, Orig. 23, 371 (1896).
456. Lozeron, H. A., and W. Szybalski, *Biochem. Biophys. Res. Commun.*, **23**, 612 (1966).
457. ———. *J. Mol. Biol.*, **30**, 277 (1967).
458. Lunt, M. R., and K. Burton. *Biochim. Biophys. Acta*, **55**, 1005 (1962).
459. Lunt, M. R., and E. A. Newton. *Biochem. J.*, **95**, 717 (1965).
460. Lunt, M. R., J. C. Siebke, and K. Burton. *Biochem. J.*, **92**, 27 (1964).
461. Luria, S. E. *Proc. Nat. Acad. Sci.*, **33**, 253 (1947).
462. ———. *Biochem. Biophys. Res. Commun.*, **18**, 735 (1965).
463. Luria, S. E., and J. E. Darnell, Jr. *General Virology*, 2nd edition, John Wiley and Sons, 1967.
464. Luria, S. E., M. Delbrück, and T. F. Anderson. *J. Bact.*, **46**, 57 (1943).
465. Luria, S. E., and M. L. Human. *J. Bact.*, **59**, 551 (1950).
466. ———. *J. Bact.*, **64**, 557 (1952).
467. Luzzatti, D. *J. Bact.*, **92**, 1435 (1966).
468. Maalöe, O., and G. Stent. *Acta Path. Microbiol. Scand.*, **30**, 149 (1952).
469. Maalöe, O., and N. Symonds. *J. Bact.*, **65**, 177 (192).
470. Maass, D., and W. Weidel. *Biochim. Biophys. Acta*, **78**, 369 (1963).
471. MacHattie, L. A., D. A. Ritchie, C. A. Thomas, Jr., and C. C. Richardson. *J. Mol. Biol.*, **23**, 355 (1967).
472. Mackal, R. P., B. Werninghaus, and E. A. Evans, Jr. *Proc. Nat. Acad. Sci.*, **51**, 1172 (1964).
473. Maestre, M. F., and I. Tinoco, Jr. *J. Mol. Biol.*, **12**, 287 (1965).
474. ———. *J. Mol. Biol.*, **23**, 323 (1967).
475. Magee, W. E. *Virology*, **17**, 604 (1962).
476. Magee, W. E., and O. V. Miller. *Virology*, **31**, 64 (1967).
477. Mahler, H. R., and M. B. Baylor. *Proc. Nat. Acad. Sci.*, **58**, 256 (1967).

478. Maitra, U., and J. Hurwitz. *Proc. Nat. Acad. Sci.*, **54**, 815 (1965).
479. Maley, G. F., D. U. Guarino, and F. Maley. *J. Biol. Chem.*, **242**, 3517 (1967).
480. Maley, G. F., and F. Maley. *J. Biol. Chem.*, **237**, PC 3311 (1962).
481. ———. *J. Biol. Chem.*, **241**, 2176 (1966).
482. Markert, A., and W. Zillig. *Virology*, **25**, 88 (1965).
483. Markham, R., S. Frey, and G. Hills. *Virology*, **20**, 88 (1963).
483a. Marmur, J. Personal communication.
484. Marmur, J., and C. M. Greenspan. *Science*, **142**, 387 (1963).
485. Marmur, J., C. M. Greenspan, E. Palacek, F. M. Kahan, J. Levine, and M. Mandel. *Cold Spring Harbor Symp. Quant. Biol.*, **28**, 191 (1963).
486. Marshak, A. *Proc. Nat. Acad. Sci.*, **37**, 299 (1951).
487. Marshak, A., and H. J. Vogel. *J. Biol. Chem.*, **189**, 597 (1951).
488. Marvin, D. A. *J. Mol. Biol.*, **15**, 8 (1966).
489. Marvin, D. A., and H. Hoffmann-Berling. *Z. Naturforsch.*, **18b**, 884 (1963).
490. Marvin, D. A., and H. Schaller. *J. Mol. Biol.*, **15**, 1 (1966).
491. Masamune, Y., K. Hori, and Y. Takagi. *J. Biochemistry (Tokyo)*, **56**, 92 (1964).
492. Mathews, C. K. *J. Bact.*, **90**, 648 (1965).
493. ———. *J. Biol. Chem.*, **241**, 5008 (1966).
494. ———. *J. Biol. Chem.*, **242**, 4083 (1967).
495. ———. *J. Virology*, 1, 963 (1967).
496. ———. Personal communication.
497. Mathews, C. K., F. Brown, and S. S. Cohen. *J. Biol. Chem.*, **239**, 2957 (1964).
498. Mathews, C. K., and S. S. Cohen. *J. Biol. Chem.*, **238**, 367 (1963).
499. ———. *J. Biol. Chem.*, **238**, PC 853 (1963).
500. Mathews, C. K., and R. H. Kessin. *J. Virology*, 1, 92 (1967).
501. Mathews, C. K., and K. E. Sutherland. *J. Biol. Chem.*, **240**, 2142 (1965).
501a. Matsubara, K., K. Shimada, and Y. Takagi. *J. Mol. Biol.*, **29**, 297 (1967).
502. Matsubara, K., M. Takai, and Y. Takagi. *Biochem. Biophys. Res. Commun.*, **11**, 372 (1963).
503. Matsubara, K., A. Taketo, and Y. Takagi. *J. Biochemistry (Tokyo)*, **54**, 225 (1962).
504. Mazaitis, A. J., and E. K. F. Bautz. *Proc. Nat. Acad. Sci.*, **57**, 1633 (1967).

505. McAuslan, B. R., and W. K. Joklik. *Biochem. Biophys. Res. Commun.*, **8**, 486 (1962).

506. McClain, W. H., and S. P. Champe. *Proc. Nat. Acad. Sci.*, **58**, 1182 (1967).

507. McCorquodale, D. J. *Fed. Proc.*, **25**, 651 (1966).

508. Melechen, N. E., and P. D. Skaar. *Virology*, **16**, 21 (1962).

509. Mennigmann, H. D. *J. Gen. Microbiol.*, **41**, 151 (1965).

510. Miller, C. S. *J. Am. Chem. Soc.*, **77**, 752 (1955).

511. Minagawa, T. *Virology*, **13**, 515 (1961).

512. Miovic, M. L., and L. I. Pizer. *Fed. Proc.*, **27**, 802 (1968).

513. Mitra, S., P. Reichard, R. B. Inman, L. L. Bertsch, and A. Kornberg. *J. Mol. Biol.*, **24**, 429 (1967).

513a. Mittleman, A., R. H. Hall, and J. T. Grace. *Cancer Res.*, **27**, 1409 (1967).

514. Mokulskaya, T. D., J. M. Gorlenko, L. A. Zamchuck, E. S. Bogdanova, M. A. Mokulsky, D. M. Goldfarb, and R. B. Khesin. *Folia Microbiologica*, **12**, 107 (1967).

515. Monod, J., and E. Wollman. *Ann. Inst. Pasteur*, **73**, 937 (1947).

516. Moody, M. F. *Virology*, **26**, 567 (1965).

517. Moore, E., and S. S. Cohen. *Biochem. Biophys. Res. Commun.*, **25**, 501 (1966).

518. Morris. D. W., and N. O. Kjeldgaard. *4th Meeting European Biochemists, Oslo, July 1967*, Abstract 161.

519. Mosig, G. *Proc. Nat. Acad. Sci.*, **56**, 1177 (1966).

520. Mosig, G., and H. R. Revel. *Virology*, **31**, 397 (1967).

520a. Mukai, F., G. Streisinger, and B. Miller. *Virology*, **33**, 398 (1967).

521. Murakami, W. T., H. Van Vunakis, L. Grossman, and L. Levine. *Virology*, **14**, 190 (1961).

522. Murakami, W. T., H. Van Vunakis, H. I. Lehrer, and L. Levine. *J. Immunol.*, **89**, 116 (1962).

523. Murakami, W. T., H. Van Vunakis, and L. Levine. *Virology*, **9**, 624 (1959).

524. Murata, K., and T. Miyamoto. *J. Vitaminology*, **10**, 237 (1964).

525. Nakata, A., and F. W. Stahl. *Genetics*, **55**, 585 (1967).

526. Naono, S., J. Ronvière, and F. Gros. *Biochim. Biophys. Acta*, **129**, 271 (1966).

527. Nathans, D., G. Notani, J. H. Schwartz, and N. D. Zinder. *Proc. Nat. Acad. Sci.*, **48**, 1424 (1962).

528. Neidhardt, F. C. *Bact. Rev.*, **30**, 701 (1966).

529. Neidhardt, F. C., and C. F. Earhart. *Cold Spring Harbor Symp. Quant. Biol.*, **31**, 557 (1966).

530. Newell, P. C., and R. G. Tucker. *Biochem. J.*, **100**, 512, 517 (1966).

531. ———. *Nature*, **215**, 1384 (1967).

532. Nierlich, D. *Proc. Am. Soc. Microbiol.*, Los Angeles, May 1966.
533. Nishihara, M., A. Chrambach, and N. V. Aposhian. *Biochemistry*, 6, 1877 (1967).
534. Nomura, M., B. D. Hall, and S. Spiegelman. *J. Mol. Biol.*, 2, 306 (1960).
535. Nomura, M., K. Matsubara, K. Okamoto, and R. Fujimura. *J. Mol. Biol.*, 5, 535 (1962).
536. Nomura, M., K. Okamoto, and K. Asano. *J. Mol. Biol.*, 4, 376 (1962).
537. Nomura, M., C. Witten, N. Mantei, and H. Echols. *J. Mol. Biol.*, 17, 273 (1966).
538. Northrop, J. H. *J. Gen. Physiol.*, 34, 715 (1951).
539. Northrop, J. H., M. Kunitz, and R. M. Herriott. *Crystalline Enzymes*, New York, Columbia University Press, 1948, p. 299.
540. Novogrodsky, A., and J. Hurwitz. *Fed. Proc.*, 24, 602 (1965).
541. ———. *J. Biol. Chem.*, 241, 2923 (1966).
542. Novogrodsky, A., M. Gefter, U. Maitra, M. Gold, and J. Hurwitz. *J. Biol. Chem.*, 241, 1977 (1966).
543. Novogrodsky, A., M. Tal, A. Traub, and J. Hurwitz. *J. Biol. Chem.*, 241, 2933 (1966).
544. Nygaard, A. P., and B. D. Hall. *J. Mol. Biol.*, 9, 125 (1964).
545. Oeschger, M. P., and M. J. Bessman. *J. Biol. Chem.*, 241, 5452 (1966).
546. Oeschger, M. P., and D. Nathans. *J. Mol. Biol.*, 22, 235 (1966).
547. Ogawa, H., and J. Tomizawa. *J. Mol. Biol.*, 23, 265 (1967).
548. Okada, Y., E. Terzaghi, G. Streisinger, J. Emrich, M. Inouye, and A. Tsugita. *Proc. Nat. Acad. Sci.*, 56, 1692 (1966).
549. Okamoto, K., Y. Sugino, and M. Nomura. *J. Mol. Biol.*, 5, 527 (1962).
549a. Okazaki, R., and A. Kornberg. *J. Biol. Chem.*, 239, 269 (1964).
550. Okubo, S., B. Strauss, and M. Stodolsky. *Virology*, 24, 532 (1964).
551. Oleson, A. E. *Fed. Proc.*, 25, 275 (1966).
552. Oleson, A. E., and J. F. Koerner. *J. Biol. Chem.*, 239, 2935 (1964).
553. Oleson, A. E., and I. R. Lehman. *Proc. Nat. Acad. Sci.*, 57, 1426 (1967).
554. Olivera, B. M., and I. R. Lehman. *Proc. Nat. Acad. Sci.*, 57, 1700 (1967).
555. Orias, E., and T. K. Gartner. *J. Bact.*, 91, 2210 (1966).
556. Orengo, A., and T. T. Tchen. *Biochem. Biophys. Res. Commun.*, 6, 261 (1961).
557. Orr, C. W. M., S. T. Herriott, and M. J. Bessman. *J. Biol. Chem.*, 240, 4652 (1965).

558. Ortiz, P. J., J. T. August, M. Watanabe, A. M. Kaye, and J. Hurwitz. *J. Biol. Chem.*, **240**, 423 (1965).

559. Osawa, T., and Y. Nakazawa. *Biochim. Biophys. Acta*, **130**, 56 (1966).

560. Osawa, S., and I. Watanabe. *Biochem. Biophys. Res. Commun.*, **6**, 427 (1961).

561. Pardee, A. B., and L. S. Prestidge. *Biochim. Biophys. Acta*, **37**, 544 (1959).

562. Pardee, A. B., and I. Williams. *Arch. Biochem. Biophys.*, **40**, 222 (1952).

563. ———. *Ann. Inst. Pasteur*, **84**, 147 (1953).

564. Park, B. H. *Virology*, **2**, 711 (1956).

565. Pene, J., and J. Marmur. *J. Virology*, **1**, 86 (1967).

566. Pfefferkorn, E., and H. Amos. *Virology*, **6**, 299 (1958).

567. Pfeiffer, D. Z. *Vererbungslehre*, **92**, 317 (1961).

568. Piechowski, M. M., and M. Susman. *Virology*, **28**, 386 (1966).

569. ———. *Virology*, **28**, 396 (1966).

570. Pitts, J. D., and R. L. Sinsheimer. *J. Mol. Biol.*, **15**, 676 (1966).

571. Pizer, L. I. Personal communication.

572. Pizer, L. I., and S. S. Cohen. *J. Biol. Chem.*, **235**, 2387 (1960).

573. ———. *Biochim. Biophys. Acta*, **53**, 509 (1961).

574. ———. *J. Biol. Chem.*, **237**, 1251 (1962).

575. ———. *Methods in Enzymology*, Vol. 6, S. P. Colowick and N. O. Kaplan (eds.), New York, Academic Press, 1963, p. 131.

576. Poglazov, B. F., S. N. Borhsenius, and E. M. Belavtseva. *Virology*, **25**, 650 (1965).

577. Poglazov, B. F., and V. V. Mesyanzhinov. *Virology*, **31**, 449 (1967).

578. Pratt, D., H. Tzagoloff, and W. S. Erdahl. *Virology*, **30**, 397 (1966).

579. ———. *Virology*, **30**, 397 (1966).

580. Pratt, D., H. Tzagoloff, W. S. Erdahl, and T. J. Henry. *Molecular Biology of the Viruses, Symposium at Edmonton, Canada*, New York, Academic Press, 1967, p. 219.

581. Pratt, E. A., S. Kuno, and I. R. Lehman. *Biochim. Biophys. Acta*, **68**, 108 (1963).

581a. Price, A. R., and H. R. Warner. *Fed. Proc.*, **27**, 592 (1968).

582. Pricer, W. E., Jr., and A. Weissbach. *J. Biol. Chem.*, **242**, 1701 (1967).

583. Primosigh, J., H. Pelzer, D. Maass, and W. Weidel. *Biochim. Biophys. Acta*, **46**, 68 (1961).

584. Pritikin, W. B., and W. R. Romig. *J. Bact.*, **92**, 291 (1966).

585. Protass, J. J., and D. Korn. *Proc. Nat. Acad. Sci.*, **55**, 832 (1966).

586. ———. *Proc. Nat. Acad. Sci.*, **55**, 1089 (1966).

587. Prystaš, M., and F. Šorm. *Coll. Czech. Chem. Commun.*, **31**, 1053 (1966).

588. Ptashne, M. *Proc. Nat. Acad. Sci.*, **57**, 306 (1967).

589. ———. *Nature*, **214**, 232 (1967).

589a. Puck, T. T., and H. H. Lee. *J. Exp. Med.*, **101**, 151 (1955).

590. Putnam, F. W., D. Miller, L. Palm, and E. A. Evans, Jr. *J. Biol. Chem.*, **199**, 177 (1952).

591. Radding, C. M., and D. C. Schreffler. *J. Mol. Biol.*, **18**, 251 (1966).

592. Radding, C. M., J. Szpirer, and R. Thomas. *Proc. Nat. Acad. Sci.*, **57**, 277 (1967).

593. Raff, R. N., and S. S. Cohen. *J. Bact.*, **60**, 69 (1950).

594. Raina, A., and S. S. Cohen. *Proc. Nat. Acad. Sci.*, **55**, 1587 (1966).

595. Ray, D. S., H. Bscheider, and P. H. Hofschneider. *J. Mol. Biol.*, **21**, 473 (1966).

596. Ray, D. S., A. Preuss, and P. H. Hofschneider. *J. Mol. Biol.*, **21**, 485 (1966).

597. Regueiro, B., R. Amelunxen, and S. Grisolia. *Biochemistry*, **1**, 553 (1962).

598. Reichard, P., A. Baldesten, and L. Rutberg. *J. Biol. Chem.*, **236**, 1150 (1961).

599. Reichard, P., Z. M. Canellakis, and E. S. Cannellakis. *Biochim. Biophys. Acta*, **41**, 558 (1960).

600. Reichard, P., and L. Rutberg. *Biochim. Biophys. Acta*, **37**, 554 (1960).

601. Reiter, H. *Virology*, **21**, 636 (1963).

602. Revel, H. R. *Virology*, **31**, 688 (1967).

603. Revel, M., and F. Gros. *Biochem. Biophys. Res. Commun.*, **27**, 12 (1967).

604. Revel, H. R., S. Hattman, and S. E. Luria. *Biochem. Biophys. Res. Commun.*, **18**, 545 (1965).

605. Richardson, C. C. *Proc. Nat. Acad. Sci.*, **54**, 158 (1965).

606. ———. *J. Biol. Chem.*, **241**, 2084 (1966).

607. ———. *J. Mol. Biol.*, **15**, 49 (1966).

608. Richardson, C. C., C. L. Schildkraut, and A. Kornberg. *Cold Spring Harbor Symp. Quant. Biol.*, **28**, 9 (1963).

609. Ritchie, D., C. A. Thomas, Jr., L. MacHattie, and P. Wensink. *J. Mol. Biol.*, **23**, 365 (1967).

610. Roepke, R. R. *J. Bact.*, **93**, 1188 (1967).

611. Roepke, R. R., and F. E. Mercer. *J. Bact.*, **54**, 731 (1947).

612. Roscoe, D. H., and R. G. Tucker. *Biochem. Biophys. Res. Commun.*, **16**, 106 (1964).

613. ———. *Virology*, **29**, 157 (1966).

614. Rose, I. A., and B. S. Schweigert. *J. Biol. Chem.*, **202**, 635 (1953).
615. Roth, T. F., and M. Hayashi. *Science*, **154**, 658 (1966).
616. Royaumont Symposium. *Ann. Inst. Pasteur*, **84**, 1–318 (1953).
616a. Rueckert, R. R., and W. Zillig. *J. Mol. Biol.*, **5**, 1 (1962).
617. Rüst, P., and R. L. Sinsheimer. *J. Mol. Biol.*, **23**, 545 (1967).
618. Rutberg, B., and L. Rutberg. *J. Bact.*, **90**, 891 (1965).
619. ———. *J. Bact.*, **91**, 76 (1966).
620. ———. *Virology*, **22**, 280 (1964).
621. Rutten, F. J., K. C. Winkler, and P. G. DeHaan. *Brit. J. Exp. Path.*, **31**, 369 (1950).
622. Sagik, B. P., M. H. Green, M. Hayashi, and S. Spiegelman. *Biophysical J.*, **2**, 409 (1962).
623. Salas, M., M. B. Hille, J. A. Last, A. J. Wahba, and S. Ochoa. *Proc. Nat. Acad. Sci.*, **57**, 387 (1967).
624. Salivar, W. O., T. J. Henry, and D. Pratt. *Virology*, **32**, 41 (1967).
625. Salivar, W. O., H. Tzagoloff, and D. Pratt. *Virology*, **24**, 359 (1964).
626. Salser, W., R. F. Gesteland, and A. Bolle. *Nature*, **215**, 588 (1967).
627. Salzman, L. A., and A. Weissbach. *Virology*, **31**, 70 (1967).
628. Sambrook, J. F., D. P. Fan, and S. Brenner. *Nature*, **214**, 452 (1967).
629. Sarabhai, A. S., A. O. W. Stretton, S. Brenner, and A. Bolle. *Nature*, **201**, 13 (1964).
630. Sarkar, S., N. Sarkar, and L. M. Kozloff. *Biochemistry*, **3**, 517 (1964).
631. Scarano, E. *Biochim. Biophys. Acta*, **29**, 459 (1958).
632. ———. *J. Biol. Chem.*, **235**, 706 (1960).
633. ———. *J. Biol. Chem.*, **235**, 3556 (1960).
634. Scarano, E., G. Geraci, A. Polzella, and E. Campanile. *J. Biol. Chem.*, **238**, PC 1556 (1963).
635. Scarano, E., G. Geraci, and M. Rossi. *Biochemistry*, **6**, 192 (1967).
636. Scheiner, J. M., E. Kostelak, and R. Duschinsky. *Fed. Proc.*, **16**, 242 (1957).
637. Schildkraut, C. L., J. Marmur, and P. Doty. *J. Mol. Biol.*, **4**, 430 (1962).
638. Schildkraut, C. L., K. L. Wierzchowski, J. Marmur, D. M. Green, and P. Doty. *Virology*, **18**, 43 (1962).
639. Schlesinger, M. *Nature*, **138**, 508 (1936).
640. Scott, D. B. M. *Biochem. J.*, **63**, 587 (1956).
641. Seaman, E., E. Tarmy, and J. Marmur. *Biochemistry*, **3**, 607 (1964).

642. Séchaud, J., and G. Streisinger. *Virology*, **17**, 387 (1962).

643. Sekiguchi, M. *J. Mol. Biol.*, **16**, 503 (1966).

644. Sekiguchi, M., and S. S. Cohen. *J. Biol. Chem.*, **238**, 349 (1963).

645. ———. *J. Mol. Biol.*, **8**, 638 (1964).

646. Sellin, H. G., P. R. Srinivasan, and E. Borek. *J. Mol. Biol.*, **19**, 219 (1966).

647. Sercarz, E. *Virology*, **28**, 339 (1966).

648. Sertic, V. *Comp. Rend. Soc. Biol.*, **100**, 477 (1929).

649. Shalitin, C. *J. Virology*, **1**, 569 (1967).

650. Shalitin, C., and R. Ben-Ishai. *Proc. Israel J. Chem.*, **4**, 61p (1966).

651. Shalitin, C., and E. Katchalski. *Arch. Biochem. Biophys.*, **99**, 508 (1962).

652. Shalitin, C., and S. Sarid. *J. Virology*, **1** (June 1967).

653. Shapiro, D. M., and J. Eigner. *Fed. Proc.*, **23**, 271 (1964).

654. Sharon, N. *Proc. Roy. Soc.*, **167B**, 402 (1967).

655. Shedlovsky, A., and S. Brenner. *Proc. Nat. Acad. Sci.*, **50**, 300 (1963).

656. Sheid, B., P. R. Srinivasan, and E. Borek. *Biochemistry*, **7**, 280 (1968).

657. Shemiakin, M. F., and R. B. Khesin, *Doklady Akad. Nauk. SSSR*, **145**, 937 (1962).

658. Shen, S. R., and R. R. Schmidt. *Arch. Biochem. Biophys.*, **115**, 13 (1966).

659. Shen, An-Ya, J. Eisenstadt, and P. Lengyel. *Proc. Nat. Acad. Sci.*, **56**, 1599 (1966).

660. Short, E. C., and J. F. Koerner. *Proc. Nat. Acad. Sci.*, **54**, 595 (1965).

661. Shuster, R. C., T. R. Breitman, and A. Weissbach. *J. Biol. Chem.*, **242**, 3723 (1967).

662. Sicard, N., and R. Devoret. *Compt. Rend. Acad. Sci.*, **255**, 1417 (1962).

663. Sicard, N., G. Simonnet, and L. Astrachan. *Biochem. Biophys. Res. Commun.*, **26**, 532 (1967).

664. Siegel, A., M. Zaitlin, O. P. Sehgal. *Proc. Nat. Acad. Sci.*, **48**, 1845 (1962).

665. Siegel, J. E. D., and M. Hayashi. *J. Mol. Biol.*, **27**, 443 (1967).

665a. Silver, S. *J. Mol. Biol.*, **29**, 191 (1967).

666. Simon, E. H., and I. Tessman. *Proc. Nat. Acad. Sci.*, **50**, 526 (1963).

667. Simon, L. D., and T. F. Anderson. *Virology*, **32**, 279 (1967).

668. Sinsheimer, R. L. *Science*, **120**, 551 (1954).

669. ———. *Proc. Nat. Acad. Sci.*, **42**, 502 (1956).

670. ———. *J. Mol. Biol.*, **1**, 37 (1959).

671. Sinsheimer, R. L., C. A. Hutchinson, and B. H. Lindqvist. *Molecular Biology of the Viruses, Symposium at Edmonton, Canada,* New York, Academic Press, 1967, p. 175.

672. Sinsheimer, R. L., M. Lawrence, and C. Nagler. *J. Mol. Biol.,* **14,** 348 (1965).

673. Sinsheimer, R. L., B. Starman, C. Nagler, and S. Guthrie. *J. Mol. Biol.,* **4,** 42 (1962).

674. Skalka, A. *Proc. Nat. Acad. Sci.,* **55,** 1190 (1966).

675. Skalka, A., B. Butler, and H. Echols. *Proc. Nat. Acad. Sci.,* **58,** 576 (1967).

676. Sköld, O., and J. M. Buchanan. *Proc. Nat. Acad. Sci.,* **51,** 553 (1964).

677. Slavik, K., and S. F. Zakrzewski. *Mol. Pharmacol.,* **3,** 370 (1967).

678. Smith, J. D. *4th Meeting European Biochemists, Oslo, July 1967,* Symposium Paper.

679. Smith, J. D., J. N. Abelson, B. F. C. Clark, H. M. Goodman, and S. Brenner, *Cold Spring Harbor Symp. Quant. Biol.,* **31,** 479 (1966).

680. Smith, J. D., and G. R. Wyatt. *Biochem. J.,* **49,** 144 (1951).

681. Smith, M., and G. R. Greenberg. *Fed. Proc.,* **23,** 271 (1964).

682. Smith Lomax, M., and G. R. Greenberg. *J. Biol. Chem.,* **242,** 109 (1967).

683. ———. *J. Biol. Chem.,* **242,** 1307 (1967).

683a. Snyder, L., and E. P. Geiduschek. *Proc. Nat. Acad. Sci.,* **59,** 459 (1968).

684. Somerville, R., K. Ebisuzaki, and G. R. Greenberg. *Proc. Nat. Acad. Sci.,* **45,** 1240 (1959).

685. Spahr, P. F., and R. F. Gesteland. *4th Meeting European Biochemists, Oslo, July 1967,* Abstract 297.

686. Spahr, P. F., and D. Schlessinger. *J. Biol. Chem.,* **238,** PC 2251 (1963).

687. Speyer, J. F. *Biochem. Biophys. Res. Commun.,* **21,** 6 (1965).

688. Spiegelman, S. *Informational Macromolecules,* H. J. Vogel, V. Bryson, and J. O. Lampen (eds.), New York, Academic Press, 1963, p. 27

689. Stacey, K. A. *Brit. Med. Bull.,* **21,** 211 (1965).

690. Stahl, F. W., N. E. Murray, A. Nakata, and J. M. Crasemann. *Genetics,* **54,** 223 (1966).

691. Stanley, W. M. *Science,* **81,** 644 (1935).

692. Stanley, W. M., and T. F. Anderson. *J. Biol. Chem.,* **139,** 325 (1941).

693. Stent, G. S. *Molecular Biology of Bacterial Viruses,* San Francisco, W. H. Freeman and Co., 1963.

694. ———. *Proc. Roy. Soc.,* **164B,** 181 (1966).

695. Stent, G. S., and S. Brenner. *Proc. Nat. Acad. Sci.,* **47,** 2005 (1961).

696. Stent, G. S., and N. K. Jerne. *Proc. Nat. Acad. Sci.,* **41,** 704 (1955).

697. Stern, J. L., H. D. Barner, and S. S. Cohen. *J. Mol. Biol.,* **17,** 188 (1966).

698. Stern, J. L., and S. S. Cohen. *Proc. Nat. Acad. Sci.,* **51,** 859 (1964).

699. Stern, J. L., M. Sekiguchi, H. D. Barner, and S. S. Cohen. *J. Mol. Biol.,* **8,** 629 (1964).

700. Stewart, C. D., and M. J. Bessman. *Fed. Proc.,* **26,** 396 (1967).

701. Stollar, D., L. Levine, H. I. Lehrer, and H. Van Vunakis. *Proc. Nat. Acad. Sci.,* **48,** 874 (1962).

702. Stollar, D., L. Levine, and J. Marmur. *Biochim. Biophys. Acta,* **61,** 7 (1962).

703. Stone, A. B. *Biochem. Biophys. Res. Commun.,* **26,** 247 (1967).

704. Stone, A. B., and K. Burton. *Biochem. J.,* **85,** 600 (1962).

705. Streisinger, G. *Nat. Canc. Inst. Monograph,* **18,** 1 (1965).

706. Streisinger, G., R. S. Edgar, and G. H. Denhardt. *Proc. Nat. Acad. Sci.,* **51,** 775 (1964).

706a. Streisinger, G., J. Emrich, Y. Okada, A. Tsugita, and M. Inouye. *J. Mol. Biol.,* **31,** 607 (1968).

707. Streisinger, G., S. Emrich, and M. M. Stahl. *Proc. Nat. Acad. Sci.,* **57,** 292 (1967).

708. Streisinger, G., F. Mukai, W. J. Dreyer, B. Miller, and S. Horiuchi. *Cold Spring Harbor Symp. Quant. Biol.,* **26,** 25 (1961).

709. Streisinger, G., Y. Okada, J. Emrich, J. Newton, A. Tsugita, E. Terzaghi, and M. Inouye. *Cold Spring Harbor Symp. Quant. Biol.,* **31,** 77 (1966).

710. Streisinger, G., and J. Weigle. *Proc. Nat. Acad. Sci.,* **42,** 504 (1956).

711. Strominger, J. L., and J. M. Ghuysen. *Science,* **156,** 213 (1967).

712. Stryer, L., A. Holmgren, and P. Reichard. *Biochemistry,* **6,** 1016 (1967).

713. Subak-Sharpe, H., and I. Hay. *J. Mol. Biol.,* **12,** 924 (1965).

714. Subak-Sharpe, H., R. Burk, L. Crawford, J. Morrison, I. Hay, and H. Keir. *Cold Spring Harbor Symp. Quant. Biol.,* **31,** 737 (1966).

715. Subak-Sharpe, H., and I. Hay. *J. Mol. Biol.,* **12,** 924 (1965).

716. Subak-Sharpe, H., W. I. H. Shedden, D. H. Watson, and P. Wildy. *Virology,* **30,** 154 (1966).

717. Subak-Sharpe, H., and W. M. Shepherd. *4th Meeting European Biochemists, Oslo, July 1967,* Abstract 205.
718. Subbaiah, T. V., C. D. Goldthwaite, and J. Marmur. In *Evolving Genes and Proteins,* V. Bryson and H. J. Vogel (eds.), New York, Academic Press, 1965, p. 435.
719. Sueoka, N., and T. Kano-Sueoka. *Proc. Nat. Acad. Sci.,* **52,** 1535 (1964).
720. Sueoka, N., T. Kano-Sueoka, and W. J. Gartland. *Cold Spring Harbor Symp. Quant. Biol.,* **31,** 571 (1966).
720a. Summers, W. C., and W. Szybalski. *Virology,* **34,** 9 (1968).
721. Sugiyama, T., and D. Nakada. *Proc. Nat. Acad. Sci.,* **57,** 1744 (1967).
722. Susman, M., and M. M. Piechowski. *Virology,* **26,** 163 (1965).
723. Sutherland, I. W. *Biochem. J.,* **104,** 278 (1967).
724. Sutherland, I. W., and J. F. Wilkinson. *J. Gen. Microbiol.,* **39,** 373 (1965).
725. Symonds, N., K. A. Stacey, S. W. Glover, J. Schell, and S. Silver. *Biochem. Biophys. Res. Commun.,* **12,** 220 (1963).
726. Szer, W. *J. Mol. Biol.,* **16,** 585 (1966).
727. Szer, W., and D. Shugar. *J. Mol. Biol.,* **17,** 174 (1966).
728. Szybalski, W., H. Kubinski, and P. Sheldrick. *Cold Spring Harbor Symp. Quant. Biol.,* **31,** 123 (1966).
729. Takahashi, I. *J. Gen. Microbiol.,* **31,** 211 (1963).
730. Takahashi, I., and J. Marmur. *Biochem. Biophys. Res. Commun.,* **10,** 289, (1963).
731. ———. *Nature,* **197,** 794 (1963).
732. Takanami, M. *Cold Spring Harbor Symp. Quant. Biol.,* **31,** 611 (1966).
733. Tanaka, F., S. Takeuchi, and H. Yonehara. *J. Antibiotics,* **Ser. A,** **15,** 197 (1962).
734. Tanaka, F., N. Tanaka, H. Yonehara, and H. Umeyawa. *J. Antibiotics,* **Ser. A,** **15,** 191 (1962).
735. Tanenbaum, S. W., and S. M. Beiser. *Proc. Nat. Acad. Sci.,* **49,** 662 (1963).
736. Taylor, A. R. *J. Biol. Chem.,* **165,** 271 (1946).
737. Taylor, K., Z. Hradecna, and W. Szybalski. *Fed. Proc.,* **26,** 449 (1967).
738. ———. *Proc. Nat. Acad. Sci.,* **57,** 1618 (1967).
739. Terzaghi, E., Y. Okada, G. Streisinger, J. Emrich, M. Inouye, and A. Tsugita. *Proc. Nat. Acad. Sci.,* **56,** 500 (1966).
740. Terzi, M. *J. Mol. Biol.,* **28,** 37 (1967).
741. Terzi, M., and C. Levinthal. *J. Mol. Biol.,* **26,** 525 (1967).

742. Tessman, E. S. *Virology,* **25,** 303 (1965).

743. ———. *J. Mol. Biol.,* **17,** 218 (1966).

744. ———. *Molecular Biology of the Viruses, Symposium at Edmonton, Canada,* New York, Academic Press, 1967, p. 193.

745. Tessman, I., H. Ishiwa, S. Kumar, and R. Baker. *Science,* **156,** 824 (1967).

746. Tessman, I., S. Kimar, and E. S. Tessman. *Science,* **158,** 267 (1967).

747. Tessman, I., and E. S. Tessman. *Proc. Nat. Acad. Sci.,* **55,** 1459 (1966).

747a. Thang, M. N., D. C. Thang, and M. Grunberg-Manago. *Biochem. Biophys. Res. Commun.,* **28,** 374 (1967).

748. Thelander, L. *J. Biol. Chem.,* **242,** 852 (1967).

749. Thomas, C. A., Jr. *Prog. Nucleic Acid Res. and Mol. Biol.,* **5,** 315 (1966).

750. Thomas, C. A., Jr., and L. A. MacHattie. *Proc. Nat. Acad. Sci.,* **52,** 1297 (1964).

751. Thomas, C. A., Jr., and I. Rubenstein. *Biophys. J.,* **4,** 93 (1964).

752. Thomas, C. A., Jr., and S. R. Suskind. *Virology,* **12,** 1 (1960).

753. Tiselius, A., K. O. Pedersen, and T. Svedberg. *Nature,* **140,** 848 (1937).

754. Tocchini-Valenti, G. P., M. Stodolsky, A. Aurisicchio, F. Graziosi, M. Sarnat, S. B. Weiss, and E. P. Geiduschek. *Proc. Nat. Acad. Sci.,* **50,** 935 (1963).

754a. Tomizawa, J., and N. Anraku. *J. Mol. Biol.,* **8,** 516 (1964).

755. Tomizawa, J., N. Anraku, and Y. Iwamu. *J. Mol. Biol.,* **21,** 247 (1966).

756. Tomizawa, J., and S. Sunakawa. *J. Gen. Physiol.,* **39,** 553 (1956).

757. Tonegawa, S., and M. Hayashi. *Biochim. Biophys. Acta,* **123,** 634 (1966).

758. Traub, P., and W. Zillig. *Hoppe-Seyler's Z. Physiol. Chemie,* **343,** 246 (1966).

759. Traub, P., W. Zillig, R. L. Millette, and M. Schweiger. *Hoppe-Seyler's Z. Physiol. Chemie,* **343,** 261 (1966).

760. Trilling, D. M., and H. V. Aposhian. *Proc. Nat. Acad. Sci.,* **54,** 622 (1965).

761. Tsugita, A., M. Inouye, E. Terzaghi, and G. Streisinger. *J. Biol. Chem.,* **243,** 391 (1968).

762. Tsuji, M. *Biochem. Pharmacol.,* **12,** 135 (1963).

763. Tsutsui, E., P. R. Srinivasan, and E. Borek. *Proc. Nat. Acad. Sci.,* **56,** 1003 (1966).

764. Twort, F. W. *Lancet,* (2) 1241 (1915).

765. Twort, F. W., and G. L. Y. Ingram. *Proc. Roy. Soc.*, **B84**, 517 (1912).
766. Ulbricht, T. L. V. *Prog. Nucleic Acid Res. and Mol. Biol.*, **4**, 189 (1965).
767. Ulbricht, T. L. V., and C. C. Price. *J. Org. Chem.*, **21**, 567 (1956).
768. van de Pol, J. H., G. Veldhuisen, and J. A. Cohen. *Biochim. Biophys. Acta*, **48**, 417 (1961).
769. Van Vunakis, H., W. H. Baker, and R. K. Brown. *Virology*, **5**, 327 (1958).
769a. Verses, C., M. Lute, L. Crosby, and L. M. Kozloff. *Bacteriol. Proc.*, 153 (1968).
770. Vidaver, G. A., and L. M. Kozloff. *J. Biol. Chem.*, **225**, 335 (1957).
771. Viñuela, E., M. Salas, and S. Ochoa. *Proc. Nat. Acad. Sci.*, **57**, 729 (1967).
772. Volkin, E. *J. Am. Chem. Soc.*, **76**, 5892 (1954).
773. ———. *Proc. Internat. Congress of Biochemistry, 4th, Vienna, 1958*, **7**, 212 (1959).
774. ———. *Proc. Nat. Acad. Sci.*, **46**, 1336 (1960).
775. ———. *Fed. Proc.*, **21**, 112 (1962).
776. Volkin, E., and L. Astrachan. *Virology*, **2**, 149 (1956).
777. ———. *Virology*, **2**, 433 (1956).
778. ———. In *The Chemical Basis of Heredity*, W. McElroy and B. Glass (eds.), Baltimore, Johns Hopkins Press, 1957, p. 686.
779. Volkin, E., and A. Ruffilli. *Proc. Nat. Acad. Sci.*, **48**, 2193 (1962).
780. Wacker, A. *Prog. Nucleic Acid Res. and Mol. Biol.*, **1**, 369 (1963).
781. Wade, H. E., and S. Lovett. *Biochem. J.*, **81**, 319 (1961).
782. Wagner, K., and W. Katz. *Z. Naturforsch.*, **190**, 230 (1964).
783. Wahba, A. J., and M. Friedkin. *J. Biol. Chem.*, **236**, PC 11 (1961).
784. Wainfan, E., P. R. Srinivasan, and E. Borek. *Biochemistry*, **4**, 2845 (1965).
785. ———. *J. Mol. Biol.*, **22**, 349 (1966).
785a. Walter, G., W. Seifert, and W. Zillig. *Biochem. Biophys. Res. Commun.*, **30**, 240 (1968).
786. Warner, H. R., and J. E. Barnes. *Virology*, **28**, 100 (1966).
787. ———. *Proc. Nat. Acad. Sci.*, **56**, 1233 (1966).
787a. Warner, H. R., and M. D. Hobbs. *Virology*, **33**, 376 (1967).
788. Warner, H. R., and N. Lewis. *Virology*, **29**, 172 (1966).
789. Watanabe, I., *Biochim. Biophys. Acta*, **25**, 665 (1957).
790. Waters, L. C., and G. D. Novelli. *Proc. Nat. Acad. Sci.*, **57**, 979 (1967).
791. Waters, L. C., E. Volkin, and G. D. Novelli. *Fed. Proc.*, **26**, 733 (1967).

792. Watson, J. D., and F. H. C. Crick. *Nature*, **171**, 737 (1953).
793. ———. *Nature*, **171**, 964 (1953).
794. Weed, L. L., and S. S. Cohen. *J. Biol. Chem.*, **192**, 693 (1951).
795. Weed, L. L., and T. A. Courtenay. *J. Biol. Chem.*, **206**, 735 (1954).
796. Weidel, W. *Bull. Soc. Chem. Biol.*, **42**, 1833 (1960).
797. Weidel, W., and W. Katz. *Z. Naturforsch.*, **16b**, 156 (1961).
798. Weigert, M. G., and A. Garen. *J. Mol. Biol.*, **12**, 448 (1965).
799. Weigert, M. G., E. Lanka, and A. Garen. *J. Mol. Biol.*, **14**, 522 (1965).
800. ———. *J. Mol. Biol.*, **23**, 391 (1967).
801. Weiss, B., T. R. Live, and C. C. Richardson. *Fed. Proc.*, **26**, 395 (1967).
802. Weiss, B., and C. C. Richardson. *Proc. Nat. Acad. Sci.*, **57**, 1021 (1967).
803. ———. *J. Mol. Biol.*, **23**, 405 (1967).
804. ———. *J. Biol. Chem.*, **242**, 420 (1967).
805. Weiss, J. J. *Prog. Nucleic Acid Res. and Mol. Biol.*, **3**, 103 (1964).
806. Weissbach, A., and D. Korn. *Biochim. Biophys. Acta*, **87**, 621 (1964).
807. Weygand, F., and O. P. Swoboda. *Z. Naturforsch.*, **11B**, 369 (1956).
808. Weygand, F., A. Wacker, A. Trebst, and O. P. Swoboda. *Z. Naturforsch.*, **12B**, 184 (1957).
809. Wiberg, J. S. *Proc. Nat. Acad. Sci.*, **55**, 614 (1966).
810. Wiberg, J. S., and J. M. Buchanan. *Proc. Nat. Acad. Sci.*, **51**, 421 (1964).
811. Wiberg, J. S., M. Dirksen, R. H. Epstein, S. E. Luria, and J. M. Buchanan. *Proc. Nat. Acad. Sci.*, **48**, 293 (1962).
812. Wierzchowski, K. L., and D. Shugar. *Acta Biochim. Polonica*, **6**, 313 (1959).
813. Williams, A. M., and F. J. Bollum. *Proc. Soc. Exp. Biol. Med.*, **112**, 701 (1963).
814. Wilson, R. G., and M. J. Caicuts. *J. Biol. Chem.*, **241**, 1725 (1966).
815. Winocour, E., A. Kaye, and V. Stollar. *Virology*, **27**, 156 (1965).
816. Wu, R., and A. D. Kaiser. *Proc. Nat. Acad. Sci.*, **57**, 170 (1967).
817. Wulff, D. L., and K. Metzger. *Virology*, **21**, 499 (1963).
818. Wyatt, G. R., and S. S. Cohen. *Nature*, **170**, 846 (1952).
819. ———. *Nature*, **170**, 1072 (1952).
820. ———. *Ann. Inst. Pasteur*, **84**, 143 (1953).
821. ———. *Biochem. J.*, **55**, 774 (1953).
822. Yankofsky, S. A., and S. Spiegelman. *Proc. Nat. Acad. Sci.*, **48**, 108 (1962).

823. Yeh, Y.-C., and G. R. Greenberg. *J. Biol. Chem.*, **242**, 1307 (1967).
824. Yudelevich, A., and M. Gold. *Fed. Proc.*, **26**, 450 (1967).
825. Zgaga, V. *Virology*, **31**, 559 (1967).
826. Zimmerman, S. B., and A. Kornberg. *J. Biol. Chem.*, **236**, 1480 (1961).
827. Zimmerman, S. B., S. R. Kornberg, and A. Kornberg. *J. Biol. Chem.*, **237**, 512 (1962).
828. Zimmerman, S. B., J. W. Little, C. K. Oshinsky, and M. Gellert. *Proc. Nat. Acad. Sci.*, **57**, 1841 (1967).
829. Zinder, N. D., D. Engelhardt, and R. E. Webster. *Cold Spring Harbor Symp. Quant. Biol.*, **31**, 251 (1966).
830. Zinder, N. D., R. C. Valentine, M. Roger, and W. Stoekenius. *Virology*, **20**, 638 (1963).
831. Zograff, Y. N., V. G. Nickiforov, I. A. Bass, and M. F. Schemyakin. *Conference of Kurchatov's Institute of Atomic Energy, Moscow, June 1966.*

INDEX

Acetylase, 253

Actinomycin D: head abnormalities, 165; inhibition of DNA condensation, 166; phage 2C infection, 185; lysozyme synthesis, 212; maturation, 212, 231; RNA degradation, 224; inhibition of synthesis of virus-induced RNA, 224, 231, 232; similarity to oxidized spermine, 251

Adenine, 29, 125, 126, 225

Adsorption, bacteriophage, 5–7, 56

Allosteric controls: dCMP deaminase, 105–7, 183, 184; ribonucleotide reductase, 113, 114; absence in SP8 dCMP deaminase, 183, 184

Amber mutants (am): in permissive host, 86, 87, 149; enzyme stability, 87, 150–55; conditional lethality, 86, 150–55; dCMP hydroxymethylase, 86, 87, 124, 154; dCTPase, 98; deoxynucleotide kinase, 101; DNA polymerase, 117, 118; complementation by T* phage, 124; production of 5'-polynucleotide phosphatase, 132; polynucleotide ligase, 132, 134; T4, 150–55; φX 174, 150, 193, 194; S13, 150, 193, 194, 242; M13, 150, 197, 198; lambda, 152, 154; suppressors for nonsense mutations, 153; as nonsense mutations, 153, 158, 159; complementation tests, 155, 158; head proteins, 158, 159; tail elements and self-assembly, 170; transcription of e gene, 237–39; polarity effects, 242

Aminoacyl tRNA synthetase: host enzymes in infection, 139; thermolabile valyl enzyme and infection, 139

Aminopterin, 110, 111

Antibodies: to glucosylated phage DNA, 41; to other DNA, 41; to nucleic acid constituents, 41; to dCMP hydroxymethylase, 67, 68; to virus and induced proteins, 90; to DNA polymerase, 116, 117; fluorescent, 233

D-Arabinose: D-arabinose-5-phosphate, 16; enzymatic synthesis, 16; cell wall, 16; araCMP in dCMP hydroxymethylase reaction, 67

Assembly of phage: proflavine, 22, 95, 159–65; puromycin, 162, 163; 5-methyltryptophan, 162, 163; mechanism, 169–71; in vitro assembly of heads and tails, 169–71; T4 mutants, 169–71; lambda systems, 169; P22 mutants, 170, 171

5-Azacytidine, 231

6-Azadeoxynucleosides, 32, 42

Bacimethrin, 30, 31

Bacterial chromosome: association with bacterial membrane, 198, 204–8; conjugation after infection, 202, 206, 207

Bacterial DNA: degradation in phage infection, 202, 203; chloramphenicol and synthesis after infection, 202, 203

Bacterial membrane, see Membrane, bacterial

Bacterial pili, see Pili

Bacterial syntheses: arrest by T-even phage infection, 9–12, 202–8; arrest of RNA accumulation, 202; arrest of ribosome synthesis, 202; lack of arrest in SP8, φX174, λ infections, 202; degradation of DNA and conjugation, 202; chloramphenicol and host synthesis, 202, 203; hypotheses on T4 infection arrest, 202–6; protein synthesis in arrest, 203; lack of mutants for arrest, 203; T4 infection of Shigella, 204; arrest by nuclease-deficient phage, 206; ghosts, 206; polylysine-inactivated T2, 206; arrest of rRNA without protein synthesis, 213, 214

Bacterial virus, see Virus